THE MENTALLY
RETARDED CHILD

Development, Education
and Treatment

SECOND EDITION

THE MENTALLY RETARDED CHILD

Development, Education and Treatment

SECOND EDITION

MAX L. HUTT
Clinical Psychologist and Psychotherapist, Consultant, Michigan Department of Mental Health. Formerly, Department of Psychology, University of Michigan, Ann Arbor, Michigan.

ROBERT GWYN GIBBY
Chief Psychologist, McGuire Veterans Administration General Medical and Surgical Hospital, Richmond, Virginia.

ALLYN AND BACON, INC.   Boston

TO MY MOTHER
who taught the "difficult ones"

R. G. G.

TO MY FATHER
who taught me the deepest meanings of true companionship

M. L. H.

Library of Congress Catalog Card Number:
65–18950

Printed in the United States of America

Eighth printing . . . January, 1972

In Memoriam
John Fitzgerald Kennedy 1917-1963

Much of the world's population still strives for mere survival; others for domination of the weaker. Our aim is individual and national dignity. Our fortune is scientific and technological ability. Our obligation is to search for the secrets of the human mind and to share our knowledge throughout the world.

From *Statement by President John F. Kennedy Regarding the Need for a National Plan in Mental Retardation,* October 11, 1961.

PREFACE TO THE
SECOND EDITION

In the preface to the first edition of this work we stated, "There has been such marked improvement in our understanding of the retarded child over the past decade that dissemination of this knowledge and implementation of home and school programs have not kept adequate pace." But, even in the short period that has elapsed since we made the comment, our knowledge in this area has increased enormously and community and school programs designed to stimulate the maximal growth of retarded individuals have undergone a virtual revolution. Similarly, interest in the problem of retardation has not waned but, rather, has broadened and deepened. And, once again, as we attempted to do in the first edition, we have sought to integrate the newer findings and methodologies and make them available to the teaching community and to the general public.

Our basic orientation to the problem of mental retardation has remained constant; the retarded individual is a unique personality, as are all individuals, and to understand him in all of his complexity and uniqueness, we must seek to understand the multiple causes, direct and indirect, of his current status so that we can apply in a creative and constructive manner the optimal methods of education, guidance, and treatment. We still believe that every retardate can have a meaningful and productive place in our society *if* society is willing to offer him appropriate opportunities to develop his full potential and to offer him suitable guidance and training. But we have also learned from recent and ongoing research, as well as from experimental programs with the retarded, that our knowledge of the great many varieties of retardation is far from complete and our methods of dealing with these problems are still halting and unsure.

Most, if not all, educators are aware of the special adjustment problems of the retarded individual—problems originating in part by virtue of his own limitations, but often made more difficult by society's failure to understand him or to provide suitable education and guidance for him. Increasingly, educators and research workers alike have come to recognize more fully that mental retardation itself may sometimes be symptomatic of emotional difficulties causing, in turn, inhibition of cognitive and social development. It has become increasingly evident that socio-cultural deprivation may contribute to, or even cause, many instances of apparent retardation. Hence, we have emphasized those factors in the total-personality development of retarded individuals. This revision attempts to marshal the new as well as old evidence which may contribute to our understanding of the developmental and adjustive processes, and cites case studies and clinical findings which may be relevant.

It is in the light of these considerations that the present edition was planned. We are grateful to many colleagues who wrote critiques of the former edition and suggested sources of evidence or shortcomings which needed to be considered. Although we may not have been able to take as much advantage of these suggestions as they would have liked, we have made every effort to do so. Each of the chapters of the first edition has been revised, and most have been enlarged, to summarize the trends in research and experience which workers in the field have gained. The following major revisions and additions may be noted by comparing the two editions.

The recent findings on many aspects of etiology and classification of retardation have been added and integrated into the text. The chapters on personality development have been markedly revised, enlarged, and reorganized. The psychoanalytic position is given emphasis but research findings that are not necessarily consistent with this position have been included where feasible. Only still additional research will enable the workers in this field to arrive at a more universally acceptable understanding of the full role of personality factors in retardation. Considerable research evidence has also been slowly accumulating on the adjustment problems of retardates and we have tried to cite significant examples of this evidence.

The chapter on education and guidance in the first edition has been expanded into the two present enlarged chapters, with more specific discussion of educational problems of administration, organization of classes, and general and specific methods of teaching. We hope this modification will provide more assistance to educators. We have also summarized studies on the special learning problems of the retarded and the application of learning theory to such problems. In the chapter on parental reactions we have culled the new evidence and discussed some of the newer implications of such evidence. We have also added a number of photographic illustrations in an attempt to make our presentation more interesting and vivid. We acknowledge with gratefulness the cooperation of those individuals and organizations that have made these photographs available to us. Our special thanks are offered to Dr. Robert I. Jaslow, Medical Superintendent of the Plymouth State Home and Training School of Michigan, and to the Department of Education, State of Virginia.

We wish to express our gratitude to Mrs. Catherine E. Gibby, who assumed responsibility for the multiplicity of details in the preparation and assembly of the manuscript.

The last word on mental retardation has certainly not been written. Each of us—the workers in this field—undoubtedly has his prejudices. If, at times of enthusiastic exposition of a viewpoint which seems reasonable to us we have seemed to be dogmatic, we hope the reader will understand that this is not the fault of overwhelming evidence but, rather, of insufficient evidence which still needs to be emphasized. Our exposition is intended to be constructively provocative and we trust that the reader will review both argument and evidence and test these out in the light of his own experience as well as that of additional evidence.

M. L. H.
R. G. G.

TABLE OF CONTENTS

THE MENTALLY RETARDED CHILD

Development, Education and Treatment

SECOND EDITION

ch. 1

THE PROBLEM OF

MENTAL RETARDATION

C HILDREN VARY TREMENDOUSLY IN THE DEGREE OF INTELLECTUAL capacity with which they function, ranging from extremely inferior to extremely superior levels. If we measure their intellectual capacity by means of an intelligence test, we find that a large percentage clusters around the middle portion of the range. By definition, we call these children "average." A small percentage ranks at such a low level that we term them "feebleminded," and an equally small percentage ranks at such a high level that we term them "genius." Between the highest and the lowest levels there is a very large range—a *continuum*—which comprises all the intervening levels of intellectual capacity.

Children range *all along* this continuum, differing from each other in both the *amount* of intelligence they possess (quantity) and the *kinds* of intelligence they display (quality). There is no sharp break along this continuum. For convenience, we may term those who rank *below* some *arbitrarily* selected point as feebleminded, just as we may term those who rank *above* some *arbitrarily* selected point as very superior. Those who fall within the lowest range on this scale, and whom we call feebleminded, also differ significantly among themselves. They do not fall at only one point on the scale, but range over a considerable section of it, from the mildly inferior to the severely inferior. This *total* inferior range of the scale is the mentally retarded group.

This book discusses those inferior or mentally retarded children who

1

are incapable, because of limited mental capacities, of adapting adequately to their environment. Although there have always been inferior children, in recent years a more adequate recognition of the nature of their specific characteristics and problems has developed. Moreover, society has shown a greater willingness to meet the problems they present, and a relatively fresh approach to them is evolving.

We do not have an accurate measure of the extent of the problems presented by mentally retarded children. We have learned much about the nature of retardation, but there is still far more to be learned. We can calculate fairly accurately the number of children who are placed in institutions for special care, but these are only the *most severely* retarded. We do not know exactly how many mildly and moderately retarded children there are; we can only estimate their numbers by a variety of methods. An indication of the seriousness of the problems, however, is the fact that aroused communities are finally focusing considerable attention on their solutions.

It is, of course, important that we be concerned with the child who is so severely retarded that institutional care is the only apparent solution, but the problems of the more mildly retarded children are greater in extent. Such children are capable of making an adequate social adjustment in the community *provided* their problems are recognized and they are given the care, attention, guidance, and treatment they need so desperately.

Mentally retarded children, in the not-so-distant past, were frequently regarded with feelings of scorn and deprecation by other more fortunate persons, and were often, due to lack of adequate knowledge, a source of shame to their families. Today we find a somewhat more enlightened attitude toward such children, and more people are beginning to appreciate the true nature of their disabilities. We are also becoming aware of society's responsibilities in providing more adequate programs for their treatment and care. However, despite the increase in total care programs for the retarded, society still has not shouldered its full responsibilities.

In this first chapter we shall first present a case study of a mentally retarded boy. Next, we shall turn attention to the concept of mental retardation, review its historical background, and be concerned with the magnitude of the problem.

THE CASE OF JOHNNY JONES

The case of Johnny illustrates some of the problems of a mildly retarded child. Johnny is, in many respects, typical of other mentally retarded children, but like all other human beings, Johnny is also a unique individual, with his own special characteristics.

Johnny appears to have lived a life full of varied frustrations. When one first meets him, in his fourth-grade class, he is struck by his attitude of despair and hopelessness. He is about a year older than his classmates (he has just turned ten years of age), sits alone in his seat near the window, and fumbles with the pages of the book on his desk. The teacher is reading some material from the fourth-grade reader, but Johnny seems to be uninterested. The rest of the children are following the teacher in their own texts, but Johnny's attention appears to be wandering. Soon, the teacher, after a few reproving looks in his direction, walks over to him to see whether she can be of help. She finds Johnny is looking at the wrong page, questions him about what he has been doing, finally finds the right page for him, and walks back to her desk to continue with her reading. The class is annoyed by this interruption in the exciting material the teacher was reading, and has waited impatiently for her to resume. But Johnny has lost interest, and soon his head drops upon his book as he gives up his hopeless task of attempting to follow the print.

Johnny has not learned to read! He can understand many spoken words and even some simple phrases, but he is unable to gain a comprehensive understanding of the material even when it is read to him. He seems to get tired easily when the reading lesson arrives and he frequently gives up and goes to sleep. This has been a problem for him from the beginning of his school days in the first grade, but became a serious obstacle in the second grade (which he was forced to repeat).

When he was entered in school at the age of six years, his mother had a conference with his teacher. She told the teacher that Johnny had always "seemed a little slow," but that he was a good boy, and she asked that he be given special help and encouragement. He had seemed to be a perfectly normal baby, she told the teacher. He was the first child in a family of three children, with a brother two years younger and a sister three years younger. He was slow in beginning to talk, but was able to say a few words at two years of age. His speech had "always" been infantile, and he seemed to prefer "baby talk" even when he was six years of age. He had also been slow in learning to walk, despite special efforts to encourage him by his parents. Shortly after he had begun to walk, at two years of age, his brother was born, and Johnny, due to the fact that he received less attention and love, reverted to creeping and crawling. He was also late in learning bladder and bowel control, his mother explained, and after he had established fairly good control, he went back (*regressed*) to soiling and wetting at five years of age. With help he overcame this difficulty, however, and was fully trained once again at the age of six.

His mother stated that he had never been a "problem" at home although he had had severe temper tantrums from two and a half to four years of age. She thought that his tantrums were "brought on" by measles and scarlet fever, because he had seemed temporarily more irritable after these illnesses. When his teacher asked about his relations with his brother and sister (*siblings*), his mother commented that there had been some jealousy and rivalry, but that the parents would not tolerate this. Johnny soon learned to get along with his siblings and preferred the company of his brother to other children of his own age. This became something of a problem because the brother tired of Johnny's constant companionship and Johnny was often left to play by himself. He had never seemed to be interested in or able to get along with boys of his own age. Frequently these boys would take advantage of him and lead him into mischievous behavior. At other times, they would engage in games but would not include him. Gradually, Johnny had begun to stay by himself and play with his dog or work with his Erector set. He learned to use a few simple tools and would spend hours making things.

Johnny never liked school. In the first grade he managed to get along, but frequently had to be prodded into going to school. His teacher reported that he was the slowest child in the group. He was not particularly troublesome but he had difficulty learning any of the things the other children seemed to learn easily. He usually stayed by himself and had to be urged to participate in group activities. He would seem listless and fatigued. When he did show some interest in something, it soon waned. At times he would doze off in the classroom. It was suspected that there was something wrong physically, but a medical examination was entirely negative, and it was finally concluded that he was "lazy." However, he did show considerable drive and continued interest when he was engaged in "making things" in school.

He was promoted to the second grade because it was the school policy not to "fail" children at the end of the first year. His second year at school was much more difficult for him. He had difficulty in all school subjects except handwriting and spelling, in both of which he did fairly well. His greatest trouble was with reading, but he had almost as much difficulty with simple arithmetical computation. He was given some special help at school and a tutor was employed at home, but to no avail. Finally, he was referred to the school counselor, who reported that Johnny was retarded in intelligence. An intelligence test score of 63 was reported for him on the basis of a group test of intelligence given to him by this counselor. It was suggested that he should be given continued special help in school and that he should probably be made to repeat the second grade.

During his second experience in the second grade, Johnny's school work continued to be very inferior. The principal, who had a conference with Johnny's mother, suggested that Johnny needed placement in a class for retarded children; but since none was available in this school, the teacher was asked to provide a simplified program of studies for him. But his school conduct became more unsatisfactory despite this special program. Occasionally he would "play hookey." He would have to be brought to school by his mother to ensure his attendance. He seemed to resent his younger brother who was attending the first grade in the same school and who was doing good school work. Near the end of the year Johnny was referred to a child guidance clinic in a nearby city. There it was determined that his I.Q. score on an individual intelligence test was 67 but that his school achievement was below the level expected of his mental age. He was reported as being unable to read phrases or sentences, as having poor memory abilities, and as being unable to concentrate for any extended period of time. The clinical psychologist reported that Johnny felt hostile toward both of his siblings and was highly ambivalent toward his mother. In addition to inferior intelligence, he was reported as having a moderate emotional maladjustment due to frustrations in school work and excessive pressures upon him from the home to do well in school. It was suggested that the pressures be reduced and that Johnny be transferred to a school with a class for retarded children of his own age group. The parents resented these suggestions and were unwilling to move the family from the small town where they lived to a larger city whose school system provided "special classes." Further tutoring was attempted at home to get Johnny "up to grade." The parents could not "understand" why Johnny was so dull. After all, the mother explained to the teacher, both of the parents had graduated from high school and both of the other children seemed to be above average.

Despite unsatisfactory work, Johnny was promoted to the third grade. In this grade he seemed to like his teacher, who took a special interest in him. He was permitted to spend most of his time drawing and making things and his interest in school increased. He no longer had to be "urged" to go to school. The teacher was a very warm person who tried to deal with each child on an individual basis. Even Johnny's reading of words began to improve, although no special tutoring was provided at this time. Johnny reported at home that he liked the class because it was smaller than his previous classes and because he could spend so much time on his "projects." His reading vocabulary reached the beginning second-grade level, although his reading comprehension was still well below this level.

Since Johnny's school work continued to be very poor in the fourth grade and his withdrawal behavior became more pronounced, he was referred again to the psychological clinic in the nearby city. This time a more extensive evaluation was made. Once again he attained an I.Q. rating of "retarded," his score this time being 71. Interviews with both Johnny and his mother revealed that Johnny was often despondent, that he flared up occasionally at home, that both of his parents were severely disappointed in him, and that they made frequent unfavorable comparisons with the younger brother. It was also learned that Johnny was unwanted at the time he was born. The parents had felt that they did not want a child at that time because of their precarious financial situation. His father had been particularly upset by the financial burden that a child presented. The parents attempted to accept their new child, but it was admitted that their resentment often showed in their early attitudes toward him. Johnny's slow progress added to their irritations and subsequently, when their second child was born, at a time when their financial position had become more favorable, the parents tended to show more interest and pleasure in the new arrival. It became more clear that Johnny's problems were complicated by the unfortunate attitudes of the home toward him and by the unfavorable comparisons that were frequently made with his siblings. The clinic staff came to the conclusion that his difficulties due to inferior intellectual capacities were greatly increased by this home situation, by the explicit and implicit pressures exerted upon him by the home and the school, and by his growing sense of rejection and inadequacy. They proposed a "total program" of mental hygiene in the home, a carefully specified special program of school activities, and psychological guidance for both Johnny and his mother.

There is a great deal that can be learned from Johnny's case. At this time one can note some of the crucial factors and reserve for discussion in later chapters some of the other issues. Johnny is a boy with limited general intelligence (a mildly retarded child). His three reported I.Q. scores of 63, 67, and 71, which were reasonably close in agreement, indicated that he had retarded intelligence. (A child with exactly average intelligence would hypothetically score 100 on an intelligence test.) Thus, a major factor in Johnny's poor school work was his relatively limited intelligence. Such children usually progress much more slowly in many aspects of their general development and learn much more slowly in school, particularly in the traditional academic subjects. Under optimal conditions, when home and school expectancies are geared to the child's actual abilities and potentialities, special provision can be made to adapt their environment to their actual level of ability. Such was not the case in Johnny's circumstance.

However, Johnny was not doing as well in school as his actual mental ability would warrant. At the time of his last clinical examination, when he obtained an I.Q. score of 71 at the age of ten years and four months, his obtained *mental age* was seven years and three months. This meant that his average mental level of development was equal to that of average children who were seven years and three months old. He therefore had the potential of doing school work at the level of children near the beginning of the second grade. Yet the clinic found that in academic subjects (principally reading and arithmetic), he was even below this level. This was true despite the fact that he had repeated the second grade and that he had obtained special tutoring at school and at home. His emotional maladjustment and his frustrations with his school environment had probably contributed significantly to his relatively inferior achievement for his mental level.

From a review of the history of this case it becomes clear that many factors in the home may have contributed, in the first place, to Johnny's poor emotional adjustment. The initial attitudes of his parents, their inappropriate expectations of him, the unfortunate comparisons with his more fortunate siblings (who were apparently not retarded) played their part. The illnesses that occurred shortly after his brother was born probably added to his difficulties, both in their direct effect upon his reduced ability, temporarily resulting from their physical effects, and in their indirect effect, in gaining him some measure of additional special attention and in fostering regressive behavior. Thus were developed the initial stages of his maladjusted behavior, which in turn contributed to his later difficulties in adjusting to the school program.

Johnny's withdrawal behavior (his aloneness, his depression, his "dozing," his "laziness," and his infantile mannerisms) may be interpreted as defensive attempts to cope with his problems. His truancy may be similarly understood. The attempts to get him to learn more rapidly and adequately, by parents, teachers, and tutors, were probably perceived by him as further evidence of rejection and as further evidence of his inadequacy. It is interesting to note that he had the greatest success with his "warm" teacher in the third grade who made no attempt to pressure him, who respected his integrity as an individual, and who provided him with a program in which he could both feel and be successful.

This case raises many questions concerning methods of guidance that might have been effective for Johnny and his parents, and many questions concerning school policies that might be developed for such children. There are many issues that need to be raised concerning areas of accomplishment that one may reasonably expect in such cases. These matters will be deferred, however, until later sections of this book in which their discussion will be more appropriate.

THE CONCEPT OF MENTAL RETARDATION

Psychology, like any other science, has its difficulties with words. Many of the terms that have been devised mean essentially the same thing even though they are intended to convey very subtle differences in meaning. Often such differences turn out to be more fancied than real. Sometimes a new term or phrase has been introduced because an older expression has become "loaded" with emotional tones that are thought to be undesirable.

Many "labels" have been applied to the child who is below average in intelligence. These include such terms as: mental defective, mentally subnormal, mentally retarded, intellectually defective, intellectually subnormal, intellectually retarded, oligophrenic, feebleminded, amental, exceptional, and slow learning. In reality there is little difference among them, although some do carry more positive emotional connotations than others.

Although Chapter Three presents a detailed conception of mental retardation, a very brief first glance at the problem is worthwhile now. Many attempts have been made to define precisely what is meant by the concept of "mental retardation." Some authorities have attempted to define the condition in terms of the intelligence quotient that an individual achieves on a suitable intelligence test. This approach has been particularly characteristic of authorities in the United States where the use of intelligence tests has flourished. In such cases the usual procedure is to define intellectual retardation in terms of an intelligence quotient score which is below 70.[1] However, a child who obtains an intelligence

---

[1] In more recent years, this kind of approach has been "refined" on the basis of more adequate statistical data. For example, the 1959 manual of the American Association on Mental Deficiency defines four levels of retardation based on a

quotient of 68 is not necessarily more retarded mentally than a child with one of 72, since many factors must be taken into consideration in the interpretation of intelligence test scores, such as the validity of the scores, the absence of culturally depriving factors, and the like.

Other authorities have attempted to include some of these considerations in their definitions. Tredgold, for example, defines mental retardation as follows:[2]

. . . a state of incomplete mental development of such a kind and degree that the individual is incapable of adapting himself to the normal environment of his fellows in such a way as to maintain existence independently of supervision, control or external support.

We may note that this definition stresses the degree of social adequacy of the person—how well he is able to adjust to the demands of society in comparison with others of his age group. "Inability to adapt" is emphasized as an important factor.

Doll's definition is more explicit than that of Tredgold. He defines feeblemindedness as follows:[3]

Mental deficiency is a state of social incompetence obtained at maturity, resulting from developmental arrest of intelligence because of constitutional (hereditary or acquired) origin: the condition is essentially incurable through treatment and unremediable through training except as treatment and training instill habits which superficially compensate for the limitations of the person so afflicted while under favorable circumstances and for more or less limited periods of time.

Doll also stated:[4]

. . . we observe that six criteria by statement or implication have been generally considered essential to an adequate definition and concept. These are (1) social incompetence, (2) due to mental subnormality, (3) which has been developmentally arrested, (4) which obtains at maturity, (5) is of constitutional origin and (6) is essentially incurable.

Again we find "social incompetence" stressed as the ultimate criterion. Doll distinguishes between "feeblemindedness" and "intellectual retarda-

---

deviation from the average in measured intelligence of more than one standard deviation. This problem will be discussed more fully in Chapter Three.

[2] Tredgold, A. F., and Soddy, K., *A Textbook of Mental Deficiency*, 10th Ed. Baltimore: The Williams & Wilkins Co., in prep.

[3] Doll, E. A., "Definition of mental deficiency," *Train. Sch. Bull.*, 1941, *37*, 163–164.

[4] Doll, E. A., "The essentials of an inclusive concept of mental deficiency," *Amer. J. ment., Defic.*, 1941, *46*, 214–219.

tion." "Feeblemindedness," to Doll, is an incurable condition characterized *always* by social incompetence, while "intellectual retardation" implies that there is a possibility of attaining social competence. Doll insists that a diagnosis of feeblemindedness cannot be made until all six criteria listed above are met.

Benoit has expressed dissatisfaction with many definitions of mental retardation because they usually state the existence of a functional defect without reference to the total socio-cultural background of the individual (the *social milieu*), or they define the behavioral problem of retardation in "dead-end" terms.[5] He offers as a substitute a formulation based upon Hebb's theory of the organization of behavior.[6] Benoit views mental retardation:

. . . as a deficit of intellectual function resulting from varied intrapersonal and/ or extrapersonal determinants, but having as a common proximate cause a diminished efficiency of the nervous system thus entailing a lessened general capacity for growth in perceptual and conceptual interpretation and consequently in environmental adjustment.

According to Benoit, this "Hebbian" type of definition is more fruitful than others in the literature since it directs attention to how a basic lack in the individual originates, and suggests that retardation is due to impaired efficiency of the nervous system. Benoit deplores the dichotomy of "organic vs. familial" etiology, and feels his definition avoids this pitfall since it places all retarded individuals in the same group, as the Hebbian formulation "neither assumes nor denies a structural defect in the central nervous system at the root of the diminished capacity for perceptual and conceptual integration."

The American Association on Mental Deficiency defines mental retardation as follows:[7]

Mental retardation refers to subaverage general intellectual functioning which originates during the developmental period and is associated with impairment in one or more of the following: (1) maturation, (2) learning, and (3) social adjustment.

The term "subaverage" is further defined as a level of performance which is at least one standard deviation below the population mean for the

[5] Benoit, E.. "Towards a new definition of mental retardation," *Amer. J. ment. Defic.*, 1959, *63*, 559–565.
[6] Hebb, D., *The Organization of Behavior.* New York: John Wiley & Sons, Inc., 1949.
[7] Heber, R., "A manual on terminology and classification in mental retardation," *Amer. J. ment. Defic.*, 1959, *64*, Monograph Supplement.

age group involved.* The upper age limit of the "developmental period," although not rigidly specified, is regarded as being approximately 16 years. Even though this definition of mental retardation has precipitated some controversy (see Chapter Three), it may be helpful in that it clearly delineates a highly specific group of individuals according to sharply defined criteria. This definition of mental retardation will be employed in the present text.

At this point it would be helpful to differentiate between *retarded* mental development and *arrested* mental development. *Retarded* mental development refers to a slow or inferior developmental rate present in the child from the *time of birth*. *Arrested* mental development refers to a cessation or diminution in the rate of mental growth due to injury or disease that occurs *after birth*. (These points will be elaborated upon in following chapters.)

It should be noted that mental retardation can also vary in *degree* or *level*. The American Psychiatric Association attempts to deal with this problem by distinguishing three major levels, as follows:

a. *Mild deficiency.* Children at this level can profit from a simplified school curriculum, and *can* make an adequate, though modest, social adjustment.
b. *Moderate deficiency.* Such children need special academic and vocational training and guidance, but do not require institutional care.
c. *Severe deficiency.* These children need institutional or some type of custodial care.

A detailed discussion of systems of classification of mental retardation will be found in Chapter Three.

The World Health Organization has proposed that those children whose intellectual deficit is sufficiently severe so as to result in academic disability be regarded as *mentally retarded* children, bearing in mind, however, that academic achievement is not the sole criterion on which such a diagnosis is based. (See Chapter Nine.) If one accepts this point of view, then the total range of degree of intellectual deficit encompassed by the group is considerable.

The condition of mental retardation, in fact, includes other groups of children in addition to the so-called trainable and educable mentally retarded children who first come to mind, and upon whom attention primarily has been focussed in the past. It also includes those children who,

---

* The *standard deviation* is a statistical measure which indicates the manner in which a group of scores are clustered around the average or mean score in a normal distribution of scores. It is represented by the Greek letter "sigma" (σ) and is also abbreviated as S.D. For a full discussion of the meaning and derivation of sigma the reader is referred to an elementary text on statistics.

due to limited intellectual capacities, find it impossible to keep up with their chronological age group in the elementary school or to complete successfully an academic high school course. There is, therefore, a considerable range in the *degree* of mental retardation.

The behavioral reactions of the mentally retarded child are the product of *many interacting forces.* The attitudes and actions of the child's family, his neighbors and schoolmates, and society generally, as well as his inferior intellectual capacities, *co-determine* the child's reactions. We are concerned primarily with the reasons *underlying* his behavioral reactions. Such an approach is termed a *dynamic approach.* It is different from the traditional manner in which mental retardation has been regarded. As Perry has so well pointed out:[8]

A dynamic interpretation of mental deficiency or behavior cannot be approached when one holds the traditional view of mental deficiency, for it requires a complete reassessment of the nature of mental deficiency—in effect a redefinition. Each mentally defective person must be considered, not as belonging to a homogeneous category called deficiency, but as an individual: his subnormal intellectual functioning must be considered, not as constitutionally or organically determined, but as an interdependent complex of constitutional or physiological processes, interpersonal processes, and sociocultural processes; and from a research standpoint the mentally defective must be approached, not with an assumption of irreversibility and permanence, but with the assumption that benevolent intervention may lead to a reversibility or improvement of the condition.

SOME HISTORICAL BACKGROUND

Prior to the 20th century, interest in mentally retarded children had waxed and waned for several hundred years. In the 19th century the nature of mental retardation was brought to spectacular public attention by Jean Itard. He undertook the task of educating "up to a civilized state" a young boy who had been living in a wild and savage-like condition in the woods of France. This boy, called the "Wild Boy of Aveyron," was about eleven years of age at that time. Although Itard did not apparently meet with much success in his educative attempts, the publicity the case attracted served to stir up considerable interest in the problems of mental retardation. Several schools for the mentally retarded were established in Europe. The prevalent theory at that time was that mental defect was amenable to education. It soon became apparent, however, that even though the children placed in special schools did show remarkable growth and progress, particularly in areas of habit develop-

[8] Perry, S. E., "Some theoretic problems of mental deficiency and their action implications," *Psychiat.,* 1954, *17,* 46.

ment, there were limits beyond which they could not reach. The work of Itard was followed up in Europe by Edward Seguin, who later migrated to the United States where he became a leader in educating state legislatures and the public to the problems of the mental defective.

In 1875 Dugdale's report, *The Jukes*, appeared.[9] He studied the social adaptations of five generations of a single family, whose members had extensive antisocial records. Although Dugdale concluded that "crimes against society" were transmitted along family lines, he did *not* believe that this transmission was necessarily on an hereditary basis. Society, however (probably because of its tendency to project its inner fears), jumped to the conclusion that hereditary transmission of mental retardation was proved by Dugdale's study, despite the fact that only *one* out of the 709 subjects studied by Dugdale had a certified record of feeble-mindedness.

Many misconceptions were held both by the general public and by professional workers during this period. Some of these were: that mental deficiency was a disease; that delinquent and criminal behaviors were a direct consequence of mental deficiency; that education was of no value in the treatment of mental deficiency; and that mentally retarded individuals should be kept in prisons or in homes for paupers. Thus, whereas some attempt at segregation of the mentally retarded individuals was attempted, there was very little provision made for either their special education or training.

In the early part of the 20th century some attempts at differentiation in the segregation and treatment of the mentally retarded began to appear. Institutions and special schools were established for their care and training. Probably much of this more desirable attitude was made possible by the development of intelligence tests. (It is interesting to note that this movement originated in France.) In 1904 Alfred Binet and Thomas Simon developed the now famous Binet-Simon test to identify mentally retarded children in the public schools. It has been translated and revised for use in many countries throughout the world. In this country the best known revisions were made by Goddard, Yerkes, Kuhlman, and Terman.* Intelligence tests made the measurement and detection of mental retardation more accurate, and their use stimulated important movements in planning more effectively for children in the public schools.

During World War I intelligence tests, particularly those designed

---

[9] Appendix, entitled "A Record and Study of the Relations of Crime, Pauperism and Disease," in 31st annual report of N.Y. Prison Assoc., 1875.

* See Chapter Nine for a full discussion of the Binet-Simon test and its many revisions.

to be administered to groups of persons at the same time (group intelligence tests) were widely used in the armed forces. The country was shocked to hear that almost half of all the Army recruits had a mental age of 12 years or less. Later, surveys of school populations yielded similar results. This raised a storm of controversy regarding the whole issue of the nature of intelligence and the meaning of the term "feebleminded." It was first decided that something was wrong with the tests and the interpretations made of their results. Soon, however, it became apparent that test results were invalidated by many conditions, such as educational and cultural experiences, that the intelligence quotient alone was not an adequate criterion of mental retardation, and that there were many other problems concerning the proper use and interpretation of intelligence test scores.

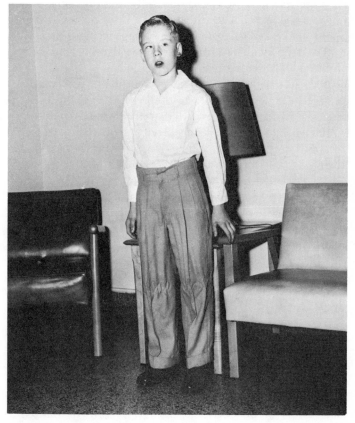

A FAMILIAL MENTAL DEFECTIVE—A MODERATE CASE (Courtesy the Fort Wayne Training School, Photo by L. Richard Young)

Research was stimulated, and many studies were done on such problems as the inheritance of mental capacity, racial differences in intelligence, relation of I.Q. to occupational level, and the like. Many previously held conceptions were found to be invalid and had to be discarded. The oversimplified concept that intelligence was a unitary trait transmitted on a Mendelian hereditary basis had to be thrown overboard. It was seen that the apparent race differences in intelligence were often the result of the bias of the test in favor of one racial group over another. It was also evident that many factors other than intelligence were significant in predicting ultimate vocational and educational levels.

The over-all products of the ferment of the early part of the 20th century were quite valuable. More and more understanding of the concepts of mental retardation was developed. More and more specialized provisions were made for training mentally retarded individuals, particularly in the public schools. Probably the chief outcomes were the reorganizations of the attitudes and concepts in regard to mental retardation and the establishment of more adequate provisions to meet the unique problems that retarded individuals present.

Of course these developments did not occur in isolation, but accompanied far-reaching developments in other areas, notably those relating to mentally disturbed individuals. Research programs continue to grow, and even though many are not specifically directed at the problem of mental retardation they are nonetheless of extreme value.

In reviewing the history of the treatment of the retarded child, Hungerford has stressed the role played by the modern parent.[10] He feels that there have been three major areas in work with mentally retarded children. The first was during the period of 1850 to 1900, which was characterized by the development of institutions. The second was from 1900 to 1950, which was highlighted by the stress on day-school special classes. The third is the present-day period, from 1950 on. As he points out, institutions were "built to last, and unfortunately they did." He feels that although they have not deteriorated, they have not kept pace with modern developments. Hungerford feels also that the day-school special classes have failed, but that they did produce a significant movement among the *parents* of retarded children. This movement of the parents has resulted in three important gains, according to Hungerford. First, by education it has made mental retardation more respectable, and killed forever the idea that heredity is its major cause. The public is now more aware of the fact that mentally retarded children are en-

<hr>

[10] Hungerford, R. H., "Editor's page," *Amer. J. ment. Defic.*, 1955, *60.*

titled to treatment and a chance for happiness. Second, by getting together, the parents have themselves grown in their understanding of the problems of mental retardation. Third, by refusing to believe that the less able retarded children were doomed to lives of perpetual custody, the parents have conducted the most practical research of the last 15 years.

This is where we are at present—not only willing but eager to look at the assets of the retarded child in a positive manner. Many of the older misconceptions have been swept away, and we are tending to substitute a more dynamic approach which is characteristic of 20th century science. However, we still have a long way to go.

THE MAGNITUDE OF THE PROBLEM

As pointed out earlier, the exact extent of intellectual retardation is not known. However, we do know how many retarded persons are reported as being cared for in either public institutions or in private homes and schools. Table 1 summarizes such data for the various sections of the United States.

TABLE 1. PERSONS IN HOMES AND SCHOOLS FOR THE MENTALLY RETARDED*

Area	Total population	Public and private	Rate per 100,000	Public	Rate per 100,000
U.S.	150,697,361	134,189	89.00	125,650	83.37
N. East	39,477,986	50,048	126.77	45,273	114.67
N. Central	44,460,762	50,997	114.70	48,696	109.53
South	47,197,088	18,838	39.91	18,038	38.22
West	19,561,525	14,306	73.13	13,643	60.74

* Reproduced from Sloan, W., "Some statistics in institutional provisions for the mentally handicapped," *Amer. J. ment. Defic.*, 1955, *59*, 380–387.

The data included in Table 1 indicate that, for the country as a whole, 89 out of every 100,000 persons are so mentally retarded that they need institutional care. It also shows a great amount of variation from one section of the country to another. Note that the lowest rate is in the southern area (39.91) and the highest in the northeastern area (126.77). This reflects the varying provisions for the care of mentally retarded individuals in different areas of the country.

It has been estimated that almost 1% of our total population is so severely retarded mentally as to require some sort of special institutional care. But not *all* such individuals are given such special attention and "treatment." (Moreover, the less severely retarded individuals often have no provision made for them.) The data contained in Table 2 indicate the adequacy of the various states in meeting the needs for institutional care.

North Dakota, which ranks first in rate per 100,000 individuals in institutions, ranks 42nd in population. Arkansas, which ranks 30th in population, ranks 48th in number of individuals per 100,000 in institutions. It is reasonable to assume that the percentage of mentally retarded individuals does not vary significantly from one state to another—certainly not as significantly as the rates of institutional placement quoted in this table. The rate for North Dakota (rank 1) is 164.77 per 100,000 for example, and that for Arkansas is only 4.50. It is probable that the differences in rates reflect the relative extent of facilities that are provided, and are not all due to the fact that there are relatively more retarded individuals in some states than in others.

Another important fact to be noted is that there were 7,800 *first* admissions of mental defectives to institutions in 1949.[11] Sabagh and Windle have analyzed data relative to changing admission rates of mental defectives to institutions from 1936–38 to 1953–55.[12] They concluded that: (1) the trend of admission rates over the years was not uniform in all age groups, (2) there was an increase in admission rates for children and a decrease for adults and adolescents, (3) the decrease in older ages was directly proportionate to mental level, while the increase in younger ages was inversely related to mental level, and (4) there was a tendency for admission rates of males to increase more than those of females, and for this trend to be directly proportionate to age and mental level. It was felt that the increase in admission rates for the younger children indicates an increased stress upon the medical treatment of retarded individuals. Further, the data indicate that placement is now occurring for the higher grades of mentally retarded children and at an earlier chronological age. It may be concluded that this indicates more sensitivity on the part of the general public to the problems of retarded children, and a growing awareness of the need for positive programs of treatment.

Dingman and Tarjan have attempted to estimate the total number of mentally retarded individuals in the United States, even though they believe the true number can only be estimated in the crudest fashion.[13] Conservatively, it is estimated that there are 87,500 individuals with I.Q.'s between 0 and 20; 350,000 with I.Q.'s between 20 and 50; and

[11] Perry, *op. cit.*

[12] Sabagh, G., and Windle, B., "Recent trends in institutionalization rates of mental defectives in the United States," *Amer. J. ment. Defic.*, 1960, *64*, 618–624.

[13] Dingman, H., and Tarjan, G., "Mental retardation and the normal distribution curve." *Amer. J. ment. Defic.*, 1960, *64*, 991–994.

TABLE 2. PERSONS IN HOMES AND SCHOOLS FOR THE MENTALLY RETARDED*

Rank	State	No. in pub. inst.	Rate per 100,000	Pop. rank	Rank	State	No. in pub. inst.	Rate per 100,000	Pop. rank
1	N.D.	1,021	164.77	42	25	Mont.	526	89.00	43
2	Conn.	2,910	144.97	28	26	Md.	1,935	82.59	24
3	Minn.	4,315	144.68	18	27	Wis.	2,801	81.55	14
4	Wyo.	415	142.84	48	28	Pa.	8,132	77.46	3
5	Mass.	6,640	141.56	9	29	S.C.	1,320	62.35	27
6	Iowa	3,660	139.64	22	30	Colo.	824	62.18	34
7	N.H.	731	137.09	45	31	Tex.	4,715	61.14	6
8	Del.	433	136.13	47	32	R.I.	484	61.12	37
9	Idaho	794	134.89	44	33	Va.	1,965	59.21	15
10	Me.	1,224	133.95	35	34	Calif.	6,218	58.74	2
11	Mich.	8,333	130.78	7	35	Okla.	1,279	57.27	26
12	N.Y.	19,366	130.58	1	36	Mo.	1,844	46.63	11
13	Neb.	1,611	121.54	33	37	Ala.	1,209	39.49	17
14	N.J.	5,834	120.65	8	38	La.	979	36.48	21
15	Ind.	4,590	116.67	12	39	Ariz.	252	33.62	38
16	Vt.	436	115.42	46	40	Ky.	725	24.62	19
17	S.D.	752	115.21	41	41	Tenn.	749	22.75	16
18	Kan.	2,169	113.84	31	42	N.C.	892	21.96	10
19	Utah	783	113.67	39	43	Ga.	717	20.82	13
20	Ill.	9,733	111.72	4	44	Fla.	542	19.56	20
21	Wash.	2,570	108.03	23	45	Miss.	363	16.66	25
22	Ohio	7,867	99.00	5	46	N.M.	113	16.59	40
23	D.C.	750	93.50	36	47	W.Va.	129	6.43	29
24	Ore.	1,400	92.02	32	48	Ark.	86	4.50	30

* Reproduced from Sloan, W., "Some statistics in institutional provisions for the mentally handicapped," *Am. J. ment. Defic.*, 1955, *59*, 380–387.

5,276,755 with I.Q.'s between 50 and 70. In all, Dingman and Tarjan estimate that there are 5,714,255 individuals in the United States with an intelligence quotient of below 70.

Many traits and capacities of the child are either directly or indirectly related to the degree of mental retardation. The capacity for academic achievement is one of the most important of such relationships. Ingram states that approximately 2% of all school children are so severely retarded that they are in need of a highly differentiated and specialized academic program.[14] But, in addition to this group, Ingram points out that another 15% to 18% of school children have abilities below the normal range (these are children with I.Q. scores of 70 to 90). Such children are likely to present varying degrees of academic disability. If we regard Ingram's figures as being reasonably correct (and they have been generally substantiated by other studies), approximately 20% of all school children, due to lowered mental ability, will show some significant degree of academic disability. This is no small number!

An appreciable number of mentally retarded children are so severely retarded as to require extensive modification of their scholastic program. These are the so-called "trainable" retarded children, who, even though not requiring institutional placement, are not intellectually capable of profiting even from the special class program designed for the more educable child. Goldberg has summarized data relating to the incidence of such trainable retarded children in the general population of school-age children. [15] He states that in 1954 the National Association for Mentally Retarded Children estimated this to be .4%. In 1955, the New York State Department of Education estimated the incidence of such children (defined as children with a mental age of at least 3 years, and with an I.Q. of below 49) to be approximately 3.3 per 1,000 population, or about .3% of the 7- to 15-year-old population. There is considerable agreement that the incidence of trainable mentally retarded children is between .3% and .4% of the school-age population. Goldberg points out that in September, 1956 the total school-age population was approximately 32,000,-000. Therefore, at that time there were estimated to be 95,000 to 130,000 children sufficiently retarded to be termed "trainable and not educable" in the United States. This large group presents society with many unresolved problems.

Tizard studied the prevalence of mental retardation, and his findings

---

[14] Ingram, C. P., *Education of the Slow Learning Child*. New York: The Ronald Press Company, 1953.

[15] Goldberg, I., "Current status of education and training in the United States for training mentally retarded children," *Except. Child.*, 1957, *24*, 146–154.

are felt to be of such importance as to deserve quoting directly from his article.[16] In regard to the number of children involved, he states:

At the present time the proportion of children considered educationally subnormal in different countries varies from about 1% to 4%; a further 6% to 9% are so dull as to require special assistance within the normal school system.

Further, in regard to the provisions available for such retarded children, he states:

All [surveys] have revealed a much higher prevalence of subnormality than any society is known to make provision for. In particular, the needs of infants and preschool children have been overlooked, and it is evident that much uncared for subnormality must exist within children of preschool age.

[16] Tizard, J., "The prevalence of mental subnormality," *Bull. World Hlth. Org.,* 1953, *9,* 423–440.

ch. 2

CONCEPTS OF

INTELLIGENCE AND

INTELLIGENCE TESTS

I N THIS CHAPTER WE SHALL FIRST DISCUSS THE MAJOR CON-
cepts of intelligence. Then we shall turn our attention to some of the more important problems related to the use of intelligence tests.

SOME MAJOR CONCEPTS OF INTELLIGENCE

The mentally retarded child, by definition, is significantly below average in intellectual functioning. But what is meant by "intellectual functioning"? In order to deal with this fundamental problem, there is presented first an overview of the general nature of intelligence, then a brief review of some of the major theories which have been formulated in an attempt to define its characteristics. Next, there is a discussion of the manner in which intelligence is *distributed* in the total population, and finally, there is a look at the varied patterns of intellectual maturation.

Definitions of Intelligence

There are many theories which purport to explain the nature of intelligence. As one studies them he soon becomes aware of the fact that there is a great deal of disagreement among "authorities" concerning the concept of "intelligence." In fact, it has been said that "intelligence is what intelligence tests test," and one may well speculate about the implications of such a statement. Major hypotheses in regard to the nature of intelligence are summarized in the following paragraphs, but due to limitations of space they cannot be presented in detail. For a more complete elaboration of a particular theoretical approach the reader is referred to the appropriate bibliographical references.

Hutt and Gibby state that, from one point of view, the major theories in regard to the nature of intelligence may be ordered on a scale.[1] Toward one end of the continuum are those theories which regard intelligence as a *unitary* phenomenon. Toward the other end are those which regard it as a highly *specific* phenomenon.

The unitary concepts of intelligence are best exemplified by the work of Spearman.[2] Following extensive research and integration of existing data, Spearman concluded that there is one fundamental *general factor* that underlies *all* manifestations of intelligence. He termed this factor *g*. According to Spearman, individuals are born with different amounts of *g*, although *g* is also influenced by experiences in life. The *g* factor is involved to some extent in all behavior of the individual, and some behavior is very heavily dependent upon the amount of this factor. Some types of behavior are dependent upon specific abilities, called *s*. In addition behavior is influenced by group personality factors and by non-intellectual traits. The *s* factor is specific to a given activity. Spearman thus postulates that there are two major factors involved in all intelligent behavior: a common factor *g*, and a specific factor *s*. He believes that differences in intelligence from one child to another are essentially functions of the differences in the amount of *g* that is present. According to this theory the mentally retarded child has a significantly lesser amount of the *g* factor than normal or superior children.

In direct opposition to this unitary concept of Spearman's is the concept proposed by Thorndike.[3] He has concluded that intelligent behavior is the function of highly specific abilities, and that general intelligence is merely the aggregate of these specifics. Unlike Spearman, Thorndike does not believe there is such a trait as *general intelligence*, but, rather, he believes there are a number of *specific intelligences*. According to Thorndike there are many of these; in fact, there may be as

[1] Hutt, M. L., and Gibby, R. G., *The Child: Development and Adjustment*. Boston: Allyn and Bacon, Inc., 1959.

[2] Spearman, C., *The Abilities of Man*. New York: The Macmillan Co., 1927.

[3] Thorndike, E. L., *et al.*, *The Measurement of Intelligence*. New York: Bureau of Publications, Teachers College, Columbia University. 1926.

many specific intelligences as there are different kinds of intelligent behaviors. However, he also believes that all of these specific intelligences
may be grouped into three major categories. Thorndike calls these categories *abstract, mechanical,* and *social* intelligence. Of the three, abstract
intelligence correlates the most highly with achievement in academic
subjects.

There are other theories that fall between the extremes maintained
by Spearman and Thorndike. Specifically, Thurstone, for example, states
that there is no single general factor of intelligence, but rather there are
twelve *primary mental abilities.*[4] He named seven of these which he felt
had been well delineated as follows: *V* (verbal relations), *S* (spatial relations), *P* (perceptual abilities), *W* (words), *M* (memory), *N* (numerical abilities), and *I* (induction). The other five factors have not been so
specifically identified. Thurstone believes that all twelve factors are essentially independent of each other and influence various behaviors in
different proportions.

Wechsler deplores the fact that many people feel that intelligence
is not adequately defined.[5] He states that the difficulty is not so much
that psychologists cannot agree on a definition of intelligence, but that
intelligence itself is not a tangible entity. Rather, it is a limiting construct—an abstract rather than a material fact—and for this reason, it is
known only through its properties and effects. According to Wechsler,
any definition must be concerned ultimately with what intelligence involves and what it distinguishes, rather than with what it is. As he suc-
cinctly states: "We know intelligence by what it enables us to do."
Wechsler defines intelligence operationally as the aggregate or global
capacity of the individual to act purposefully, to think rationally, and to
deal effectively with his environment. Further, he stresses the fact that
many determinants other than intellectual ability *per se* are involved in
intelligent behavior. These would include: the goal-directed nature of
the behavior, drive, incentive, and personality variables.

It is the authors' contention that any definition of intelligence is a
rather arbitrary matter at the present time. Intelligence may be conceptualized as the "ability to learn or profit from experience," or as an "abstract conceptual ability," or as "an aggregate of a variety of factors,"
or in one of many other such ways. But in each instance *different measures of intelligence, based upon different conceptions of the nature of in-*

---

[4] Thurstone, L. L., *Vectors of the Mind: Multiple Factor Analysis for the Isolation of Primary Traits.* Chicago: University of Chicago Press, 1935.

[5] Wechsler, D., *The Measurement and Appraisal of Adult Intelligence.* Baltimore: The Williams & Wilkins Co., 1958.

telligence, will correlate differently with different criteria. Further, if one examines the most commonly used tests of intelligence, he will readily conclude that they are heavily loaded with abilities of a verbal nature, and also that they are really composites of measures of ability to *learn, remember* and *synthesize* experiences, especially of a verbal nature. All such abilities are measured by means of intelligence test items that are very closely related to the academic elements of the school curriculum and to the verbal experience that is so highly emphasized in our Western culture.

Changing concepts of intelligence

A much needed reorientation is thus apparently taking place in the manner in which we view the nature of intelligence. There is, however, a basic issue that remains to be resolved in regard to our concept of intelligence. On the one hand we can regard a person's intellectual *capacities* as being relatively fixed and static. That is, a person might be born with a *fixed* intellectual capacity that is manifested from birth onward— it is a constant. On the other hand, we might *not* need to regard intellectual *functioning* as being such a constant, but as a *variable* depending upon the interaction of many complex forces both internal and external to the individual. It is thus a resultant—a product. As Perry points out:[6]

If, however, intelligence—again as measured and observed—is regarded as a product of the hypothetical constant intelligence gift—that is, innate biological capacity—and the experience that the person has been through, then it is conceivable that *differences in experience* (as well as biological gift) will help determine what is measurable and observable as intelligence. The idea that intelligence is a variable product of interaction and not a constant is becoming more generally held.

He also points out that this is another instance of the 20th century's basic scientific revolution in ways of thinking about humans and other phenomena—as interaction processes rather than as discrete entities. The manner in which we regard intelligence thus assumes a position of major importance. If, as Perry points out, we assume that intelligence is constant, then programs for mentally retarded individuals will need to move in directions of improvement of their custodial care and vocational training as persons of limited basic capacities. If we accept the interactional concept, then we will endeavor to see what can be done to improve

---

[6] Perry, S. E., "Some theoretic problems of mental deficiency and their action implications," *Psychiat.*, 1954, *17*, 51.

the operating level of mentally retarded individuals—to raise their "intelligence operating level." As Perry states:

The one concept implies making the most of what there is in the capacity of the subnormal person; the other concept implies seeing what can be done to intervene in his subnormal functioning.

We are faced on the one hand with accepting the status quo of the individual, or on the other with rejecting the fact that his condition is fixed. Further, important action implications stem from these two concepts of intelligence. If we accept the interactional concept, then we may do much more from the preventive standpoint. Influences or factors involved may be manipulated, and this may prevent the end-product that is labeled defective intelligence. If we accept the constancy concept, then possible prevention programs become more limited.

The older theories of intelligence tended to view it as a sort of separate entity within the child, relatively independent of outer influences such as environmental and social institutions and values. Gradually this viewpoint began to change, and the effects of outer influences were recognized. However, even then intelligence continued to be regarded as a separate entity. Newer approaches view intelligence as but one part of the total dynamics of the child, one which is related to his total personality and its functioning. The human being functions as a total organism, and so the manifestations of intelligence cannot be separated from the total functioning of the child—it is part of his total personality picture.

Fromm and Hartman have dealt extensively with this point of view.[7] They discuss the many factors that interfere with the manifestation of the child's "true" intellectual potentials. These include: (1) neurotic inhibitions, such as inhibition of curiosity and aggression, physical handicaps, or emotional deprivation; (2) learning disabilities, such as inhibited curiosity or specific fears; and (3) temporary intellectual dysfunctioning based on emotional conflict, such as examination fear, fear of exhibitionism, or need to exceed potentials.

Thinking cannot be separated from feeling—it is but one aspect of the total behavior of the child. The approach, therefore, to an understanding of the retarded child must be a dynamic one, based upon an understanding of his total personality. This is the approach followed in this book.

---

[7] Fromm, E., and Hartman, L., *Intelligence: A Dynamic Approach.* Garden City, N.Y.: Doubleday & Company, Inc., 1955.

Distribution of Intelligence

We all know that there are vast differences in the range of intellectual ability among children. Some children are markedly inferior, and others, by contrast, are markedly superior in intelligence. Most children, however, cluster around a central point in the distribution of intelligence that is called the *mean* or "average." A particular child may rank at any point on this total continuum from very inferior to very superior, from the standpoint of the amount of intelligence he possesses (*quantity* or degree). In addition, he may differ from others in the kind of intelligence (*quality*) which is characteristic of him.

It is important that we consider how intelligence, from a quantitative point of view, is *distributed* (that is, "spread out") in the general population. Most human characteristics are distributed among the total population in a characteristic pattern. For example, if we took all the people in the world and arranged them in order according to their height from tallest to shortest, we would find that a very small percentage would be exceedingly tall in stature, the greatest percentage would be "average" in height, and a very small percentage would be exceedingly short in stature. If we plotted the number of people of each height so as to form a graphic representation, we could construct a curve similar to that shown in Figure 1. Any given individual would rank, according to his height, at the appropriate point in this distribution.

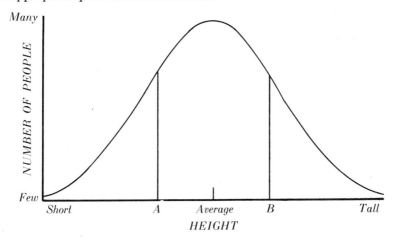

FIGURE 1. NORMAL DISTRIBUTION CURVE

The distribution depicted by this curve is representative of most human traits, such as height, weight, mechanical aptitude, physical strength, dependency upon others, aggressiveness, or any of a multitude of other characteristics. This curve is known as the *normal distribution* curve, or the curve of *normal probability*. Such a curve also results when the distribution of intelligence in the general population is plotted. When a human characteristic is distributed in this way there is a clustering around the average for that characteristic, and decreasing frequencies as we move toward either *tail* (end) of the curve.

One of the representative curves of the distribution of intelligence in white American-born children has been constructed by Terman and Merrill.[8] They plotted such a curve for the I.Q. of 2,904 children between 2 and 18 years of age. It is reproduced in Figure 2.

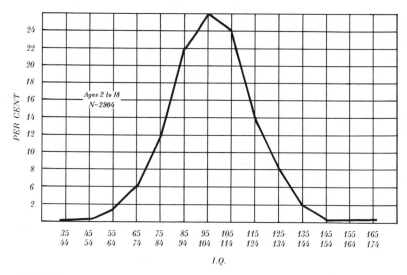

FIGURE 2. DISTRIBUTION OF COMPOSITE I.Q.'S OF STANDARDIZATION GROUP*

According to the data accumulated by Terman and Merrill, the statistical average in I.Q. is calculated to be 100 (on the 1937 revision of the Binet intelligence test), but children whose I.Q.'s fall between 95 and 104 are considered to be "average" or "normal" in intelligence. Approximately 3% of the total group are considered to be "feebleminded," and fall below an I.Q. of 65.

It is also important that we pay particular attention to the nature

---

[8] Terman, L. M., and Merrill, M. A., *Measuring Intelligence*. Boston: Houghton Mifflin Company, 1937, p. 37.

* Reported from Terman, L. M., and Merrill, M. A., *Measuring Intelligence* Boston: Houghton Mifflin Company, 1937, p. 37.

of the distribution of I.Q.'s around the *mean*. The standard deviation (S.D.) of the curve plotted by Terman and Merrill is 16.4 I.Q. points. Statisticians have determined that the following statistical relationships *always* hold for any normal distribution of measurements: 68.26% of the population fall between points one S.D. above and one S.D. below the mean; 95% of all cases fall between points two S.D.'s above and below the mean; and 99.7% of all cases fall between points three S.D.'s above and below the mean.

Since the mean of the distribution of I.Q.'s on the *Terman-Merrill* test is 100, and the S.D. is 16.4 points in I.Q., approximately 68% of all children have I.Q.'s (on this particular test) between 84 and 116 (between one S.D. above and one S.D. below the mean); 95% have I.Q.'s between 67 and 133 (between two S.D.'s above and two S.D.'s below the mean); and approximately 99% (almost all) have I.Q.'s between 51 and 149 (between three S.D.'s above and three S.D.'s below the mean). Although the numerical value of the mean I.Q. and the size of the S.D. vary according to the specific intelligence test utilized (since any specific test has some errors of measurement), it is believed that intelligence is distributed over the total population in a similar manner, regardless of the test utilized for its measurement.

Some authorities believe that, even though intelligence is normally distributed over an unselected population, the lower range of the total distribution is not normally distributed.[9] In support of such a contention some surveys have indicated that there are, in actuality, many more persons of lowered intelligence than would be predicted from the normal curve.

Dingman and Tarjan have made an analysis of such expected and actually occurring frequencies of mental retardation.[10] They estimated that there were actually 334,421 more persons below I.Q. of 70 than would be predicted from the normal distribution curve, and then con-

[9] See:
  (a) Burt, C., "The inheritance of mental ability," *Amer. Psychologist,* 1958, *13,* 1–15.
  (b) Larsson, T., and Sjogren, T., "A methodological, psychiatric, and statistical study of a large Swedish rural population," Ejnar Muuksgaard. Copenhagen: *Acta Psychiatrica et Neucelogica,* Scandinavica Supplement u m, 1954, *89.*
  (c) Penrose, L., *The Biology of Mental Defect.* London: Sidgewick and Jackson, 1954.
  (d) Thompson, G., *Social Implications of the 1947 Scottish Method Survey.* London: University of London Press, 1953.

[10] Dingman. H., and Tarjan, G., "Mental retardation and the normal distribution curve," *Amer. J. ment. Defic.,* 1960, *64,* 991–994.

structed a new curve based upon their data. This curve is shown in Figure 3.

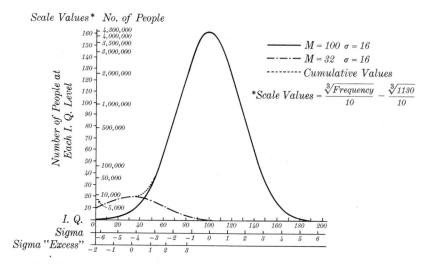

FIGURE 3. Frequency Distribution of I.Q.'s (Assuming a Total Population of 179,000,000)*

The distribution of intelligence depicted is in fact a "combined" curve, made up of two components: (a) a normal curve based on the theoretical "general population"; and (b) a truncated normal curve based on the excess frequencies. According to Dingman and Tarjan, the mentally retarded segment of the curve is composed of two subgroups. One represents the lower end of the normal distribution curve of intelligence, and the other the "excess" instances with a separate frequency distribution. The curve of the latter group is cut sharply at I.Q. zero, since this degree of retardation is "incompatible with life."

From inspection of the curve represented in Figure 3, it is apparent that mental retardation is *not* a point on the curve, but is, rather, an area under the curve which describes a *range* in intelligence. Thus, mentally retarded children range over a significant portion of the total scale. So do "normal" or "bright" children. In other words, any particular grouping of children designated by any descriptive term varies in degree of intelligence, and often will show as much (or even more) inter-group as intra-group variability.

* Reproduced from Dingman, H., and Tarjan, G., "Mental retardation and the normal distribution curve," *Amer. J. ment. Defic.*, 1960, *64*, 991–994.

Patterns of Mental Growth

Many studies have been concerned with the relationships of growth in mental abilities to increase in chronological age.[11] There are some points of difference in these studies, largely because different investigators have utilized different measures of mental ability or have applied them to different groups of children. But if these facts are taken into consideration the major findings of such studies tend to agree quite closely.

The curve representing the growth of intelligence, when smoothed out, assumes the form of a modified semi-parabola. Inspection of this

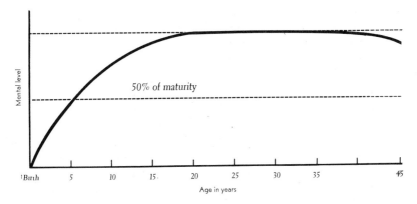

FIGURE 4. Growth in Intellectual Ability, From Birth to 45 Years*

curve indicates that mental abilities grow rapidly in the periods of infancy and early childhood. This period of rapid growth is followed by one of slower growth, which is continued until the *apogee* (maximum) is reached during early adulthood. Thorndike states that there is a cessation in growth of mental ability at about age 21, and most authorities tend to agree that measured intelligence shows no increment beyond

[11] Summaries of these have been made by:
  (a) Bayley, N., "On the growth of intelligence," *Amer. Psychologist,* 1955, *10,* 805–818.
  (b) Lorge, I., "Intellectual changes during maturity and old age," *Rev. Educ. Res.,* 1947, *17,* 326–332.
  (c) Wechsler, D., "Cognitive, conative, and non-intellectual intelligence," *Amer. Psychologist,* 1950, *5,* 78–83.
  (d) Jones, H. E., and Conrad, H. S., "The growth and decline of intelligence: A study of a homogeneous group between the ages of ten and sixty," *Genet. Psychol. Monogr.,* 1933, *13,* No. 3.
  *Reproduced from Hutt, M. L., and Gibby, R. G., *The Child: Development and Adjustment.* Boston: Allyn and Bacon, Inc., 1959, p. 204.

about this age.[12] When this point is reached no apparent change occurs for a period of years (there is a *plateau* in the curve). But in the middle years of life there is a slight decrement in intellectual functioning, and this decrement increases with increasing chronological age. In *senescence* (old age) there is a gradually increasing decrement in mental abilities as measured by present intelligence tests.*

The curve of mental growth, depicted in Figure 4, has other significant characteristics. It may be observed that there is a continuing regular decrement in acceleration of mental growth from the point of its origin until the apogee is reached. For this reason the curve is described as one of *negative acceleration.* By the age of three to five years, approximately one-half of the total mental growth of the individual has taken place. At the age of 30, there is a tendency for decrements to appear in intellectual functioning. This latter aspect of the maturation of intelligence has become the center of a great deal of controversy. Some authorities, such as David Wechsler, support such a point of view. Others criticize it on the grounds that most intelligence tests place a premium on speed and academic abilities, and so the intellectual functions of the older person are not validly measured. Further, critics point out that perceptual deficiencies serve to depress the intelligence test scores of older persons, since scores on some test items (particularly on non-verbal items) are significantly correlated with muscular control and vision.

Garrison has pointed out that even though the mental growth curves of superior, average and dull children differ in some respects, they all conform to the same general pattern.[13] This point is illustrated in Figure 5.

The three curves represent the mental development of (1) superior, (2) average, and (3) dull children. It should be observed that although the pattern of growth is essentially the same for each group, the differences on the curves become greater with increased chronological age. As Garrison points out, the backward child tends to become more inferior when compared with the average as he gets older, and the superior child becomes even more superior.

The uniqueness of the pattern of mental growth of each individual is shown in Figure 6.[14] Note that the mental age for each of the five

---

[12] Thorndike, E. L., *et al., op. cit.*

* This does not mean that people cannot learn anything more after young adulthood or even in old age, but only that mental *capacity,* or the general *rate* of learning, reaches a peak in young adulthood and decreases in later life.

[13] Garrison, K., *Psychology of Adolescence,* 5th Ed. Englewood Cliffs, N.J.: Prentice-Hall, Inc., 1956, p. 79.

[14] Garrison, *op. cit.,* p. 83.

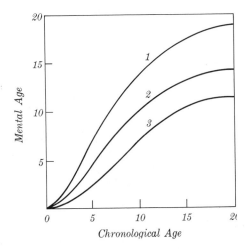

FIGURE 5. The Mental Development of (1) Superior, (2) Average, and (3) Dull Children*

subjects (all boys) was the same at the chronological age of seven years, but that at age seventeen the differences in mental ages were pronounced. The *rates* of growth also are markedly different from one child to another, with each child having his own unique pattern of mental development. Garrison points out that merely because a child develops slowly one should not conclude that he is mentally inferior. He states that a superior child may be slow in getting started, while a dull child may make an impressive beginning.

INTELLIGENCE TEST PERFORMANCE

We are all probably familiar to some extent with the intelligence test. Possibly we have taken one ourselves for educational guidance. It is very difficult to discuss mental retardation without in some way making reference to intelligence tests and the performance made on them by mentally retarded children. Yet the relationships of an intelligence test score to the level of intelligence or of intelligence test scores to intelligence itself need to be thoroughly examined and clarified. There is much misunderstanding of these relationships, which has led to confusion and considerable muddy thinking on the part of many people.

---

* Reproduced from Karl C. Garrison, *Psychology of Adolescence*, 5th Ed. © 1956, by permission of Prentice-Hall, Inc., Englewood Cliffs, N.J., p. 79.

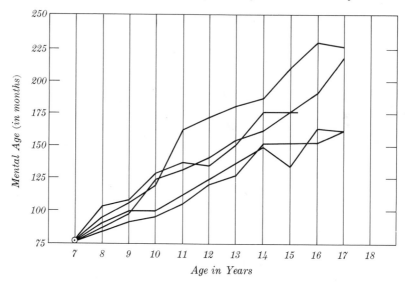

FIGURE 6.   DIVERGING INDIVIDUAL MENTAL GROWTH CURVES*

We shall take a brief look at two concepts relating to intelligence tests at this point. These are the concepts of *mental age* and *intelligence quotient*. They will be discussed in more detail in Chapter Nine. The *mental age* that a child achieves on an intelligence test is derived from the total score that he makes on that test. It indicates the intellectual level at which the child is functioning. Thus, a mental age of six years indicates that the child has a mental age equal to that of the average six-year-old child; a mental age of ten years means that he has a mental age equivalent to that of the average ten-year-old child. The mental age *by itself*, however, tells us very little about the child's mental capacities. It must be considered in relation to the child's physical (or *chronological*) age. A child six years of age who achieves a mental age of ten years is much different from a child with a chronological age of sixteen years who achieves a mental age of ten years. The first child would be considerably advanced in intellectual functioning; the second would be retarded. The *intelligence quotient* (the *I.Q.*) is a convenient way of representing the relationship between the child's mental and chronological age. It is calculated by dividing the mental age by the chronological age, and multiplying the obtained quotient by 100 (to remove the decimal figures). For example, if a child with a chronological age of eight years and four months (100 months) achieves a mental age of

* Reproduced from Garrison, *op. cit.*, p. 83.

six years and 10 months (82) months), his resulting I.Q. is 82. This is a much oversimplified presentation, but it will suffice for the present. (Some intelligence tests do not consider mental age, but convert the score directly into an I.Q. An example of such a test is the *Wechsler*, which is discussed in Chapter Nine.)

One basic point that certainly needs clarification is the common tendency to identify a particular test score with a particular category or degree of intellectual deficit (*i.e.*, Jacky achieves an I.Q. score of 76 on a particular test, and therefore is called a mentally retarded child). From this point of view, the test performance tends to be seen as an absolute measure of intellectual deficit. Such a concept is fallacious; the intelligence test score and the degree of intellectual capacity of the child are not synonymous. We must constantly bear in mind the fact that the intelligence test score is a representation of a *single* sample of the behavior of a child *at a particular time*, and that this sample may be highly biased and subject to considerable fluctuation from one time to another. Any intelligence test score is a product of many factors. It is a function, first, of the total capacities and personality characteristics of the child. Second, since no psychological measurement may be made with absolute accuracy, it is a function of the inaccuracies in measurement of the particular test utilized. This is called the *error of measurement*. The amount of this error varies from one intelligence test to another. It also varies from time to time with the same test, even when given to the same child. Third, it is a function of many factors external to the child, such as social and cultural influences, the examiner, the situation in which the test is given, and the like. Since it is subject to so many different influences, it is not possible to equate directly any given intelligence test score with any given level of intellectual functioning. Two children, for example, may achieve precisely the same intelligence test score and yet be of widely separated intellectual levels. Joe and Billy may both achieve an intelligence test score of 55. Following evaluation of the factors involved, it may be concluded that Joe is a mentally retarded child, but that Billy is a child of above-average intelligence whose functioning has been inhibited by some emotional disorder.

As early as 1925 Bisch stated that mental tests were employed to objectify mental processes and in this sense they were quantitative measures.[15] He felt that their greatest value consisted in liberating the diagnostician from the old-time vagueness and uncertainty which resulted

[15] Bisch, L. E., *Clinical Psychology*. Baltimore: The Williams & Wilkins Co., 1925.

from purely subjective standards. The authors do not agree completely with this point of view. After a child has been examined, the examiner needs to evaluate the performance carefully and determine what possible factors might have influenced the obtained test score (in either a positive or negative direction). This demands a high degree of professional skill, and the interpretation of a test score is *not* the mechanical process that Bisch implies, but is intricate and difficult, involving many subjective observations and judgments on the part of the examiner. For example:

Carole, a seven-year-old girl, achieved an intelligence test score of 68. The examiner, despite the lowered level of her test performance, noted that she was a child of good average intelligence, and that the test score was depressed because of her severe fear of the testing situation. She had formerly attended a one-room school, and was now attending a large city elementary school. He recommended re-evaluation at a later date after she had become accustomed to her changed situation.

Why do we tend to depend so much upon the intelligence test score? It might well be that we cannot yet agree on the nature of mental retardation, as Burton points out.[16] We then gain "putative satisfaction" by leaning upon intelligence tests, even though we know their inadequacies. We tend to look upon them as being infallible. There is a further danger in this regard. The overemphasis upon the use of the intelligence test leads to an oversimplification of the whole concept of mental retardation. As Burton puts it, the conception then changes "from a multidimensional to a unitary one. It has again resulted in accentuating the intellectual at the expense of the total personality."

McCulloch and his co-workers raise questions as to the applicability of intelligence tests to all individuals.[17] They conclude, following a study of word learning by mental defectives, that the results are consistent with the hypothesis that intelligence tests directly measure apprehension *grasp* rather than ability for repetitive learning, and so carry implications that these tests are inadequate for prediction in a large segment of human behavior. This further implies that all intelligence tests do not have the same meaning for all people.

Constancy of intelligence test scores

This brings us to a consideration of the much debated topic of the constancy of the intelligence test score—that is, how stable is such

16 Burton, A., "Psychotherapy with the mentally retarded," *Amer. J. ment. Defic.*, 1954, *58*, 486–489.

17 McCulloch, T. L., Reswick, J., and Irving, R., "Studies of word learning in mental defectives," *Amer. J. ment. Defic.*, 1955, *60*, 133–139.

a score over a period of time? The research literature is replete with apparently conflicting studies; some maintain that it remains fairly constant, others stress the fact that it is variable and shows considerable fluctuation. Much of the difficulty in dealing with this problem may stem partly from attempts to overgeneralize about the matter of constancy as well as from a tendency to identify test scores with behavioral aspects of intellectual functioning. In part we need to consider the characteristics of various groups of children in talking about I.Q. constancy rather than attempting to generalize for all children. The I.Q. has different "meanings" depending upon the group to which it is applied. Thus, an I.Q. derived for a mentally retarded group has a *different* reliability than one for an "average" group. Similarly, an I.Q. for an infant is less reliable than that for an adolescent.

Let us, for example, consider measures of intelligence on young children. How constant are their intelligence test scores from year to year? Goodenough raises some objections to the results of intelligence tests given to infants and children two or three years of age.[18] She points out that: (1) they do not necessarily have the same predictive value for later mental development as those given after school age; and (2) they are not necessarily reliable. Goodenough feels that tests given in early life have little value for prognosis; further, they are often inaccurate even for the time of administration. There is some additional evidence to substantiate this point of view.[19] Honzig, following a study of repeated tests on a group of preschool children, concluded:[20]

These results suggest the impossibility of making an accurate prognosis of future ability on the basis of a simple mental test given before the age of two, but suggest further that repeated tests and tests at later ages of the preschool span have increasing predictive value.

Further, the constancy of the measured intellectual functions fluctuates with the intellectual level of the group examined. In general, as

[18] Goodenough, F. L., "Experiments of raising the I.Q.," in *Readings in Child Psychology* (W. Dennis, ed.). Englewood Cliffs, N.J.: Prentice-Hall, Inc., 1951, pp. 320–328.
[19] See the following references:
  (a) Anderson, J. E., "The limitations of infant and preschool tests in the measurement of intelligence," *J. Psychol.*, 1939, *8*, 351–379.
  (b) Bayley, N., "Mental growth during the first 3 years; A developmental study of 61 children by repeated tests," *Genet. Psychol. Monogr.*, 1932, *14*, No. 1.
[20] Honzig, M. P., "The constancy of mental test performance during preschool periods," *J. genet. Psychol.*, 1938, *52*, 285–302.

pointed out earlier, those children with I.Q.'s around the average tend to have more constant I.Q.'s when tested a second time than either the very bright or very dull children. We are here concerned only with the constancy of measured intellectual capacities in the below-average groups. Thus, the true scores of children with low intelligence test scores contain a larger probable error of measurement than those scoring around the average.

We know that marked fluctuations in the I.Q.'s of children testing below average do occur, apart from the statistical variation cited above, when they are retested. Repeated studies have been made of children who were reared in undesirable environments and later placed in more favorable surroundings. In such instances there have been, at times, considerable increases in intelligence test scores. Examples of such recent studies are detailed in the following paragraphs.

Skeels and Dye studied the effects of differential stimulations on mentally retarded children.[21] Originally they were interested in two illegitimate children whose mothers were feebleminded, and who were placed in an orphanage. At the age of one and a half years these children were examined on the *Kuhlman-Binet Test* and achieved I.Q.'s of 46 and 35 respectively. Behaviorally their actions were also quite typical of mentally retarded children. They were accordingly transferred to an institution for feebleminded children. Six months later they were re-examined, and found to have I.Q.'s (again on the *Kuhlman-Binet*) of 77 and 87. A year later their I.Q.'s were found to be 100 and 88. At about three and a half years of age they were 95 and 93. It was found that the two children had been greatly liked by the ward attendants, who played with them, took them for rides, and in general provided them with a positive *therapeutic* climate. Following this initial experience, 13 children were then transferred from the orphanage to the institution for feebleminded. The mean I.Q. of the group was about 64, with a range of 35 to 89. The children also showed the behavioral characteristics of retarded children. As a control, they were compared with 12 children of similar intellectual level and behavior who were retained in the orphanage. In the institution for the feebleminded the children were placed in wards with older and brighter children. According to Skeels and Dye, the environment of the transferred group was positive and stimulating, while that of the control group tended to be the opposite. They were then re-ex-

---

[21] Skeels, H. M., and Dye, H. B., "A study of the effects of differential stimulation on mentally retarded children," *Proceedings of the American Association on Mental Deficiency*, 1939, *44*, 114–136.

amined psychologically. The experimental group showed a mean increase in I.Q. of 27.5 points, but the children in the control group all *decreased* in I.Q.

There are, of course, many factors to be taken into consideration in evaluating the Skeels and Dye study. The positive emotional environment provided for the experimental group may be of importance, as well as the fact that deprivation at an early age is generally believed to hinder the psychological growth of the child. On the other hand, one might argue that the reason for the change in I.Q. was that the tests given were unreliable, or that they were administered improperly, and so forth. We are not, however, concerned at this point with the reason for the change *per se.* The important fact is that the original measure of intellectual functioning did *not* remain constant, but *did change* over a relatively short period of time.

Marchand studied a group of 123 retarded individuals before and after being placed in employment outside an institution. He concluded that:[22]

1. Eighty per cent of these individuals had higher I.Q.'s after having had such employment experiences. Of the group, 50 per cent increased from 1 to 9 I.Q. points, while 38 per cent increased from 10 to 31 points in I.Q.
2. There are consistent differences in the drive, attitudes, and façades of the individuals who developed significantly as well as those who did not show such change.
3. The average rise of the experimental group was 9.2 points of I.Q., while the group with which they were compared (the control group) showed a mean drop of 1.4 I.Q. points.

He states: "We score the quantitative output of the patient who may be blocked and deterred because of many emotional and/or organic reasons." Marchand readily admits that the bare I.Q. has little significance in itself, other than to give a barren level *at which an individual is functioning at a precise period in his life.* He is emphatic in stating that outside vocational experiences have not been the sole cause of the increase in I.Q. Further, Marchand feels that the enriching and satisfying experiences that result give the person a better chance to respond at a maximal level of functioning on standardized intelligence tests. As he states, the increase appears to be caused by an opening-up process of the dull emotional tone of the retarded individual.

Cultural factors also may affect the intelligence test score. This con-

[22] Marchand, J., "Changes of psychometric test results in mental defective employment care patients," *Amer. J. ment. Defic.,* 1956, *60,* 852–859.

clusion has been demonstrated repeatedly. A recent study of this is reported by Fahmy.[23] He tested a group of children from an extremely restricted environmental section of Egypt. Four tests were given to the group. On the *Porteus* the mean score was 76, on the *Goddard* 74, and on the *Goodenough* 50, but on the *Alexander* it was 97. The children tested had no adequate conceptions of straight lines, and had no drawing experience. These were heavily weighted in the first three tests. However, the *Alexander* test involves the manipulations of colored blocks, and colors were much emphasized in the children's culture. Fahmy feels that this study furnishes ample evidence of the effect of culture on the intelligence test score. If a child is removed to a different culture, then changes in his test score may be expected.

Tizard quotes an unpublished study by Clarke and Clarke.[24] In a very carefully controlled study they found that adolescents who came into an institution for retarded children from "very bad" home environments showed a mean gain of ten I.Q. points after a period of two years at the institution. Those who did not come from such a "bad" home environment to the institution did not show such increases.

Collmann and Newlyn studied changes in the *Terman-Merrill* I.Q.'s of 182 retarded children, who were retested within a period of one year following the original test.[25] The correlation between the two obtained I.Q.'s was .93, and of the total of 182 cases, only two of the I.Q.'s rose by nine points and only five cases fell six points. These were the extreme shifts which occurred in I.Q. from test to retest. This study suggests that the I.Q.'s of retarded children tend to be stable within a period of one year.

Alper and Horne studied I.Q. changes in a group of 50 children institutionalized over a long period of time.[26] Originally they had been tested with the 1916 *Binet*, and were all retested with the *Wechsler Adult Intelligence Scale*. The minimum retest interval was 17 years and 9 months, the maximum was 35 years and 3 months, and the mean time between tests was 25 years and 9 months. It was found that in some cases there was considerable shifting of I.Q. within a narrow range, but that extreme shifts were very few in number. The difference between the mean *Binet*

[23] Fahmy, M., *Initial Exploring of the Skilluk Intelligence*. Cairo, Egypt: Dar Misr Printing House, 1954.

[24] Tizard, J., "The prevalence of mental subnormality," *Bull. World Hlth. Org.*, 1953, *9*, 423–440.

[25] Collman, R., and Newlyn, D., "Phases in Terman-Merrill I.Q.'s of mentally retarded children," *Amer. J. ment. Defic.*, 1958, *63*, 307–311.

[26] Alper, A., and Horne, B., "Changes in a group of institutionalized mental defectives over a period of two decades," *Amer. J. ment. Defic.*, 1959, *64*, 472–475.

and mean *Wechsler* total I.Q. scores was not significant. It was concluded that there is a tendency for the I.Q. of institutionalized children to remain relatively consistent.

Honzig *et al.* studied the mental test scores of a group of 252 children over the period from 21 months to 18 years of age.[27] They found that the I.Q.'s of 60 per cent of the group changed 15 points or more, while in the case of 9 per cent the I.Q. changed 30 points or more. These are by no means minor shifts in I.Q. These findings are in sharp contrast to what is still a commonly held view: that the I.Q. is quite constant for all individuals throughout the life span. We must emphasize, therefore, how hazardous it is to attempt to predict the late I.Q. of a supposedly retarded child from a single I.Q. measure obtained on a single test at an early period of life!

When we review the available evidence we are forced to conclude that intelligence test scores need not remain constant from time to time. This is particularly true when we consider the performances of a particular individual as opposed to those of a group. Social and cultural forces, personality factors within the child, the circumstances surrounding the test administration, as well as statistical artifacts of test construction, are all factors that influence the production of an intelligence test score. (These will be discussed in detail in Chapter Nine.)

Intelligence is a product of the total functioning of the child. It is not a separate entity in itself, but is related to all aspects of the child's growth and development. Therefore, we need not expect an intelligence test score for a particular child to remain constant throughout his life. (We have noted the variability of intelligence test scores in the case of Johnny.)

Pseudofeeblemindedness

The confusion of thinking in regard to the relationships between intelligence test scores and behavioral manifestations of intelligence has given rise to the concept of *pseudofeeblemindedness*. According to this concept, an individual who initially behaved and tested at a mentally retarded level, but who later functioned and tested at about the average level of intelligence, was formerly functioning as a *pseudofeebleminded* person. The change in the child's performance may occur spontaneously, or it may be the result of active intervention by another individual (such as removal of the child to a more positive environment, the use of psy-

[27] Honzig, M., MacFarlane, J. and Allen, L., "The stability of mental test performance between two and eighteen years," *J. exp. Educ.*, 1948, *17*, 309–324.

chotherapy or medication, correction of a sensory defect, etc.). Porteus summarizes this point of view when he states:[28]

Very wide differences in intellectual status merely indicated that the first diagnosis was wrong. Any child who finally functions at a normal level proves thereby that he was never feebleminded.

Cantor has also discussed the problem of pseudofeeblemindedness.[29] He states:

The various definitions of pseudofeeblemindedness which have been offered all appear to connote the same general idea, namely, that an individual labeled mentally defective at one time may possibly be labeled "dull-normal" or "normal" or even "superior" at a later date. When such a change occurs, one says that this individual was not "really" mentally defective originally, but, rather, was pseudofeebleminded. But if one is to utilize strictly operational criteria, it becomes apparent that the question of whether an individual is "really" defective is a meaningless one.

As Clarke and Clarke point out, and as previously cited studies indicate, it is clear that an early adverse environment has what may be termed a "crippling" effect on mental development.[30] When this is removed or corrected in some way, the *apparent* intellectual retardation is not as pronounced, and increases in intelligence scores result. They suggest that there may be two types of developmental arrest, one permanent and the other impermanent. They point out that impermanent mental defect is not uncommon, particularly among "subcultural" defective children. As they state:

Mental defectives, of non-organic pathology, like others of normal mentality, are not necessarily static, but capable of change within limits, which are not yet precisely ascertained, nor are the factors influencing and limiting such changes really understood.

There are some children who function somewhat or considerably below their "native potential" for intellectual functioning. Just how many cases of this kind there are is not known, although widespread clinical experience which has been reported and some recent research suggest

[28] Porteus, S. D., *The Practice of Clinical Psychology.* New York: American Book Company, 1941.

[29] Cantor, G. N., "On the incurability of mental deficiency," *Amer. J. ment. Defic.*, 1955, *60*, 362–365.

[30] Clarke, A. D. B., and Clarke, A. M., "Pseudofeeblemindedness, some implications," *Amer. J. ment. Defic.*, 1955, *59*, 507–509.

that the number may be very great. In fact, Tarjan, who differentiates two groups of mental retardates as *physiological* (those who rarely show stigmata and whose retardation is attributable to psychogenic or functional causes), and *pathological* (those who have some demonstrable organic basis for their retardation and show concomitant somatic involvements), estimates that the former group outnumbers the latter by a ratio of 16 to 1.[31] (See page 99.) Many children may tend to function as mental retardates due to types of personality disturbances which produce *inhibition in intellectual functioning*. When and if these personality disturbances are resolved, they may then begin to function at considerably higher mental levels.

Thus, it may be seen that some cases of *apparent* mental retardation may test and function at an intellectual level which falls within the range of mental retardation, but may, under improved conditions, test and function at higher levels, including the average and superior levels of intellectual functioning. These are the cases that may properly be called *pseudofeebleminded* since their true potential is not being manifested. We prefer the term *mental impairment*, since such cases are not, in fact, cases of true mental retardation, and since there has been an impairment in functioning which, in theory at least, is remediable. The term *mental retardation*, then, would be reserved for those cases in which there is a true and permanent inferiority in mental development.

Although the concept of mental impairment is a complex one, and will be discussed in various chapters throughout this book, it would be well to provide further preliminary discussion at this point.

Mental impairment may be said to exist whenever an individual is functioning below the intellectual level of which he would be capable were it not for some interfering and remediable factor. It is *not* to be confused with a test rating of mental retardation due to invalid or faulty administration of the test. In contrast, in mental impairment the individual not only tests lower than his potential but behaves in his total adaptation to the world at an inferior level.

Three main categories of factors may produce or contribute to mental impairment. One of these is *cultural deprivation*. Cultural deprivation is frequently, but not necessarily, associated with very low socioeconomic status. It may be due to cultural poverty in the home, to very inadequate and inferior schooling, or to serious inconsistencies in cultural experiences. In any case, the environment is seriously deficient in

---

[31] Tarjan, G., "Research in mental deficiency with emphasis on etiology," *Bull. Menninger Clin.*, 1960, *24,* 57–60.

providing stimulation for intellectual growth and, after a period of time, the individual may then behave as though he were retarded in native intellectual endowment. (See Chapter Six, especially, for further discussion of this problem.)

A second major category of causes of mental impairment is that of *physical injury or disease*. Sometimes, a disease may so debilitate an individual that he is unable to function in terms of his mental potential until this condition has been corrected or compensated for. Severe anemia is one example of such a condition; tuberculosis is another. Other diseases may affect the functioning of the individual for shorter periods but may nevertheless cause impairment in mental ability during such periods. Injuries, especially those causing sensory impairment, may adversely affect mental functioning. Other conditions, such as severely enlarged adenoids, may interfere with effective sensory functioning or with general physical well-being, and so indirectly affect mental functioning. In general, the kinds of conditions we are discussing produce a *temporary arrest* in mental development and an *impairment* in mental functioning as a consequence. Such conditions should be distinguished from those which affect the central nervous system, and particularly the cortex, in which permanent arrest and retardation may ensue.

Finally, there is the category of *psychological factors* which may cause impairment in mental functioning. This is a highly complex category. All of us have heard of cases of severe psychological disturbances, notably cases of *psychosis* (insanity), in which impairment in mental functioning may occur. But even much milder cases of personality disturbance may produce some degree of mental impairment. Common examples of such cases include the under-achiever in school who functions below his mental potential, but who does not necessarily show mental impairment of the degree which would cause him to be confused with a case of mental retardation.

Due to a great variety of etiological factors, impairment in mental functioning may be associated with various types of personality difficulties. Fear of failure, low aspiration level in achievement, fear of rejection, fear of group situations, and fear of teachers may be associated with mental impairment. When any of these or other conditions contribute to impaired mental functioning severe enough to cause the individual to function on intelligence tests and in his other behavior as if he were a case of true mental retardation, the individual may be categorized as showing mental impairment.

We should like to highlight one type of psychological disturbance which can contribute to this end result and which frequently goes undetected. This is the type of case in which severe anxiety, especially when present from infancy, may cause the individual to *withdraw* from full interaction with and participation in his environment. As a result of the anxiety the personality may become *autistic* or *schizoid*, that is, it may *avoid* responding to stimulation. Such children may not show any bizarre behavior manifestations; they may be quiet and even compliant; they may not look outwardly disturbed. But their *resulting inhibition in mental functioning* may closely resemble the condition of true mental retardation. The mental inhibition and impairment may, in such cases, actually be the major clinical symptom of the personality disturbance. In these, and in all other types of personality disturbances in which impaired mental functioning occurs, improvement in the personality adjustment, together with whatever other corrective measures might be indicated, can be followed by improved total behavioral functioning including that in the intellectual area.

Relation of mental retardation to intelligence test score

There is grave danger in equating a lowered intelligence test score with a lowered level of intelligence. The I.Q. is simply a score or ratio, and *in itself* may tell us very little in regard to the possible retardation of the child. Many complex and inter-related factors determine the actual obtained score. As MacFarlane states:

"A given I.Q. must be regarded as a functional composite of mature ability, opportunity, health, attitude toward intellectual achievement, habits of heightened functioning, or let-down under stress, emotional factors in the child, the nature of the test, the impact of the test, etc."[32]

Since any one of a number of factors may result in the depression of a particular I.Q., it is dangerous to estimate the degree of mental retardation from the test score by itself.

It is not on the basis of a test score alone that the diagnosis of mental retardation should rest, nor should it be based on only a careful and qualitative analysis of the responses to a given test. Rather, it should be based on a comprehensive and detailed integration of *all* of the data in regard to the total functioning of the individual in all major life areas. This conclusion has been dramatically reinforced by a recent experience of one of the authors who was attempting to evaluate the in-

[32] MacFarlane, J., "Summations of a Clinician after Three Decades of Longitudinal Research," Presidential Address, Division of Clinical Psychology, Amer. Psychol. Ass., 9/1/56.

tellectual efficiency and potential of supposedly retarded individuals who are also "deaf" or hard of hearing. It has been found in this ongoing project, The Michigan Project for the Deaf-Retarded, that sensory deprivation can profoundly influence the individual's total functioning as well as his performance on a formal intelligence test. Hence, very careful evaluation must be made of life history, personality functioning, sensory abilities, and the like, as well as performance on different kinds of intellectual tests, before a diagnostic evaluation can be attempted.

Just as there is grave danger in identifying a lowered intelligence test score with a lowered level of intelligence, so there is also grave danger in confusing lowered intellectual functioning with the condition of mental retardation. Many other factors need to be considered. As Tizard points out, there are at least six criteria to be considered in arriving at a diagnosis of mental retardation.[33] These are: (1) anatomical and physiological considerations; (2) intellectual measures; (3) educational functioning; (4) social characteristics; (5) emotional reactions; and (6) temperamental considerations. He stresses the fact that diagnosis of a severe or moderate retardation is easy to make (we would question even this) but that the diagnosis of mild retardation is difficult. The reasons for this are: (1) the criteria are unreliably measured; (2) the criteria are inadequately standardized; (3) the predictions are fallible; and (4) what constitutes abnormality is socially determined. Tizard states:

The criteria of mental subnormality are complex, uncertain and not self-consistent. Confusion arises because of errors of measurement, differences in growth patterns, environmental influences, and lack of agreement between the different criteria for diagnosis. Fluctuations in the threshold of community tolerance make the term "mental subnormality" only a relative one, useful mainly for administrative purposes. There is evidence to suggest that mild subnormality is to a large extent a culturally determined disability; it follows that cultural changes can do much to diminish its occurrence. In particular, better maternal and child health services, more adequate educational provisions, social welfare, vocational guidance and training services, and a condition of full employment would together reduce the prevalence of this, the commonest form of mental subnormality.

Sloan and Birch emphasize the same point of view.[34] They stress the fact that mental retardation refers to the *over-all* efficiency of the functioning organism, from both qualitative as well as quantitative

---

[33] Tizard, J., *op. cit.*
[34] Sloan, W., and Birch, J. W., "A rationale for degrees of retardation," *Amer. J. ment. Defic.*, 1955, *60*, 258–264.

points of view. It refers to the maturation, learning capacity, and social adjustment of the individual. *The mentally retarded person is not one who shows more or less of something like mental ability.* Intelligence *per se* is overvalued, praticularly in that it is used to "class" children. Sloan and Birch make one particularly important point which we feel cannot be overstressed. An older concept, still all too prevalent, is that persons achieving a particular intelligence test score belong to a particular class of intelligence. However, the concept should really imply that persons of a particular degree of intellectual retardation usually have an intelligence test score within a particular range. Thus, *a measure of retardation is not synonymous with a measure of intelligence.* As Sloan and Birch state, the intelligence test score should be used together with other attributes of intellectual retardation, such as vocational, social, maturational, and developmental malfunctioning, to evaluate the child (see Chapter Nine). They feel that there are three major areas that must be explored before a diagnosis of mental retardation may be properly established. These three important areas are: (1) the maturational level; (2) the learning ability; and (3) the social adjustment of the child.

ch. 3

CLASSIFICATION AND
CHARACTERISTICS OF
RETARDED CHILDREN

I N THIS CHAPTER, FIRST WE SHALL DEVOTE ATTENTION TO THE major attempts to categorize mentally retarded children. Then, we shall outline some of the characteristics of the mildly, moderately, and severely retarded children, touching briefly upon some of the more extreme pathological "types."

CATEGORIZATION OF MENTAL RETARDATION

Of primary concern are the numerous schemes which have been proposed in attempts at categorizing mental retardation. We shall present, first, characteristics of the major attempts at such categorizations. Following this presentation we shall explore - some of the fundamental problems associated with the process of classification, and finally we shall present criteria for a modern concept of mental retardation.

Attempts at classification of mental retardation

There have been many attempts at classifying in some way children who suffer from mental retardation. The lack of agreement in such attempts may be due to the fact that classification is in some respects an arbitrary matter, and that our knowledge in the field has not been precise enough to lead to an unequivocal classification. Many of the proposed systems are based on different sets of criteria: in some they are based upon some presumed etiology; in others they are based upon behavioral characteristics of the children; and in others they are based upon intelligence test performance. We shall outline several attempts at classification in the following paragraphs.

BENDA'S CLASSIFICATION. Benda was concerned with classification of those children who were regarded as being "intellectually inadequate" (those with I.Q.'s in the range from 50 to 70). According to Benda's proposed classification, there are five major categories of such children. These are:[1]

1. *Emotionally disturbed normal children.* These children score low on intelligence tests because of factors outside the intellectual field. Because of their low scores they are thought to be mentally retarded. (See discussion of pseudofeeblemindedness in Chapter Two.)
2. *Mentally ill children with low intelligence.* These children are unable to cope with the test situation in a successful manner and score low in spite of their adequate intellectual potentials. This is due to a serious emotional disorder, such as childhood schizophrenia or infantile dementia. (See Chapter Eight.)
3. *Biologically normal children with low intelligence.* These children have no demonstrable biological involvements, but have a low degree of intelligence. They are a "normal" part of our population.
4. *Oligoencephaly.* Children in this classification are considered as being pathological in terms of their over-all constitutional inadequacy.
5. *Brain-injured children.* These children are considered by Benda to be more or less "accidental" cases. The injury may result from such causes as birth trauma, infectious diseases, or metabolic disorders.

Even though Benda constantly refers to the psychological test performance in his classification scheme, the point of view is expressed that an adequate diagnosis also rests upon many additional factors.

AMERICAN PSYCHIATRIC ASSOCIATION PROPOSAL. We have mentioned, in Chapter One, a suggested approach to classification proposed by the American Psychiatric Association. In general, this is based upon the behavioral reactions of the child and the amount of care he needs.

---

[1] Benda, C. E., *Developmental Disorders of Mentation and Cerebral Palsies.* New York: Grune & Stratton, Inc., 1952.

It would be well to repeat this threefold classification at this point. The various categories are: (1) the severely deficient; (2) the moderately deficient; and (3) the mildly deficient children. These groups will be described more completely at a later point in this chapter.

STRAUSS' CLASSIFICATION. An approach to classification based, at least in part, upon *etiological* (causative) factors is made by Strauss.[2] He postulates two major groups of disorders: (1) *exogenous* conditions, and (2) *endogenous* conditions. The children forming the exogenous group are essentially brain-injured children. Damage to the brain can occur before, during, or following birth. However, Strauss does not include in this category those children who show signs of gross neurological involvement; he limits it to those with no motor disabilities but whose test performance is indicative of some brain damage. Sometimes the damage to the brain is such that neurological examination does not elicit any "signs" of the damage. It is manifested by subtle alterations in the functioning of the child as revealed by psychological tests. The endogenous classification refers to those children who have no brain damage but who are nonetheless mentally retarded.

LEWIS' CLASSIFICATION. Lewis, like many others, has suggested a twofold classification based in part on the presence or absence of organic brain damage.[3] He calls one category the *pathological* group. In this category are placed those children whose intellectual deficiencies are attributable to some organic brain damage or pathology. Such conditions are considered "abnormal variations" from the normal. He terms the second category the *subcultural* group. These children have no demonstrable brain injuries, and no other physical pathology can be found. Lewis feels that these children are the "extremes" of the normal variations in intelligence that can be expected, on the basis that abilities are distributed in the population from very low to very high. They are not "abnormal" variants like the "pathological" group, but are considered by Lewis as "normal variants."

KANNER'S CLASSIFICATION. Kanner introduced a classification of mental retardation that may be termed in effect a pragmatic grouping.[4]

---

[2] Strauss, A. A., and Lehtinen, M. A., *Psychopathology and Education of the Brain-Injured Child*. New York: Grune & Stratton, Inc., 1947.

[3] Lewis, E. O., "Types of mental deficiency and their social significance," *J. ment. Sci.*, 1933, *79*, 298–304.

[4] Kanner, L., *A Miniature Text Book of Feeblemindedness*. New York: Child Care Publications, 1949, p. 9.

Based upon the behavioral reactions of the child, he proposed three major groups:

1. *Absolute feeblemindedness.* Children are placed in this category who would stand out as "different" in any situation. Their deficiency is so great that they *cannot be helped* significantly at home and so need institionalization.
2. *Relative feeblemindedness.* In this category are placed those children whose limitations are related to the society in which they live. They cannot comply with its intellectual demands.
3. *Apparent or pseudofeeblemindedness.* These children act *as if* they were feebleminded, due to the effect of various causes, but are actually not feebleminded, and have the potential for adequate performance.

A CLASSIFICATION BASED ON THE I.Q. Traditionally, mentally retarded children have been classified, on the basis of intellectual capacities, into four major categories: idiot, imbecile, moron, and borderline. The exact limits of each of these categories are not agreed upon by all authorities. The general characteristics of each of the categories are however, fairly well established.

The lowest category of mentally retarded individuals is the *idiot* level. In terms of I.Q., the range is usually given as from 0 to 30. The diagnosis of "idiot" depends upon many factors besides the intelligence test score, (see Chapter One). Children falling in this category are usually unable to care for themselves in even the most elementary manner. They cannot learn to dress themselves, and may not, in many instances, be able to feed themselves in an adequate manner. They have to be constantly protected from physical dangers, and supervised in other ways. Speech functions are retarded, and remain at a primitive level. Many idiots are mute, and never develop speech functions. Soiling is quite frequent, and inability to control both bladder and bowel functions is not rare. These children cannot profit from the usual special-class programs, and at an adult age are not able to take care of themselves. They need continued custodial care throughout life.

The next highest category is that of *imbecile.* In terms of I.Q., the range is usually given as from 30 to 50. The child ranking at or near the upper limit of the imbecile range is able, with some help, to learn to dress himself. He is also able to learn, after an extensive training period, to control both bladder and bowel functions. He learns to feed himself, although at a later age than does the child of average intellectual capacities. Speech functions are mastered, although they are very simple. Vocabulary remains at a very rudimentary level, but the high-grade imbecile can learn to read a few words, and can, with considerable help, learn to write his name and a few simple words. Such a child can eventually be taught to do simple tasks, and occasionally develops special skills in some art or craft. However, the imbecile can never adequately function by himself in our society, and needs a great deal of close supervision, attention, and continued help.

Ranking above the imbecile is the *moron*. The range of his I.Q. is usually given as from 50 to 70. The high-grade moron usually learns to dress himself adequately, has no great problems in establishing either bowel or bladder controls, and does not usually soil himself. He feeds himself well, and is attentive to his surroundings. Speech functions, even though at a lowered level, are usually adequate, and he learns to read and write at an elementary level. He can profit from the experiences of the special class, and in general is capable of reaching a school reading achievement level equivalent to the fourth grade. He learns to do many manual tasks and, with help, is certainly capable of holding a simple job. With proper guidance, training, and help he can eventually support himself, but he needs guidance throughout his life. Many individuals at this level marry and have families, but function best if they are given the continued support and help of an understanding person. Usually they do not need institutionalization or continued custodial care.

Children ranking at a *borderline* level have difficulties in making an adequate adjustment to the demands of daily life. The I.Q. range of this group is usually from 70 to 80. The area of greatest manifest difficulty of borderline children is that of academic achievement. They are slow in learning such material. In particular, great difficulties are experienced with such school subjects as reading and arithmetic. Usually they are "carried along" in school, and fail many grades. Frequently they are promoted solely on the basis of their age and size, and so sometimes do get as far as the high-school grades. Appropriate school programs for such children are usually not available. This is unfortunate because they would profit from such programs.

THE CLASSIFICATION OF THE AMERICAN ASSOCIATION ON MENTAL DEFICIENCY. In 1959 the American Association on Mental Deficiency published a revised manual dealing with the classification of mental retardation.[5] This manual sets forth in detail both medical and behavioral

---

[5] Heber, R. F., "A manual on terminology and classification in mental retardation," *Amer. J. ment. Defic.*, 1959, *64*, Monogr. Suppl. No. 2.

classifications. We shall regard the latter attempt at classification of degree of mental retardation in the following paragraphs.

The primary classification of mental retardation, according to the Association, utilizes two dimensions: (1) the measured intelligence, and (2) the adaptive behavior of the individual. These dimensions are not conceived as being completely independent of each other, but the postulation of two dimensions is felt to be justified since there are a sufficient number of discrepancies in the levels of performance of each within a single person. Further, it was hoped that the new classification scheme would stimulate needed research on the significance of factors that were previously neglected in diagnosis. In order that a person be termed "mentally retarded," it is required that he demonstrate significant deficiencies in *both* measured intelligence *and* adaptive behavior.

The classification scheme of measured intelligence postulates five levels of retardation, each level being based upon the S.D. of the particular intelligence test employed. *Level 1* includes those individuals whose test score is more than 5 S.D.'s below the mean; *Level 2,* those whose score falls between −4.01 and −5.00 S.D. units; *Level 3,* those whose score lies between −3.01 and −4.00 S.D. units; *Level 4,* those with scores between −2.01 and −3.00 S.D. units; and, *Level 5,* those with scores between −1.01 and −2.00 S.D. units. In terms of the Revised Stanford-Binet intelligence tests (Forms L and M), the various I.Q. levels would be: Level 1, below I.Q. 20; Level 2, I.Q. 35 to 20; Level 3, I.Q. 51 to 36; Level 4, I.Q. 67 to 52; and Level 5, I.Q. 83 to 68. The selection of the particular test or tests to be utilized is the responsibility of the psychologist.

The second dimension of *Adaptive Behavior* includes two major aspects of adjustment: (1) the degree to which the individual is able to function and maintain himself independently; and (2) the degree to which he meets in a satisfactory manner the "culturally-imposed demands of personal and social responsibility." Further, the level of the adaptive behavior of the individual is always evaluated in light of his particular chronological age group. The classification scheme of the American Association on Mental Deficiency postulates four levels of adaptive behavior, as in the case of measured intelligence. It is suggested that the best available measure of adaptive behavior is furnished by the Vineland Social Maturity Scale, an instrument designed to yield a measure of social maturity based on interview data obtained from a reliable observer of the individual being rated.[6] Other tests or observa-

[6] Doll, E. A., *The Vineland Social Maturity Scale—Manual of Directions.* Vineland, N.J.: The Training School, 1935.

tional data can or should be used, "Particularly at the adolescent and adult age . . ."

The levels, based on S.D. units, are: *Level 1, Profound negative deviation,* includes those persons with scores below −4.75 S.D. units; *Level 2, Severe negative deviation,* persons with scores from −3.51 to −4.75 S.D. units; *Level 3, Moderate but definite negative deviation,* those with scores from −2.26 to −3.50 S.D. units; and, *Level 4, Mild but apparent and significant negative deviation,* those with scores from −1.00 to −2.25 S.D. units.

Garfield and Wittson have raised some objections to the definition and reference points for mental retardation in the preceding classification scheme proposed by the American Association on Mental Deficiency.[7] They feel that such a classification offers potentially too wide a range for error, since Level 5 includes those individuals who exceed only one S.D. below the mean to a maximum of two S.D.'s below the mean. This range includes approximately four times as many persons as would be found in all the other four levels of retardation combined, and therefore Garfield and Wittson feel that it allows too wide a latitude for the diagnosis of mental retardation. They would prefer to regard Level 5 (the borderline level) as a separate non-related level, and exclude it from the more specific categories of mental retardation. Thus, individuals of borderline intelligence would not be regarded as mentally retarded, according to the contention of Garfield and Wittson.

But Cantor does not feel that this criticism is of importance.[8] He states that Garfield and Wittson are bothered by the fact that they regard mental retardation as "incurable," and do not wish borderline individuals referred to as mentally retarded. Further, Cantor feels that Garfield and Wittson erroneously imply that a definite line of demarcation can be drawn between "clearly" and "not clearly" retarded individuals.

It is the opinion of the authors that the extension of the classification scheme on Level 5 as proposed by the American Association on Mental Deficiency is certainly defensible. The broadening of the total range of the mentally retarded to include the borderline individual (or the "slow learner") appears to be justified in terms of the difficulties that such a person experiences in adjusting to the problems he encounters

---

[7] Garfield, S., and Wittson, C., "Some reactions to the revised Manual on Terminology and Classification in Mental Retardation," *Amer. J. ment. Defic.,* 1960, *64,* 951–953.

[8] Cantor, A., "A critique of Garfield and Wittson's reaction to the revised Manual on Terminology and Classification," *Amer. J. ment. Defic.,* 1960, *64,* 954–956.

in daily life. These difficulties are particularly true in regard to the level of academic achievement he is able to attain. Further, according to the revised scheme of classification, an individual may not be termed mentally retarded unless he is deficient *both* in measured intelligence *and* adaptive behavior. Inclusion of an evaluation of retardation in adaptive behavior as an indispensable requirement of a diagnosis of retardation is especially to be welcomed.

Problems in classification

Classification of retarded children is important for several reasons. It serves the function of convenience, and enables us to compile data under the appropriate headings for future analysis and study. It thus aids research. Classification helps us to understand how a particular child may be expected to respond when we know some things about other children in his group or *class*. It may help us to clarify problems of etiology (or causation). Further, adequate classification would make much simpler the process of surveying the extent of the problems of mental retardation in society, and would assist us in making comparative studies of different groups.

There are, however, many problems inherent in the task of attempting to devise an adequate system of classification. If, for example, we attempt a classification based upon the behavioral reactions of retarded children (like some of the cited systems of classification), we need to take into account the fact that children with the same kinds of behavior or symptoms often have very different underlying problems. In the first place, a symptom may be the result of very different causes or processes. Let us consider, as an example, the behavioral reaction of bed-wetting (enuresis). This may be the result of some physiological disturbance on a neurological basis; it may be caused by a severe emotional maladjustment; it may be a reflection of training practices in toilet control; it may be due to a disturbance in gastrointestinal functions; *or it may* be due to conditions associated with mental retardation. In the second place, a given form of behavior may have different implications depending upon the way it is used and the personality of the particular child showing the reaction; and the same behavior may have a different significance at different times in the life history of the same person. For example, thumb-sucking is viewed quite differently in a three-year-old than in a ten-year-old child. Therefore, to base a system of classification of mental retardation upon behavioral reactions alone presents many difficulties.

If, on the other hand, we attempt to base a system of classification upon underlying causes or dynamics, our problems are complicated. The same cause may produce different reactions in different people. There is no single cause for an abnormal form of behavior; causation is complex. Several component causes may jointly contribute to the result. Let us look, for example, at birth injuries to children as a possible etiological factor in some forms of mental retardation. All classification schemes based on causation (and also some others by implication) have the "birth-injured" child (or some other designation meaning essentially the same thing) in one classification category. Although they may appear to be rather easily described, birth injuries are very difficult to classify. Several attempts have been made to relate the type and extent of a brain injury to the degree and type of mental retardation. One way of doing this is to examine the brains of mentally retarded individuals following death, then to attempt to relate the injury (if any is found) to the retardation. An example of such a study is that of Malamud.[9] He reviewed autopsy findings and noted: "It is concluded that an etiological classification of mental deficiencies is not warranted in the present state of our knowledge."

It is also unsatisfactory to base a system of classification entirely upon the results of intelligence test performance. To do so would be to assume that the results of such a test are entirely valid manifestations of intellectual capacity, and that other factors need not be considered. Such an assumption would not be true.

We have summarized some of the many attempts to devise a system of classification of mentally retarded children. None of them is completely adequate. Rather they appear to be relatively crude attempts at classification of "something" that is inadequately understood. In all fields of knowledge, the first attempts at classification are inaccurate. Such schemes are continually refined as knowledge in the area is accumulated. There is apparently a "feedback" process involved—the classification aids in the more adequate utilization of gathered data, which then leads to an improved method of classification. The unsatisfactory systems of classifications of mental retardation with which we struggle are indicative of our relative ignorance in this field. They should be viewed as tentative formulations and we should continually bear in mind their limitations.

[9] Malamud, N., "Recent trends in classification of neuropathological findings in mental deficiency," *Amer. J. ment. Defic.*, 1954, *58*, 438–447.

Criteria for a modern concept of mental retardation

We are now ready to analyze more fully the nature of mental retardation. A few widely used definitions were cited at the beginning of this chapter to serve as "working" definitions. We shall attempt to arrive at a more adequate concept—one that embodies not only more recent knowledge in regard to retardation but also the modern dynamic approaches that are characteristic of present-day science.

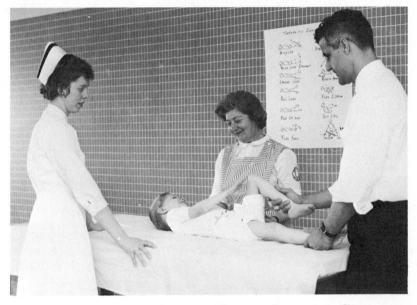

PHYSICAL REHABILITATION EXERCISES. NOTE THE INSTRUCTION CHART ON THE WALL (Courtesy of Plymouth State Home and Training School, Northville, Mich.)

Let us recapitulate certain important points. We have stressed the need for a *dynamic* approach, one that stresses the underlying causes and interacting factors in behavior rather than mere descriptions. We noted that mentally retarded children do not form a homogeneous group, but comprise a variety of conditions and are different in many respects from each other, just as they are different from other groups. Kanner's comments on this are worth noting.[10] He points out that the study of "feeblemindedness" seems at present to be entering upon a stage similar to that which existed with regard to the study of "insanity"

[10] Kanner, *op. cit.*

about 75 years ago. At that time the assumption that all insane people were alike began to be questioned. This point cannot be overemphasized. Mentally retarded children are individuals in their own right, and we can talk about "the" mentally retarded child only as an abstraction, in the same way that we talk about "the" neurotic child, or "the" person who has an elevated temperature. A neurosis or a fever can result from many different causes. So can mental retardation. It is the underlying cause that is important—not the symptom (or behavioral reaction) itself.

We have also stressed the point that it is the *whole* child who talks, thinks, and moves about—not just part of him. We cannot talk about lowered intellectual capacities in isolation, but rather must talk about a living, behaving child in his totality. In understanding his behavior we need to understand his past life history—his relationships with other people and his present integration of behaviors. Walker[11] has phrased one aspect of this problem very nicely:

Much like the situation sometimes seen in explosions when the blast effects are less important than the effect of the concussive waves set up by the explosion, we sometimes find the mental defective a problem not primarily because of his defect, but rather due to the social side effects his presence creates. We find the defective presenting a problem to society and also being trapped and affected by the social problems his presence has created. We must thoroughly understand that when an individual reacts to a situation he does not react with only so-called "intellectual" capacities, but rather he reacts *in toto*—emotionally as well as in all other ways.

We shall also see later in this chapter that there is no single cause of mental retardation. Rather, we stress the fact that it is multi-determined. We hope it is evident to the reader that a modern concept of mental retardation must embrace far more than a consideration of intellectual factors alone. It must embrace all aspects of the child's maturation—including those of personality. It must also embrace more than the child's social adjustment. The intellectual functioning of a child cannot be considered apart from his emotional and personality functioning. Each of these does not exist as a *separate* "thing." Thus we must widen the scope of our approach—we must deal with the *whole* child in all of his complexity. Perry takes a similar position when he states:[12]

[11] Walker, G. H., "Social and emotional problems of the mentally retarded child," *Amer. J. ment. Defic.*, 1950, *55*, 132–138.

[12] Perry, S. E., "Some theoretic problems of mental deficiency and their action implications," *Psychiat.*, 1954, *17*, 49.

. . . mental deficiency will be considered as a total situation complex integrated upon the basis of a presumed or observed subnormal intellectual functioning.

We shall attempt, in the remainder of this book, to integrate the data on mental retardation, building toward a better dynamic conception of the nature of the problem. We shall devote considerable attention to principles of personality development and stress the similarities and differences of such a process in the retarded as compared with the "normal" child. We shall see how he functions at home, in school, and in society, and then we shall interpret these data in terms of the criteria we have proposed.

CHARACTERISTICS OF SOME TYPES OF MENTALLY RETARDED CHILDREN

First, we shall discuss the characteristics of children of borderline abilities and mildly or moderately retarded children. Following this, we shall discuss the characteristics of the more severely retarded children, and pay attention to some specific types of conditions associated with severe mental retardation. We shall not include detailed discussion of the emotional characteristics of the children of the various levels at this point; they are so important that a full chapter is devoted to these characteristics (Chapter Eight).

Mentally retarded children are not equally deficient in all areas. Not only is there general variability among the children of this category, but there is also considerable variability within the same child among his several characteristics. One representative study illustrative of this point is that of Klausmeier and Check, who studied the relationships among 16 measures of physical, mental, achievement, and personality characteristics in children of low, average and high intelligence who were 9 years and 5 months of age.[13] The specific functions investigated were: height, weight, strength of grip, number of permanent teeth, bone development of hand and wrist (carpal age), I.Q., reading achievement, arithmetic achievement, language achievement, emotional adjustment, achievement in relation to capacity, integration of self-concept, expression of emotion, behavior pattern, and the child's estimate of his own learning abilities.

It was concluded that children of low intelligence (I.Q. 55 to 80)

[13] Klausmeier, H., and Check, J., "Relationships among physical, mental, achievement, and personality measures in children of low, average and high intelligence at 113 months of age," *Amer. J. ment. Defic.*, 1959, *63*, 1059–1068.

did not differ significantly from either the average children (I.Q. 90–110) or the high children (I.Q. 120 and higher) in nine measures: weight, number of permanent teeth, carpal age, emotional adjustment, achievement in relation to capacity, integration of self-concept, expression of emotion, behavior pattern, and estimate of own abilities. But the low I.Q. group was lower than both the average and the high I.Q. group in strength of grip, reading achievement, arithmetic achievement, and language achievement. It was also concluded that a low level of physical development in the child does not necessarily accompany low achievement in arithmetic and reading. Also, Klausmeier and Check found that intraindividual variability for each child in three functions (reading, arithmetic and language) was less for the average than for the high and low I.Q. groups.

Mildly and moderately retarded children

We shall now discuss the more important characteristics of the mildly and moderately retarded children, and leave for consideration at a later point (Chapter Eight) a more detailed analysis of the dynamics of their adjustment and related emotional problems. This first presentation should serve to provide basic orientation concerning these groups and establish a basis for some of the special problems they present. For convenience we shall refer to the mildly and moderately retarded children as "groups."

In our discussion we shall think of mildly retarded children as having an I.Q. range of 66 to 80, and the moderately retarded, 50 to 65. These are, of course, rather arbitrarily set limits, and the intelligence test score in itself does not entirely determine the particular level of deficiency. Furthermore, the children in each of the groups are not all alike—they are *not* homogeneous groupings. Each child is an individual, and as such differs from all other children in many respects. However, each of the groups does have some common characteristics.

In order to appreciate the degree of retardation let us compare the mental ages of our groups with "average" children at the time they start school (age 6) and at the time they complete the eighth grade (age 14). We shall do so for the upper and lower extremes of both the mildly and moderately retarded children. These data are summarized in Table 3.

It should be observed from the data contained in Table 3 that in the case of the mildly retarded children there is a difference of at least 1.20 to a maximum of 2.04 years of mental age from that of the average children when they enter school. For the moderately retarded the range of difference in mental age is from 2.10 to 3.00 years. At the age of

TABLE 3. COMPARISON OF MENTAL AGES OF AVERAGE, MILDLY, AND MODERATELY RETARDED CHILDREN

		Mental age (in years)			
		Mildly retarded		Moderately retarded	
Chronological age	Average	Upper extreme	Lower extreme	Upper extreme	Lower extreme
6 years	6.00	4.80	3.96	3.90	3.00
14 years	14.00	11.20	9.24	9.10	7.00

14, when the "average" child usually completes the eighth grade, the difference in mental age for the mildly retarded group is from 2.80 to 4.76 years. For the moderately retarded children the difference ranges from 4.90 to 7.00 years of mental age. This illustrates some of the striking differences in intellectual capacities between the groups.

Moderately retarded children do much better on tasks that demand motor coordination and control than they do on those that involve verbal facilities. The more concrete the task, the better they function. Retarded children are limited in such capacities as comprehension, generalization, association, symbolization, judgment, comparison, and fluidity of thought.

The moderately retarded children do not require continued custodial care. Such children usually can be taken care of at home, attend school, and usually come into frequent contact with a wide range of children, adults, and social institutions. Nevertheless, they present continuing problems to their parents and families, to the social community of which they are a part, and to *themselves*.

We shall discuss the behavioral characteristics of these children from several points of view: (1) speech and communication, (2) social interaction, (3) self-care, (4) academic abilities, (5) motor skills, and (6) vocational adjustment.

SPEECH AND COMMUNICATION. Even the most retarded of the group are able to communicate some of their needs to other people. Their vocabulary and range of intellectual interests are, of course, at a considerably lower level than those of average children, but they do respond to other persons and can talk and express themselves in a limited manner. The least retarded of the group do rather well on the whole, and are capable of initiating and sustaining adequate conversation. They have more extensive vocabularies, and their range of intellectual interests is more adequate, than the more retarded of the group.

Sirken and Lyons investigated the incidence of speech defects in

2,522 mentally deficient children.[14] They found that normal speech was present in only one-third of the cases, while speech was not present at all in one-sixth of the cases. Of those children who did speak, 60 per cent had defective speech. Furthermore, there appeared to be a relationship between degree of mental retardation and incidence of speech defects. They found speech to be absent or defective: in 43 per cent of the combined moron and borderline groups; in 74 per cent of the imbecile group; and in 100 per cent of the idiot group.

However, the presence of a speech defect in itself does not warrant a diagnosis of mental retardation, since many other factors such as illness or physical limitations, lack of speech stimulation, or emotional disturbance may result in speech disorder. Gens, for example, found that mentally retarded children suffered from the same types of speech disorders as did normal children, but showed more frequent incidence of speech pathology.[15] He did not find, however, that there were any patterns of speech that were associated only with mental deficiency.

The relationship between speech defects and mental retardation is not a simple causal relationship. As Travis states, it is not correct to view mental retardation as the *cause* of a speech defect.[16] He feels it is more accurate to view the two as manifestations, sometimes, of the same process, both being related to some defect in the development of the central nervous system, and in this way being secondarily related to each other. Thus, according to Travis' point of view, defective intelligence is not the direct cause of defective speech. It is clear, however, that speech disorders frequently occur in association with mental retardation in children, and that the incidence of defect increases with degree of retardation.

Schlanger studied the types of speech defects shown by 74 moderately and mildly retarded children.[17] He found voice defects to be the most common type (in 62 per cent of the cases), followed by articulatory defects (57 per cent) and stuttering (20 per cent).

Speech difficulties of some kind are commonly found in all children in the group, however, the most frequent defect being that of articulation. They can all profit from speech training, and it is customary for

[14] Sirken, J., and Lyons, W., "A study of speech defects in mental deficiency," *Amer. J. ment. Defic.*, 1941, *46*, 74–80.

[15] Gens, A., "The speech pathologist looks at the mentally deficient child," *Train. Sch. Bull.*, 1951, *48*, 19–27.

[16] Travis, L., *Speech Pathology*. New York: Appleton-Century-Crofts, Inc., 1931.

[17] Schlanger, B., "Speech measurements of institutionalized mentally handicapped children," *Amer. J. ment. Defic.*, 1953, *58*, 114–122.

them to be given such instruction in more progressive school systems that have established special programs for retarded children. Often their speech and the content of their conversation attracts attention to them, with possible resultant ridicule from other children. Goodenough states:[18]

. . . quietness and inconspicuousness rather than any form of exhibitionism are virtues to be cultivated. The modern stress on "self expression" must be exercised with caution in the case of the mentally deficient child. He may express much that would better have been concealed.

Goertzen has prepared an excellent summary of available studies relating to speech problems in mentally retarded children.[19] He concluded that his review of the literature left him with the feeling that there was a great deal to be done in the way of research in this area. We certainly concur in this conclusion.[20]

SOCIAL INTERACTION. The most severely retarded children of this group relate to other persons only at the most elementary level. They tend to be totally lost in more complex social situations, being ill at ease, and not perceptive of the nuances of interpersonal relationships. They can, however, learn the most important social customs and behaviors. They find it very difficult to participate in group activities, and are unable to comprehend fully the responsibilities of group membership. In general, they are the followers rather than the leaders, and come to lean very heavily upon the group leader. The children at the opposite end of the group, however, can develop a considerable degree of skill in social interaction. Those who are fortunate enough to have adequate attention and guidance often acquire what might be termed a "social veneer," and with this polish succeed in interacting with other persons in social groups with a great deal of success. They can learn to conform to social customs and usage, and participate in group activities without a great deal of difficulty. The kind of achievement they attain, however, is directly dependent upon the treatment accorded them.

[18] Goodenough, F. I., *Exceptional Children*. New York: Appleton-Century-Crofts, Inc., 1956, p. 247.

[19] Goertzen, S., "Speech and the mentally retarded child," *Amer. J. ment. Defic.*, 1957, *62*, 244–253.

[20] For a further review of research in the speech and language development of the mentally retarded child the reader is referred to: Harrison, S., "A review of research in speech and language development of the mentally retarded child," *Amer. J. ment. Defic.*, 1958, *63*, 236–240.

Many studies have shown that mildly retarded children can adjust well to varying social situations. For example, Kennedy, who studied the social adjustment of individuals ranking at a moron level, found that they compared favorably with non-morons on marital, social, educational, and vocational status.[21] Anderson compared special-class adolescents with those in regular classes at a junior high school level.[22] It was concluded that there was little difference between the two groups insofar as social competence was concerned.

SELF-CARE. Those children at the lower extreme of the group can learn, with difficulty, to take care of their bodily needs. They eventually can learn to feed themselves and to dress themselves adequately. Bladder and bowel controls are eventually attained, but with great difficulty (see the case of Johnny in Chapter One). Such successes are not achieved "overnight"; they come only with long and patient work on the part of the parents. Through training programs such children can develop proper habits of bodily care, and can learn the elements of simple bodily hygiene. They can, with some effort, be taught to be neat, orderly, and to present a well-groomed appearance. The retarded child—particularly the one at the lower extreme of the group—does not quickly respond to changed learning conditions. He learns essentially through constant repetition—repetition not only of the same act, but preferably a repetition during a short time interval and in exactly the same way. He cannot "hold things in his mind," and cannot undertake numerous tasks at the same time too well. It is best to focus upon one particular aspect of self-care, then move on to others when the first has been established.

We tend to underestimate the difficulty posed to the mentally retarded child by many tasks. For example, let us consider the job of tying shoelaces—a task that is very readily learned by the average child. It presents quite a problem to the retarded child, and he can learn to tie his laces only after a long and laborious training period. No point of the self-care program should be taken for granted, but each element should be very patiently taught.

The children at the upper end of the group do not have such great problems in this area, but even they learn more slowly than normal

[21] Kennedy, R. J. R., *The Social Adjustment of Morons in a Connecticut City.* Hartford, Conn.: Social Service Dept., 1948.

[22] Anderson, M., "Education for social maturity," *Train. Sch. Bull.*, 1937, *33,* 185–192.

children, and need a thorough program of habit training for adequate self-care.

ACADEMIC ABILITIES. Experience and research over the past quarter of a century have contributed much to our understanding of the progression in scholastic achievement of this group. However, as in most other areas, there is a great deal more to learn about the problems and possibilities. We will summarize the findings about academic achievement in three propositions, and then say a few words about each.

1. *To the extent that the specific academic subject is dependent upon general intelligence, retarded children will be unable to achieve the level of skill that average children reach.* For instance, Jacobs studied the academic performance of 293 slow learning children in the Cincinnati public schools.[23] The median chronological age of the group was 15 years, 6 months, and the mean I.Q. (measured by the Kuhlmann-Anderson Battery) was 62.8. Jacobs found the mean arithmetic grade level of the group to be 4.3, the mean reading grade level to be 3.8, and the mean language grade level to be 3.7. There were statistically significant correlations reported between the intelligence test score and the mean grade level achieved (.70 between mental age and total grade equivalent, and .67 between I.Q. and total grade equivalent).

Thus, in the case of reading comprehension and arithmetic reasoning, two subjects that are highly dependent upon the intellectual level of the child, the retarded group may be expected to show severe limitations. The usual upper limit that can be achieved in these subjects can be predicted accurately from the data given in Table 3, if conditions for learning are favorable. Children at the upper extreme of the mildly retarded group may be expected to achieve a reading level of about the sixth grade (which means that they can read reasonably well, although perhaps slowly, such things as simple books, newspaper articles, comics, and the like), whereas children at the lower extreme of the moderately retarded group will hardly be able to read anything at all, except simple words, street signs, and the like. The latter group will rarely be able to reach an academic level in reading beyond *beginning* second grade. In general, the same kind of achievement may be expected in the area of arithmetic reasoning. On the other hand, the picture is decidedly different in other subjects. For example, in arithmetic computations, retarded children profit much more from extended practice, and those at

[23] Jacobs, J., "A study of performance of slow learners in the Cincinnati public schools on mental and achievement tests," *Amer. J. ment. Defic.*, 1957, *61*, 238–243.

the upper end of the mildly retarded group may become highly proficient in many basic computational skills. The same conditions may be found in spelling. In these and other subjects that are less highly correlated with abstract intelligence and more highly correlated with appropriate practice, considerable achievement may be expected. The implication is that a specially devised and carefully planned curriculum in the academic subjects is required for retarded children. They need more practice in some areas and less in others to approach the performance of average children. Another implication is that all such children may profit considerably from an *appropriate* program of academic training so that they can adapt more effectively to social and vocational situations.

2. *The timing of the introduction and emphasis upon academic work for retarded children varies from that for average children.* Most retarded children, for example, are not ready to profit from reading instruction of a formal kind for some years after the time such instruction is normally introduced into the curriculum for other children. This is more than a matter of slower mental maturation. It is also a matter of preparing the groundwork by *pre-academic* training. An example of important and continuing research that has been stimulated by T. G. Hegge at the Wayne County Training School, in Michigan, is the study by Weiner.[24] In this study the achievement of a group of 37 retarded boys, whose academic program was delayed experimentally for an average of two years and three months, was compared with a matched group of 31 retarded boys who had a continuing academic program. Although the matched group had a higher academic level to begin with, and had had more academic instruction (since they had "no delay"), the two groups were entirely comparable in reading and arithmetic at the end of the program, some four years later. Such finding is indicative of the hypothesis regarding the importance of maturation as a prerequisite for effective learning (see Chapters Five and Six). Not only will appropriate delay in academic instruction not impair the final level of scholastic attainment, but more appropriate skills and social behaviors can result from utilization of the time made available by such delay.

3. *The selection of the kinds of academic skills to be learned by retarded children should be guided by the principle that all such training must be closely geared to the child's immediate needs and experi-*

---

[24] Weiner, B. B., "A report on final academic achievement of 37 mentally handicapped boys who had been enrolled in a prolonged pre-academic program," *Amer. J. ment. Defic.*, 1954, *59*, 210–219.

ences. This principle is, of course, also applicable to other groups of children, but is especially relevant for the retarded group. It is stated in a positive fashion to emphasize the conclusion that not only should unnecessary or too difficult academic work be eliminated but also the selection of curriculum materials should be guided by the criterion of what is *immediately* relevant and meaningful. It is based on the finding that much of the present-day curriculum in academic subjects is neither within the grasp of retarded groups nor functionally relevant for them. Delp has explored the implications of this principle in an interesting article.[25]

Motor Skills. The term "motor skills" refers to the child's ability to use muscular control in handling or manipulating objects. The child at the lower end of the intellectual scale has severe difficulties in establishing such muscular and movement controls, particularly in the use of the finer muscles. Gross muscular control is also difficult for him to establish, but eventually he gains adequate mastery in this sphere. The less severely retarded child does not have such great difficulties, and is capable, if given the opportunity to learn, of developing such skills to a relatively high degree. For example, in one study of such children, a group of boys, given training in playing volleyball, were able to more than hold their own with a group of "average" high school boys of their own chronological age and above.

Francis and Rarick determined the gross motor abilities of a group of 284 mentally retarded children in the Madison and Milwaukee public schools.[26] The I.Q. range was from 50 to 90, and the range in chronological age was from 7.5 years to 14.5 years. Measures were obtained on 11 gross motor tasks. It was concluded that the mean scores achieved by the group of retarded children were two to four years below those achieved by non-retarded children. Further, it was observed that the discrepancy between average and retarded children tended to increase with increasing age. It is of interest to note that Francis and Rarick found intelligence to be correlated with motor performance, although the correlations tended to be low.

The basic conclusion reached by Francis and Rarick, that mentally retarded children are inferior to more normal children in motor performance, has also been drawn by other investigators. For example,

---

[25] Delp, M. A., "Goals for the mentally retarded," *Amer. J. ment. Defic.*, 1951, *55*, 472–478.
[26] Francis, R., and Rarick, G., "Motor characteristics of the mentally retarded," *Amer. J. ment. Defic.*, 1959, *63*, 792–811.

Motor Control Is Difficult to Achieve (Courtesy of Plymouth State Home and Training School, Northville, Mich.)

Sloan administered the Lincoln adaptation of the Oseretsky test of Motor Proficiency to matched groups of normal and mentally retarded children.[27] He found reliable differences between the groups on six of the subtests, with the retarded group achieving at lower levels. Sloan concluded that motor proficiency is not an isolated function, but is one additional aspect of the total behavior of the human being.

Vocational Adjustment. Mildly and moderately retarded individuals are capable of holding a great many types of jobs. This is becoming increasingly evident as programs of vocational education pro-

[27] Sloan, W., "The Lincoln-Oseretsky Motor Development Scale," *Genet. Psychol. Monogr.*, 1955, *55*, 183–252.

vide these individuals with suitable preparation. Studies of former special-class pupils show that they engage in many diverse forms of work after they leave school. They successfully hold such jobs as: general and skilled factory worker, messenger boy, foundry worker, clerk, salesman, laundry worker, hospital attendant, restaurant worker, farmer, butcher, golf course attendant, and many others. The whole range of nonprofessional occupations is open to the retarded individual, and in fact, depending upon his specific capacities, training, and the job opportunities in the community, he can do any of the tasks that do not require a high degree of formal academic training.

Beckham[28] studied the specific jobs performed by retarded individuals of different mental ages. His findings are illustrated by the following examples:

> *Mental age of 5 years.* Dishwasher, simple domestic work, prepare vegetables, sew, scrub and polish floors.
> *Mental age of 7 years.* Shoe repairing, painting, plowing, knitting, braiding, ironing, carpentry (simple), domestic work.
> *Mental age of 9 years.* Printing, furniture repair, brushmaking, pottery making, automatic loom operator, vegetable and fruit harvesting, industrial operations.
> *Mental age of 11 years.* Stock-keeping, janitors, simple library work, power sealing in cannery, greenhouse attendant, keep small store, labeling and checking, learn to play first violin and other musical instruments.

We cite these only as examples of the types of jobs that mildly and moderately retarded individuals are capable of holding. They can be contributing members of society, particularly if provided with programs designed to meet their unique needs. We shall discuss the vocational adjustment of the retarded child in detail in Chapter Eleven.

The severely retarded child

We have defined severely retarded children as those who require institutional or some other type of continued custodial care. Although this book is not primarily concerned with these children, we shall study their characteristics not only because they constitute an important part of the mentally retarded population but also because other retarded children can then be more readily understood and differentiated from them. Usually severely retarded children show some gross physical abnormality or have some definite brain pathology.

---

[28] Beckham, S., "Minimum intelligence levels for several occupations," *Personnel J.*, 1930, *9*, 309–313.

Quite a few have clearly discernible physical *stigmata* (signs) that are obvious on observation. In contrast, mildly or moderately retarded children do not usually have such special *stigmata of degeneration*.

The more frequently encountered specific "types" of severe mental retardation are discussed in the following paragraphs.

MONGOLISM.   This is one of the most striking types of mental deficiency, and owes its name to the almond-shaped, slanting eyes that are prominent features of many mongoloid idiots. It was once thought that the condition was due to a racial trait which was inherited in some way. Attempts have been made to confirm this theory without success, and the theory has been totally discredited. We know that mongolism may occur in any racial group. The phrase "mongolian idiot" that is often applied to mongoloid children is a misnomer. Actually, most mongoloid children rank at an imbecile level, though some have intellectual capacities at higher and lower levels. It has been estimated that there are approximately 28,000 mongoloid persons in the United States. About 10% of all hospitalized and institutionalized mental defectives are mongoloids.

The physical symptoms of the mongoloid child are outstanding, and once one has seen such a child others are fairly easily recognized. In addition to the unusual eyes previously mentioned, the most common physical symptoms are: a fold of the skin of the eyes (*epicanthic* fold) ; a deep transverse fissure in the tongue; an absence of definite patterns in the lines of the palm of the hand; close-set, deep eyes, which are often strabismic (cross-eyes) ; flattening of the bridge of the nose; a flaccidity (*hypotonicity*) of the muscles—they appear to have little tension or tone; thick and stubby hands; very small fingers and often with only one crease; short stature; subnormal weight; lax bone joints (many are double-jointed) ; and, occasionally, peculiarly shaped deformities of the ears. There are other physical indications of mongolism, but these are the ones most often encountered. Goldstein states that there are two distinct kinds of mongols.[29] The first is the *predominantly thyroid deficient* mongol, who is short in stature, has wide facial features, short pudgy hands, walks more awkwardly, and has a comparatively higher I.Q. The second type is described by Goldstein as being taller and thinner, more restless, showing more emotional disturbance, and having a lower I.Q.

[29] Goldstein, H., "Treatment of congenital acromicria syndrome in children," *Arch. Pedag.*, 1956, *73*, 153–167.

Many theories to explain the pathological condition have been advanced. One of these relates mongolism to the advanced age of the mother at the time of birth of the child. This theory is referred to as an "exhaustion" theory, proposing that any cause that may disturb metabolic function—such as tuberculosis or syphilis—may account for the condition. A second theory suggests that the cause of mongolism is a dis-

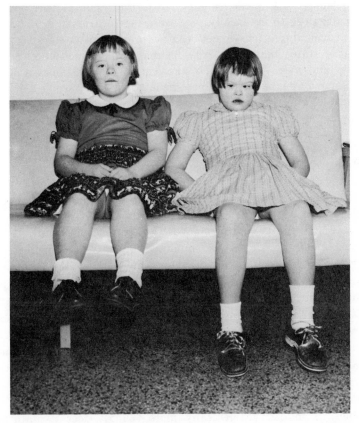

TWIN GIRLS, BOTH MONGOLOID—SEVERE CASES (Courtesy the Fort Wayne Training School; Photo by L. Richard Young)

turbance in the glandular system. However, polyglandular therapies have not been particularly impressive in alleviating the condition. Baroff has reviewed the many theories relating to mongolism.[30] He

[30] Baroff, G., "Current theories on the etiology of mongolism," *Eugen. Quart.*, 1958, *5*, 212–215.

believes that the etiology of mongolism depends upon two basic factors. First, there must be a gene-specific vulnerability to the disease, and this is one which is not a simple genetic mechanism. Second, there must be an unfavorable intra-uterine environment.

The evidence appears to be increasingly clear that the primary etiology of mongolism stems from some aberration of the chromosomes.* When one considers the complex processes involved in the creation of a sperm and an egg, in their union, and in the resultant development of the fertilized egg to eventually produce a new organism, it is surprising only that such aberrations do not occur more frequently.

Clarke states that there may be many abnormalities in both the *structure* and *number* of the chromosomes.[31] For instance, a piece of chromosome may break off, and become lost (this is known as a *deletion*); a segment of the chromosome may become inverted so that the genes will appear in the wrong order and make pairing of chromosomes impossible (*inversion*); the genes may appear twice in the same chromosome (*duplication*); two chromosomes may lose pieces, which then may be exchanged from one chromosome to another (*translocation*); chromosomes may fail to separate and so both may pass into the same gamete, with the other gamete being left without the chromosome of that pair. This is known as *non-disjunction*. The person who receives the extra chromosome is said to be *trisomic* for that chromosome pair.

Experimental evidence, as summarized by Clarke, indicates that one type of mongolism results from *non-disjunction* (the chromosomes fail to separate). The particular chromosome involved is known as the "small arocentric chromosome pair No. 21." The mongol is thus said to be *trisomic* for this chromosome, and so has a total of 47 chromosomes rather than the usual 46.

There is some doubt as to when and where the non-disjunction occurs. It could occur in the mother at time of *oogenesis* (production of the egg), or it could occur in the father at time of *spermatogenesis* (production of the sperm). Clarke states that because the mongolian child resembles its mother antigenically more than it does its father, and

---

* A chromosome is a rod-shaped body in the nucleus of the cell. It is composed of *genes*, which are the biological units of heredity. *Chromatin* is a chemical component of the cell nucleus (desoxyribose nucleic acid attached to a protein base). It is the carrier of genes in inheritance. A *gamete* is a mature ovum or sperm, and a *zygote* is the cell resulting from their union. *Oogenesis* refers to the origin and development of the ovum, and *spermatogenesis* refers to the origin and development of the sperm.

[31] Clarke, C. A., *Genetics for the Clinician*. Oxford: Blackwell Scientific Publications, Ltd., 1962.

also because mongolism is associated with the increasing age of the mother, it is more probable that the non-disjunction takes place in the mother. In addition he points out that if the non-disjunction occurs during the development of the embryo, then some *mongoloid traits* will be found in normal individuals (he will be known, genetically, as a "47/46 mosaic").

Clarke believes a second type of mongolism may result from *translocation*, even though the majority of cases are due to non-disjunction. In this instance, there is no additional chromosome present, but there does exist a condition of *extra chromation*. This results from interchange of the broken parts of one chromosome with another. Clarke notes that if a translocation is found in one of the parents, then there is an even chance of the child's being normal. If the child inherits the translocation, and the rest of its chromosomes are normal, it will be a mongol because of the extra chromatin. If it inherits the translocation, but also lacks a chromosome, it will appear normal, since there will be no excess of chromatin, but it will be a *carrier* of mongolism.

Thus, there are two types of mongolism, which result from genetic abnormality. One type is due to *trisomy* (due to non-disjunction) and the other is due to *translocation*. Both may occur in the same family.

Winschel has reviewed the etiological factors related to mongolism, and has concluded that even though many advances have been made, no single factor has been isolated as producing mongolism.[32] He speculates upon the possibility that the predisposition to mongolism may be suppressed in individuals who have good, healthy internal environments. If this is so, then Winschel raises the question as to whether or not a group of "quiescent mongols" really exists, and as to whether or not they are the real progenitors of mongolism. According to the genetic hypothesis of Clarke, we have seen that there may be carriers of the condition, depending upon the chromosome structure and number.

CRETINISM.   In sharp contrast to mongolism is the condition of cretinism. In this condition the specific cause has been well established. Cretinism is easily recognized within the first four months of the infant's life, unless the condition is very mild. It is attributable to an insufficient secretion of the thyroid glands. The cretin may be born with a rudimentary thyroid gland (*hypothyroidism*) and in some instances the gland may be entirely missing. Two types of cretinism have been identified:

[32] Winschel, I., "A review of the etiology of mongolism," *Except. Child.*, 1962, *28*, 279–286.

the *sporadic* and the *endemic*. The latter is most common in certain areas of the world; in our own country it seems to be found most frequently in the Great Lakes region and in some of the far western states. These regions are the so-called "goitrous" regions, regions in which an inadequate amount of iodine occurs naturally in the water and soil.

Cretinism manifested in early infancy is easily recognized by the presence of many physical symptoms. These include: small bodily stature (*dwarfism*); short thick legs; a disproportionately large head; short, broad hands with fingers that have square ends; dry, coarse, and "scaly" skin; a large and protruding tongue; peg-shaped and chalky teeth, which usually are delayed in eruption; everted lower lip; swollen eyelids and eyes that are half-shut; lowered basal metabolic rate with little perspiration; a short thick neck; delayed sexual development; and a hoarse, thick, and strident voice.

In temperament, cretins are, as a group, rather resistive and stubborn in their relationships with other children and adults. They tend to lack spontaneity in their behavioral reactions. Their behavior is not usually troublesome, but tends to be more placid and taciturn rather than quarrelsome and aggressive.

In intelligence, cretins show a wide range of capacities. They may range anywhere from the idiot through the moron level, and some attain a "borderline" classification.

If cretinism is untreated, it tends to become progressively worse. Then the special physical characteristics become more and more pronounced, until the cretin begins to look, in early adolescence, somewhat like a very aged and wrinkled old man. However, if medical treatment is instituted at an early age, much, if not all, of the unfavorable symptomatology may be avoided—in such instances the mental level may reach an "average" level. The later the time at which treatment is started, the more unfavorable is the prognosis. Medical treatment must be continued throughout life. However, there may be some cases in which there are complicating defects in cerebral development which thyroid treatment cannot correct even if it is initiated at a very early age. When the condition of cretinism is particularly severe, death may occur at an early age. This, however, is due to the presence of complicating factors other than the hypothyroidism itself.

Since it is important that the treatment of cretinism be initiated at as early a time as possible, the need for immediate diagnosis of the condition is evident. Lowrey *et al.* studied a group of 49 cretins in order to determine the earliest age at which a reliable diagnosis of cretinism could be made. They concluded that such a diagnosis could be made in most cases by as early an age as three months, and certainly by the age of six months.[33]

It should be emphasized that cretins need much more than medical treatment, even though this is central to their condition. Because of delayed development they experience, even at best, special problems in adjustment and adaptation. They can, as experience has shown, profit from educational, social, and vocational guidance. The parents, too, need help in understanding the problems of these children and in learning how best to help them.

About 5% or less of institutionalized mental defectives are cases of cretinism.

MICROCEPHALY. The microcephalic is one of the less frequent special "types" of mentally retarded children who require institutional or custodial care. It occurs only in about 1% of those children who are institutionalized. Like mongolism, we do not know its specific cause. The brain of the microcephalic child is extremely small and simple (comparatively) in its physical structure, and often shows very simple folds (*convolutions*) and many deformities. The head itself is usually not over 16 inches in circumference. It is a developmental condition, one in which there is inadequate growth of the brain itself (a condition known as *hypoplasia* of the brain). Some parts of the brain may even be entirely missing or present only in rudimentary form.

Many unique physical characteristics are shown by microcephalic children. These include a disproportionately small head of conical shape, with a receding forehead and flattened back part (this leads to the popular use of the term "pinhead"). The fontanelles of the brain close prematurely.

Microcephalic children have an alert and vivacious temperament. They usually have a sense of happiness and well-being (*euphoria*). Their interest shifts rapidly from one object to another. They tend to imitate the actions of other people (*echopraxia*). Their speech is highly repetitive; they will repeat the same sounds over and over (*echolalia*). Their intelligence is usually in the high range of idiocy or the low range of imbecility; some cases with limited physical anomalies may reach the moron level. Like all other types of severely retarded children, there is a possibility that they may die early, due to complications or illness, but in general they live as long as the "non-stigmatic types" of mental defectives.

[33] Lowrey, G., *et al.*, "Early diagnostic criteria of congenital hypothyroidism," *Amer. J. Dis. Child.*, 1958, *96*, 131–143.

HYDROCEPHALY. This is a condition characterized by an unusually large head formation due to the accumulation of excessive cerebrospinal fluid within the skull. In some very rare cases there may not be an actual enlargement of the head. The most frequent cause of the accumulation of cerebrospinal fluid is a blocking of the circulation of the fluid. This may, in turn, be due to many conditions such as tumors, meningeal inflammations, other types of infection, or various types of injuries. As a result of the blocking, and resultant accumulation of fluid, the ventricles of the brain increase in size, the brain tissue is thinned and destroyed, and there is a diminution in the extent of the convolutions of the brain. Hydrocephaly may occur congenitally (at birth) or it may be acquired at some later time in life. It should not be confused with a simple condition of a large head, which may occur in a "normal" person but in which there is no excessive fluid and no resultant defect of the brain tissue.

Both the physical and mental attributes of the hydrocephalic child depend, as can be expected, upon the amount of brain damage involved, and this in turn is dependent, in part, upon the amount of fluid that accumulates. In severe cases the bodies of such children are very slight, and the neck cannot support the excessive weight of the head. Usually the intellectual level of the hydrocephalic children is in the range of severe mental retardation, although it may reach an "average" level. Convulsive seizures may often complicate the clinical picture, and optic atrophy (degeneration of the optic nerves) may also be present in many cases.

Medical diagnosis is difficult, particularly in borderline cases, and depends to a great extent upon neurological findings. Treatment has been attempted by surgical intervention, and by prescription of special diets to reduce the accumulation of cerebrospinal fluid. In general, the prognosis is unfavorable, although some cases do recover. This condition is about as infrequent as microcephaly, occurring in only 1% or less of institutionalized retarded children.

AMAUROTIC FAMILIAL IDIOCY. This is an illness which, fortunately, is extremely rare in occurrence. Unlike *any* of the previously discussed conditions, there is some evidence to suggest that it might be inherited in accordance with Mendelian ratios. Although it does appear that the disease has definite familial affiliations (it appears more frequently in some families than it does in others), the precise nature of the cause of the condition is still open to question. Some recent studies suggest that there may be pathology of the adrenal and thymus glands.[34] It is known

---

[34] Marburg, O., "Studies in the pathology and pathogenesis of amaurotic familial idiocy," *Amer. J. ment. Defic.*, 1942, *46*, 312–322.

that one of a pair of the same-sexed twins may develop the disease while the other may not. This serious disease (also called Tay-Sachs disease, after two of the persons who studied it at the end of the 19th century) is a degenerative illness ending in death; nothing is now known that can reverse the process once it has begun. At first the infant appears to develop normally. Then sometime during the first few months of life he begins to regress (go back to earlier behavior) on a neurological basis, and by the age of four to ten months, mental defects begin to appear. After a time the child is not able to recognize people or objects, and finally he usually becomes totally blind. Death comes before the third year of life in most cases. Previous to this, the child may develop severe prostration, vasomotor disturbance, and become highly sensitive to noises.

ch. 4

ETIOLOGY OF

MENTAL RETARDATION

IN THE PRECEDING PAGES WE HAVE REFERRED AT TIMES TO SOME OF
the *etiological* (causative) factors contributing to mental retardation.
We have seen how various factors such as injuries to the brain, infectious
diseases, changed physiology, or glandular pathology are sometimes of
etiological importance. In addition to these more usual causes, there are
others that are apparently related to such a condition.

Mental retardation is the result of one or many more basic factors. The extensive etiological basis of the condition is well illustrated by
the medical classification scheme proposed by the American Association
on Mental Deficiency.[1] According to this classification, mental retardation may be associated with or due to the following types of factors:

1. *Diseases and conditions due to infection.* This would include both prenatal and postnatal cerebral infections.
2. *Diseases and conditions due to intoxication.* Examples of these would be
   toxemia of pregnancy and post-immunization encephalopathy.
3. *Diseases and conditions due to trauma or physical agent.* The trauma
   would result from such conditions as asphyxia at birth, mechanical injury
   at birth, or postnatal injury.
4. *Diseases and conditions due to disorder of metabolism, growth or nutri-*

[1] Heber, R. F., "A manual on terminology and classification in mental retardation," *Amer. J. ment. Defic.*, 1959, *64*, Monogr. Suppl. No. 2.

tion. These conditions would include Tay-Sachs disease, protein metabolism, hypothyroidism, and phenylketonuria.

5. *Diseases and conditions due to new growths.* Examples of such diseases would be intracranial neoplasm, tuberous sclerosis, and Von Recklinghausen's disease.
6. *Diseases and conditions due to (unknown) prenatal influence.* Here we would find included such conditions as congenital cerebral defects and mongolism.
7. *Diseases and conditions due to unknown or uncertain cause with the structural reactions manifest.* This classification would include cerebellar degeneration and diffuse sclerosis.
8. *Uncertain (or presumed psychologic) cause, with functional reaction alone manifest.* This category would include cultural-familial retardation, retardation due to environmental deprivation, retardation due to emotional disturbance or major personality disorder, and retardation due to uncertain functional cause.

In summary, the etiological factors reflected in the preceding classification system are: prenatal or postnatal infection, cerebral damage due to toxic agents, brain injury due to trauma or mechanical or physical agent, injury due to metabolic, nutritional or growth dysfunctions, damage due to new growths in the brain, retardation due to uncertain cause at or prior to birth but with a structural reaction demonstrated, retardation due to postnatal conditions in which the etiology is unknown, and, finally, retardation which occurs in the absence of any known form of organic pathology. The possible etiological factors relating to mental retardation are certainly extensive.

We shall discuss first some of the more specific somatic conditions associated with mental retardation, and then discuss the various forms of organic brain damage involved. Finally we shall discuss the importance of hereditary and cultural factors.

SOME UNIQUE SOMATIC CONDITIONS

In order to gain some conception of the significance of various etiological factors, let us examine some figures on institutionalized mental defectives.

The data in Table 4 indicate that fewer than 50% of individuals admitted for the first time to institutions for the mentally retarded are given a specific etiological diagnosis. Approximately 56% of the cases (the *familial* and the *undifferentiated* diagnoses) are not attributed to *any known* cause. Although these figures do not include the non-institutionalized mental defectives, they serve to underline the fact that there

TABLE 4. Diagnosed First Admission of Mental Defectives to 89 Public Institutions for Mental Defectives and Epileptics in the United States, 1949*

Diagnosis	Number	Per Cent
Familial	2,399	30.7
Undifferentiated	1,933	24.8
Mongolism	862	11.1
Post-traumatic	485	6.2
With developmental cranial anomalies	484	6.2
Post-infectional	427	5.5
With congenital spastic paralysis	422	5.4
Other forms	331	4.2
With epilepsy	180	2.3
With endocrine disorder	139	1.8
With other organic nervous diseases	118	1.4
With tuberous sclerosis	12	0.2
With familial amaurosis	8	0.1
TOTAL	7,800	99.9

* Reproduced from Perry, S. E., "Some theoretic problems of mental deficiency and their action implications," *Psychiat.*, 1954, *17*, 48.

is *no known, specific cause* in the majority of cases. However, in some cases there are some demonstrable somatic conditions associated with the mental retardation. Examples of these follow.

Phenylpyruvic oligophrenia (phenylketonuria)

There is an acid, known as phenylpyruvic acid, which is found in the urine when certain physiological processes within the body are disturbed. Presumably, it is not found in the urine of normal persons. It has been found, however, in certain groups of mentally retarded individuals, particularly those with severe retardation. It has been estimated that about 1% of institutionalized persons show such a condition. This condition is attributable to faulty bodily metabolism which in turn produces lowered intellectual functioning. There is some evidence to indicate that this condition tends to be transmitted along family lines—that it is possibly an inherited condition. There are no known neurological abnormalities that accompany the condition.

The history of the discovery of phenylketonuria is interesting.[2] Even though it has been told many times, we shall repeat it here. The recognition of this disease entity resulted from the fortuitous observation of a Norwegian mother of two mentally retarded children. In actively seeking

[2] Centerwell, W., and Centerwell, S. A., "Phenylketonuria, the story of its discovery," *J. Hist. Med.*, 1961, *16*, 292–296.

a specific cause for the retardation, she noticed that her children's urine smelled differently from that of other children. Eventually her observation came to the attention of Dr. A. Fölling, a physician in Oslo, who finally uncovered and described the condition known as phenylketonuria. The illness is also known as Fölling's disease, in honor of its discoverer.

The disease process is complicated, but fortunately, it is one of the few *known* and *preventable* forms of mental retardation. Blattner has estimated that the condition may occur once in every 25,000 to 40,000 births, and it has been estimated that six-tenths of one per cent of institutionalized mental defectives suffer from phenylketonuria.[3]

Studies have indicated that phenylketonuria is an inherited condition. Clarke states that it is transmitted by a single autosomal recessive gene, and that it may be possible to identify the parents who could transmit the condition to their offspring.[4] Clarke states that the biochemical lesion underlying phenylketonuria is the lack of the specific enzyme *phenylalanine hydroxylase*. In the normal individual this enzyme converts phenylalanine into *tyrosine*. At birth, the enzyme is present in all children, but in the affected child its production ceases during the first few weeks of life. In some instances, the resulting lack of tyrosine leads to a reduction of pigmentation (*melanin*), and the forming of blond hair; the parents of a phenylketonuric child often have blond hair.

This genetic defect produces abnormalities in enzyme formation, and the biochemical disturbances that then ensue are severe. Essentially, the hepatic enzyme system is not sufficiently active in phenylketonuria, and consequently the level of phenylalanine rises in various tissues of the body, including the brain. Other additional metabolic products (such as *phenylpyruvic acid* and *phenylacetic acid*) are formed, and are also found in the body tissues. Further, other enzyme systems which are necessary for normal brain functions are also adversely affected. The disease may be diagnosed as early as the third day of life by a very simple urine test, which is very fortunate, since the studies show that the earlier the disease is treated the greater is the probability that the mental defect can be arrested. It has been held that, unless treatment is initiated prior to the age of three years, the cerebral changes which result from the faulty metabolism tend to be irreversible, and that the condition of mental retardation cannot then be alleviated. Treatment consists, for

[3] Blattner, R., "Phenylketonuria: Phenylpyruria acididuria," *J. Pediat.*, 1961, *59*, 294–298.
[4] Clarke, C., *Genetics for the Clinician*. Oxford: Blackwell Scientific Publications, Ltd., 1962. For a full explanation of the technical terms employed, the reader is referred either to that text or to other standard textbooks on genetics.

the most part, of dietary manipulations to compensate for the enzyme deficiencies. A high blood concentration of phenylalanine is found in rats that have been fed on diets high in tyrosine. This high level has been found to be accompanied by a decrease in learning ability.

Mentally retarded children suffering from phenylketonuria *may* show severe maladaptive behavior. Bjornson has reported on the behavioral reactions of such children.[5] He noted that schizophrenic-like symptoms may be expected in *some cases,* but that there is no general pattern of behavioral reactions that differentiates the child with phenylketonuria from other retarded children. Bjornson did, however, observe that the condition should be suspected in children who show dull expressionless faces, negativistic behavior, unreal emotional outbursts, and speech disturbances, even though the I.Q. is not below the dull normal level. Bjornson concluded, after reviewing the available literature, that there was no consistent behavior pattern described for the phenylketonuric child, and that no "specific categorizable psychological defect exists." This conforms to our previous conclusions in regard to the behavioral reactions of organic brain-damaged individuals—that the resultant symptomology may be of many varieties, and that it is based upon the life history of the individual and upon the manner in which he reacts to the central nervous system damage. A more detailed study of phenylketonuria may be found in the references listed below.[6]

Rh factors

The Rh factor has been found to be associated with mental retardation (The Rh factors are complicated substances in the red corpuscles of the blood. The particular type that a person has is inherited.) It has been demonstrated that considerable difficulties arise when a mother with Rh negative blood type conceives a child that has Rh positive type. The mother then builds up antibodies as a protection against the Rh positive

[5] Bjornson, J., "Behavior in phenylketonuria," *Arch. gen. Psychiat.,* 1964, *10,* 65–69.

[6] For further details of phenylketonuria, see:
   (a) Allen, R., "The detection and diagnosis of phenylketonuria," *Amer. J. Publ. Hlth.,* 1960, *50,* 1600–1666.
   (b) Allen, R., Gibson, R., and Sutton, E., "Phenylketonuria with normal intelligence," *Amer. J. Dis. Child.,* 1960, *100,* 563–564.
   (c) Jervis, G., *Phenylpyruvic Oligophrenia in Genetics and the Inheritance of Integrated Neurological and Psychiatric Patterns.* Baltimore: The Williams & Wilkins Co., 1954.
   (d) Partington, J., "The early symptoms of phenylketonuria," *Pediat.,* 1961, *27,* 465–473.
   (e) Woolf, L., Griffiths, R., Moncrieff, A., Coates, A., and Dillstone, R., "The dietary treatment of phenylketonuria," *Arch. Dis. Child.,* 1958, *33,* 31–45.

blood of the foetus, and these pass through the placenta into the unborn child. This may cause considerable destruction of the blood of the foetus and damage to its central nervous system. The effects may be pronounced at birth, or they may not be clinically severe but manifested in more subtle ways at a later date. Sarason has summarized the findings of several research studies on the problem of the Rh factor. The figures cited by Sarason indicate that the Rh factor is an important cause of or factor associated with retardation. His summary is reproduced in Table 5.

TABLE 5. THE INCIDENCE OF RH NEGATIVE MOTHERS OF CHILDREN WITH MENTAL DEFICIENCY OF VARYING ETIOLOGY*

	Total Number	Mother Rh Negative		Patient Rh Positive Mother Rh Negative	
		Number	Per cent	Number	Per cent
Mongolism	23	3	13.0	3	13.0
Miscellaneous	30	3	10.0	1	3.3
Total	53	6	11.3	4	7.5
Undifferentiated	56	14	25.0	11	19.6

* Reproduced from: Sarason, S. B., *Psychological Problems in Mental Deficiency.* New York: Harper & Row, Publishers, 1949, p. 214.

X-ray irradiation

There is some evidence to indicate that excessive exposure of the pregnant female to X-ray irradiation is associated with certain forms of mental retardation. Murphy and his coworkers investigated this relationship, and reported that 51% of the children of 53 mothers who received X-ray therapy during pregnancy were in some way "abnormal."[7] Of the total group of children, 26 (or 49%) were classified as microcephalic. On the other hand, only 4% of the children of 256 mothers receiving such treatment before a pregnancy were "abnormal." Only one child in this latter group was diagnosed as being microcephalic. Courville and Edmondson state that mental deficiency resulting from exposure of the foetus to X-ray radiation is not rare, and they cite over 60 such cases which have been reported in the literature.[8] They believe that the clinical picture tends to be constant for such cases, being that of microcephaly.

[7] Murphy, D. P., *et al.*, "Microcephaly following maternal pelvic irradiation for the interruption of pregnancy," *Amer. J. Roentgenol., Rad. Ther.*, 1942, *48*, 356–359; and Murphy, D. P., "Ovarian irradiation; its effect on the health of subsequent children," *Surg., Gynec. and Obstet.*, 1928, *47*, 201–215.

[8] Courville, C., and Edmondson, H., "Mental deficiency from intrauterine exposure to radiation," *Bull. Los Angeles Neurol. Soc.*, 1958, *23*, 11–20.

These findings have been substantiated by other workers, and care is now taken not to expose pregnant women to excessive amounts of radiation.

ORGANIC BRAIN DAMAGE

Disease of or damage to the brain may occur before birth (prenatally), at birth, or after birth (postnatally). The prenatal factors may be transmitted by heredity, or they may result from a condition while the child is in the uterus. The latter conditions, which are not hereditary but with which the child is born, are referred to as *congenital* conditions. Both inherited and congenital conditions—those present *at* the time of birth without regard to the cause—are referred to as *primary* conditions. Those occurring *after* birth are referred to as *secondary* conditions.

Damage to the brain may be of many types, ranging in extent from very subtle cellular reactions to severe and obvious physical damage. There are two major types of such damage: (1) those in which there are definite *lesions* (destruction of tissue) within the brain—the *histogenic* involvements; and (2) damage resulting from physiological changes due to toxic reactions—the *chemogenic* involvements. Some brain injuries are the results of accidents. Mautner, Director of the Wrentham State School, reported finding at least 20 children institutionalized there because of various accidents.[9] Some, he felt, were caused by attempts at abortion on the part of the mother. Others were the result of very unusual accidents. For example, he reports the case of a child who, at the age of six months, was found in his crib with a cat sleeping across his mouth and nostrils. He was unconscious, cyanotic, and had to be given artificial respiration to be revived. The deprivation of oxygen (known as a state of *anoxia*) produced brain damage and resulted in loss of intellectual capacities. We shall discuss histogenic and chemogenic involvements in the following pages.

Histogenic involvements

Histogenic disorders which involve definite lesions of the brain may be of different types, including damage resulting from accidents, diseases that injure or destroy brain tissue (such as cerebral tumors or infections), or degenerative cellular changes within the brain. The actual damage to the brain structure may be demonstrated either as a grossly visual or microscopical destruction.

[9] Mautner, H., "Some unusual accidents followed by mental retardation," *Arch. Pediat.*, 1953, *70*, 40–44.

Perhaps the most common histogenic disorders of children resulting in mental retardation are those involving direct brain damage. Injuries to the brain from accidents are not rare. Many persons—probably all of us—have at one time or another suffered a severe blow to the head without any after-effects, but if, following such an accident, parents note that their child is functioning at a retarded level, then they all too frequently attribute the condition to a "brain injury." It is easier and more comfortable to do this than to look for less obvious reasons. Research studies have shown that, even though blows to the head may occasionally produce damage that is serious enough to cause a condition of retardation, they are not as important an etiological factor as is commonly thought.

Siegal has discussed the various forms of injury which may occur to the brain.[10] These are: (1) concussions, caused by a blow to the head, the effects of which are disseminated throughout the brain rather than localized; (2) contusions in which there is a definite lesion; (3) lacerations; (4) hemorrhages, which may be mild or extensive enough to involve the entire brain.

Brain damage that occurs prior to the age of three years may lead to a condition in which the child is unable to control his muscular movements. Both large and fine muscular controls may be impaired. There may be spasmodic jerkings of the hands, head, or feet; and voluntary movements such as reaching for an object are very difficult to perform. This condition is known as *cerebral palsy*. The extent of the motor involvement may vary from slight impairment to the most severe, where no voluntary controls are capable of being maintained. Sometimes the child may drool and, as may be expected, there may be very severe speech difficulties.

Although children suffering from cerebral palsy may be of average or even superior intelligence, the incidence of mental retardation is very high. Approximately half of such children tested have been reported as mentally retarded.[11] This is, of course, a far higher percentage than is found in the general population.

Probably the most common cause of histogenic brain involvement in children is that of birth trauma—the so-called *birth injuries*. Sometimes physical damage that occurs during the birth process may be very important in causing mental retardation. The birth process is often violent and, in addition to the psychological effects, may produce physical

[10] Siegal, L. J., "Cerebral traumata—Concept and valuation of psychophysiological aftermaths," *Dis. Nerv. Syst.*, 1953, *14*, 163–171.

[11] Goodenough, F. I., *Exceptional Children*. New York: Appleton-Century-Crofts, Inc., 1956, p. 353.

trauma with far-reaching consequences. Despite the plasticity of the child's brain at birth, prolonged labor, or severe physical stress or pressure, or the utilization of instruments may cause serious injury to the brain during the birth process. Hemorrhage may result, for example. Doll and his co-workers studied the significance of injury associated with the

A CASE OF CEREBRAL PALSY WITH MENTAL RETARDATION (Courtesy the Fort Wayne Training School, Photo by L. Richard Young)

birth process.[12] They showed that this factor may produce a condition of mental deficiency, even when other possible etiological factors are clearly absent.

As Whitney states, birth is one of the most acute emergencies en-

[12] Doll, E. A., Phelps, W. N., and Melcher, R. T., *Mental Deficiency due to Birth Injury*, New York: The Macmillan Co., 1932.

countered by the individual during his whole life.[13] He summarized the types of common birth injuries that may lead to mental retardation as follows: (1) asphyxia (lack of oxygen); (2) cerebral injuries to the brain itself; (3) peripheral nerve injuries; (4) fractures and resulting complicating factors; (5) soft tissue damage; and (6) injuries to the viscera.

Chemogenic involvements

As noted earlier, chemogenic involvements are those that result from the effects of various toxic agents upon the brain tissue. These include reactions to poisons taken into the body (such as alcohol and carbon monoxide); poisons resulting from internal physiological malfunctionings (such as endocrine disturbances); the toxic effects of various disease processes (such as encephalitis); or the lack of an adequate oxygen supply to the brain tissues. It might well be argued that there is destruction of tissue in chemogenic instances as well as in those that we have described as histogenic. There is, in fact, much overlap between the two classifications, but we may distinguish between the two on the basis of *primacy* of cause. If there is no chemical change preceding the damage, then it may be regarded as histogenic in character. Such a distinction, of course, is somewhat arbitrary.

Lippman *et al.* have reviewed some of the more important aspects of the biochemical bases of mental deficiency.[14] According to these researchers, differentiation should be made between conditions resulting from hereditary biochemical defects and those in which there is a biochemical trauma to the foetus. However, in either event, the behavioral anomalies which result tend to be quite similar.

When such conditions affect the neurological mechanisms they have far-reaching consequences. One of the diseases affecting children is that known as *encephalitis lethargica* (commonly referred to as "sleeping sickness"). The first serious study of this condition was made by von Economo in 1917, during the time of the great epidemic in Europe. The disease reached epidemic proportions in the United States in 1918, and at that time was often confused with influenza. Mild attacks of the disease may go unnoticed, but the behavioral residuals, such as increased irritability, aggression, and dependency, may be very serious. The mental retardation that often results may also be profound. The specific bacterial

[13] Whitney, E. A., "Mental deficiency 1955," *Amer. J. ment. Defic.,* 1955, *60,* 676–683.
[14] Lippman, R., Perry, T., and Wright, S., "The biochemical basis of mental dysfunction. II. Mental deficiency (amentia)," *Metabolism-Clin. Exp.,* 1958, *7,* 274–330.

agent responsible for the disease has not yet been definitely isolated, but it is thought to be a filtrable virus. The disease may take many forms and may be either acute or subacute in nature. It may be ushered in slowly and may be accompanied by prolonged sleep or lethargy, delirium, or various eye complaints. There may be muscular contractions ranging from tics to convulsions, or there may be postacute symptoms of over-talkativeness and hyperactivity. The extent of the resultant intellectual impairment is proportional to the involvement, and careful psychological handling, either under the supervision of a psychiatrist or a clinical psychologist, is usually desirable to deal more adequately with the after-effects.

Brain damage may result from an inadequate supply of oxygen to the brain tissues. Schreiber, who studied cerebral anoxia (*or paranatal asphyxia*) in children, stated that there were four conditions that could result in a lessened supply of oxygen to the brain.[15] There are: (1) *anoxic anoxia*, a condition in which the concentration of oxygen in the blood is low. It may be the result of strangulation or intense suffocation of the mother during pregnancy; (2) *anemic anoxia*, where the oxygen supply in the blood is low due to fewer red blood cells; (3) *stagnant anoxia*, a condition in which the quantity of blood, and hence the oxygen supply, is at a lowered level; and (4) *histotoxic anoxia*, which is due to a poisoning of the cells of the brain itself so that they are unable to absorb an adequate amount of oxygen.

In a comprehensive study of the effects of anoxia on the subsequent development of the child, some interesting and challenging results were obtained.[16] Thirty cases of anoxia were selected for study from over 40,000 babies born at the Chicago Maternity Center. Of these 30 babies, 24 had *severe apnea*, and 6 had *moderate apnea*. (Severe apnea is indicated when the baby does not breathe within 30 seconds of birth, is either livid or pallid, and appears dead.) The duration of apnea was from 10 to 30 minutes for 19 of these babies, and longer for the rest. These "experimental" children who were examined at ages 3 to 19 years, were compared with two groups of control children, matched for sex and age, one group consisting of siblings, and another of non-siblings. All of the mothers of the control groups had experienced natural labor. A variety of tests

[15] Schreiber, F., "Mental deficiency from paranatal asphyxia," *Proceedings and Addresses of the Sixty-Third Annual Session of the American Association on Mental Deficiency,* 1939, *44*, 95–106.
[16] Benaron, H. B. W., *et al.*, "Effect of anoxia during labor and immediately after birth on the subsequent development of the child," *Amer. J. Obstet. and Gynec.,* 1960, *80*, 1129–1142.

(including three different tests which could yield measures of intelligence) was administered. The finding of greatest pertinence to us was that 20 per cent of the experimental group measured mentally retarded on the intelligence tests, as compared with 2.5 per cent of the control groups.

This and related results caused the authors to conclude, ". . . that severe anoxia *may have deleterious results* in later life (*italics ours*)." The fact that not all severely anoxic children later became feebleminded reinforces the conclusion that it is not the organic deficit alone which may produce deficiency in intellectual functioning, but the way the whole organism reacts to the damage which is of particular importance. Moreover, another surprising finding, namely, that there were 4 anoxic children who had *superior* I.Q.'s (over 110) in the experimental group, but none in the control groups, reinforces this conclusion.

Although this latter finding is not statistically significant, it and related findings point up the complicated and inter-active way in which *various factors* contribute to the end result. If, indeed, it turns out that proportionately more children who had anoxia than those who experienced normal birth have superior I.Q.'s, one would have to consider how this came about: whether the organism, in defending itself against the severe trauma, compensated by developing more rapid maturational growth tendencies; whether the complicated biochemical adaptation to anoxia produces both favorable and unfavorable results in all or in only some cases; whether the special and intensive care which is given to anoxic babies contributes significantly to their pattern of development; and so on.

Again and again we are forced to the conclusion that no single factor, favorable or unfavorable, operates in isolation in determining the pace and character of the individual's development.

There are many diseases that are of importance in the production of altered intellectual functioning in children. These include: *meningitis, polioencephalitis,* and *syphilis.* Some severe forms of measles, too, may have significant results. In all of these conditions *attention should be given to the resultant psychological reactions as well as to the disease condition itself,* and the parents will profit from advice and guidance in understanding and adapting to the condition of their child.

Psychological results of brain damage

We have discussed various forms of brain damage to children, ranging from direct injury to brain tissue to damage resulting from the interaction of very complex internal processes. When the large body of literature on brain damage to children is reviewed, we find that there is a marked overlap in the effects of different types and degrees of such damage. For example, the damage to intellectual functions is not significantly different in chemogenic and in histogenic disorders. There are, however, certain basic considerations that may be summarized from such studies.

First, the specific impairment in intellectual functions is related to the area of the brain damage, regardless of the cause of the damage. Even though very little is known, comparatively speaking, concerning the characteristics of various areas of the brain, certain areas have been related to specific functions. The visual, hearing, touch, pressure, speech, and motor areas have been fairly well defined and localized, but the major portion of the brain is still an unexplored region. Moreover, experimental work is difficult. As Cobb points out, for example, lesions destroying exactly the same areas in two different brains might not result in exactly the same symptom.[17] The effects depend upon the personality and general physical characteristics of the particular child as well as on the area of the brain involved. The residual damage may vary from very severe intellectual impairment, in which the child functions at the lowest idiot level and requires complete and constant care, to very mild impairment, in which there are only slight after-effects in terms of intellectual functioning. For example, a child may function very well in most other respects, but develop a reading disability due to a birth injury that produced a mild and diffuse hemorrhage.

Secondly, the brain damage, even when it produces no deficit in intellectual functioning, may result in extensive changes in emotional reactions, which then produce impaired intellectual functioning. Such a child may then function at a somewhat lowered intellectual level, and appear to be mentally retarded even though he may still possess "average" or even "superior" intellectual capacities. Organic brain-damaged children generally tend to have lowered memory and attention spans. They tend to respond impulsively and cannot tolerate tensions. They are restless and engage in excessive motor activities to discharge their tensions. Depending, of course, upon the age at which the injury occurred, the child's psychological reactions to the injury may be profound.

Thirdly, as we have repeatedly stressed, the child reacts to his organic brain damage as a unitary organism. It is not only intellectual factors, but *all* aspects of the child that are involved. This conclusion has been particularly stressed by Goldstein in studying brain-damaged

---

[17] Cobb, S., "Personality as affected by lesions of the brain," in *Personality and the Behavior Disorders* (J. McV. Hunt, ed.). New York: The Ronald Press Company, 1944, Vol. 1, p. 553.

adults.[18] He points out that an injury to the brain produces deep changes in an individual's capacities for various performances; he can no longer do things in the same way or as well as he formerly did. He becomes a different person in many respects, both behaviorally and in basic personality characteristics.

It is possible that brain damage which produces significant decrements in behavioral functioning may be insufficient in extent to be detected by the usual neurological examination. Further, there may be different behavioral reactions resulting from slight damage as opposed to those resulting from extensive damage to the brain.

Knobloch and Pasamanick have initiated research into this area.[19] They hypothesize what they term a *continuum of reproductive casualties,* which postulates a component of cerebral damage resulting in death, and a sub-lethal component that results in a series of syndromes, depending upon the degree and location of the cerebral injury. Three specific prenatal and paranatal factors are associated with this continuum: (1) premature birth; (2) toxemia; and (3) bleeding during pregnancy. In order to investigate the effects of more minimal brain damage Knobloch and Pasamanick compared 500 premature babies with 492 normal infants up to 40 weeks of age.

It was found that the premature babies manifested evidence of cerebral damage by the presence of clear but minimal deviations from the normal neurological patterns. Of considerable significance was the finding that these deviations were more or less completely compensated for neurologically by the age of 15 to 18 months. Behaviorally, the premature children showed an increased incidence in sucking, hypertonicity, hypotonicity, twitches, convulsions, feeding problems and "crankiness" over the normal infants.

One additional finding is also of considerable importance. Knobloch and Pasamanick concluded that the degree of tension manifested by the mothers of the premature children was positively related to the degree of neurological damage present; that is, the greater the extent of the damage to the brain tissue, the more tension was manifested by the mother. In light of this evidence, it may well be that the adjustment of the brain-damaged child to the damage is made more difficult by the tension state of the mother. A follow-up of this research with longitudinal studies (as Knobloch and Pasamanick intend to carry out), will be of considerable

---

[18] Goldstein, K., *Aftereffects of Brain Injuries in War.* New York: Grune & Stratton, Inc., 1942.

[19] Knobloch, H., and Pasamanick, B., "Syndrome of minimal cerebral damage in infancy," *J. Amer. Med. Ass.,* 1959, *170,* 1384–1387.

interest in shedding light on the future patterns of behavior and degrees of impairment of functions in minimally brain-damaged children. It is of importance to determine whether later problems of the child are correlated with the degree and type of minimal brain damage manifested in early infancy.

We have seen that the results of organic damage to the same brain area vary in different children so greatly that we cannot adequately predict what psychological defects will result from damage to a specific area—or, conversely, we cannot predict precisely the area of damage from a knowledge of the symptoms alone. It is thus a mistake to talk about a generalized "brain-damaged child," as many people do. It is a *specific child* who shows such a condition. His reactions to the organic brain damage, the ways in which he deals with his changed conditions, the behavioral reactions in which he engages, and the altered emotional reactions he shows are all functions of his total personality. *What must always be considered are the total reactions of the child to the damage.*

THE ROLE OF HEREDITY AND CULTURE

Society has always been prone to attribute most maladaptive forms of behavior to the presence of an inherited trait. Criminal behavior on the part of the adult and delinquency on the part of the child have often been wrongly ascribed to heredity. Mental retardation is no exception to this tendency. Such remarks as "It's in the blood" or "It's inherited" are frequently overheard and reflect the attitude and ignorance of the public. As we pointed out in Chapter One, Dugdale's work on the Jukes was immediately interpreted by the public as evidence for the inheritance of complex behavioral maladaptations, even though his findings provided no evidence for such a conclusion.

Actually we know very little about the inheritance of intellectual characteristics, although there has been a great deal written on the subject. There are many obstacles to adequate research on this topic. Difficulties arise because of the complex nature of mental retardation itself and because of the technical problems in exploring any area of human genetics.

With respect to the nature of mental retardation, we may emphasize the following factors that make its investigation very complex. One of these concerns the criteria by which retardation is determined. We have seen that a single test of intelligence is insufficient to establish the diagnosis. In many investigations, however, the researcher does not have direct access to the subjects under study, and estimates of the degree of deficiency have to be made from judgments by those who know the subjects. Such judgments are influenced by the criteria employed by the judge as well as by his adequacy as a judge. Moreover, the ratings made by judges in former years may have little in common with those of the current period, since concepts of mental retardation vary with time. In addition to the matter of criteria, there is also the problem of the heterogeneity of the phenomena of mental retardation. Retarded persons do not, in fact, constitute a homogeneous group; a variety of biological and sociological conditions contribute to this condition. If a single type of mental deficiency is selected for study, or if a single trait of the mental defective is so selected, the results obtained are not generalizable for other types or traits. Similarly, if a particular level of retardation is studied the conclusions may be at variance with those obtained from other levels.

Another problem concerns the methodology that can be employed in such studies. Experimental manipulation of humans for breeding purposes cannot be attempted; in research on animals this problem is readily solvable. Other types of controls in research are also difficult to apply. For example, since human beings do not mate at random, the methods of statistical analysis that depend on random sampling are not appropriate. It is also difficult to measure precisely the relative effects of environmental factors upon behavioral resultants, just as it is difficult to control for variation in environmental influences by statistical means.

These and other difficulties in research on the role of heredity encourage a spurious interpretation of the results in terms of the bias of the investigator. Perry, who has made an analysis of such problems, reaches a very critical view of such matters. He states:[20]

In the end it is the assumption and predilections of the investigator which determine what interpretations are made of the heredity-environment studies. . . .

Burt has studied the role of inheritance in the etiology of mental retardation for an extended period of time. In a recent work, he reported his evaluation of 30 pairs of identical twins reared in separate homes from time of birth. Very high correlations were reported for the pairs of twins on measures of educational achievement (.68), of adjusted assessment of intelligence (.88), and of intelligence scores (.77). Burt believes strongly in the hypothesis that retardation is an inherited characteristic, and points out that his correlations tend to support this belief, since they are nearly as high as test-retest correlations for the same person. He feels

[20] Perry, S. E., "Some theoretic problems of mental deficiency and their action implications," *Psychiat.*, 1954, *17*, 58.

that both unifactor and multifactor inheritance determine retardation. Large deviations in intelligence, according to Burt, may be attributed to the influence of major genes, while smaller deviations may be a function of multiple gene effects. Burt states that three-fourths of the total variance in mental ability are due to genetic factors.[21]

It certainly is true that there have been some demonstrated relationships between mental retardation and inheritance. The evidence indicates that some conditions involving retardation are probably understandable as the result of heredity factors—amaurotic familial idiocy, tubero-sclerosis, and phenylpyruvic oligophrenia are examples. But no such clear relationships between heredity and retardation have been demonstrated for the vast majority of cases. Neuer, investigating the relationships of behavior disorders to mental deficiency in children, concluded that inheritance as a primary factor had been demonstrated for the vast majority of cases of retardation.[22] Neuer's hypothesis in regard to the role of heredity implies that maladaptive behavior (including mental retardation) is determined by a pathological physical structure; this, too, appears questionable. This structure is then assumed to be what is genetically determined. If, however, such an assumption is made, the specific limit-setting structure must be demonstrated.[23] Thus far, in general, it has not been.

Studies of the role of heredity in the etiology of mental retardation indicate that some pathological conditions are attributable to the presence of a single dominant gene within one parent. An example of such a presumed condition is *tubero-sclerosis*, which is characterized by mental deficiency, convulsive seizures, and tumors on the face. Other forms of pathology are attributed to the presence of a single recessive gene. In such cases both parents must carry the defective gene. Undetermined genetic factors, such as the effect of the interactions of multiple genes, are also assumed to be of etiologic importance in producing such conditions as brain malformations.

It is our conviction that as more adequate research is conducted, and as more and more knowledge is obtained concerning the nature of retardation, the percentage of children judged to have "inherited" the condition will decrease. This reduction is apparently taking place. Table 6 lists by year and authority the percentage of retarded individuals thought of as having inherited their disability. Notice the decline in the percentage

---

[21] Burt, C., "Inheritance of mental ability," *Eugen. Rev.*, 1957, *49*, 137–139.

[22] Neuer, M., "The relationships between behavior disorders in children and the syndrome of mental deficiency," *Amer. J. ment. Defic.*, 1947, *52*, 143–147.

[23] Anastasi, A., and Foley, J. P., "A proposed reorientation to the heredity environment controversy," *Psychol. Rev.*, 1948, *55*, 239–249.

attributed to the hereditary origin. Although many factors may explain this decrease, it seems to be related primarily to our increasing knowledge in this area.

TABLE 6. PERCENTAGE OF HEREDITARY ORIGIN OF FEEBLEMINDEDNESS*

Year	Author	Percentage
1914	Goddard	77
1920	Hollingworth	90
1929	Tredgold	80
1931	Larson	76
1934	Doll	30
1934	Penrose	29

* Adapted from Kanner, L., *A Miniature Text Book of Feeblemindedness*. New York: Child Care Publications, 1949, p. 5.

Perry raises objections to the assumption of the primary role of heredity in the etiology of retardation upon many grounds.[24] These are worth emphasizing here. He feels, first, that the demonstrated anomalies in physical structures, even though present, have not been adequately shown to be inherited characteristics. Second, there are many types of nonhereditarily determined damage to the physiological structure of the human being that are not different from those assumed to be inherited. Such damage may be produced experimentally in animals. The same may be true for human beings. For these reasons Perry does not believe that the mere presence of structural differences in mentally retarded children provides sufficient evidence for the assumption that they are inherited.

As we have seen, there are thus two opposite conclusions—that intellectual retardation is an inherited characteristic, and that it is not usually inherited. The evidence to date is not sufficiently clear to establish either hypothesis beyond reasonable doubt, but it does tend to indicate that the role of inheritance has been exaggerated. In some instances inheritance may be a primary factor, but to conclude, in general, that heredity is primarily responsible for most cases of retardation would be to go far beyond the available evidence. Moreover, mental retardation is not the result of a single factor. As we have repeatedly stressed, the child is a complex organism, and his behavioral reactions are the product of many interacting internal and external forces. Even though the potentiality for a given trait *might* be inherited, its actual manifestation depends upon many factors.

[24] Perry, *op. cit.*, 45–73.

The child lives in a culture—an environment of which he is a part. His intellectual, emotional, and other behavioral reactions are, in some measure, dependent on his environment. Many factors, particularly those of the child's immediate environment, can interfere with the adequate growth and expression of his intellectual potentials. When we consider the causal role of inheritance in this light, and perceive it as one of a large number of interacting factors, modifiable by the life experiences of the child, then heredity assumes an entirely different significance from that formerly attributed to it as "the responsible factor."

The relative effects of both heredity and environment on the development and functioning of intelligence is an especially important, if unsolved, problem. As we shall see, it is clear that inferior cultural and educational experiences can produce a significant depreciation in the functioning of intelligence, and if this is so then we must consider what are the limits within which the forces of hereditary and cultural origin can effectively operate. It is because of considerations such as these that we have tried to be careful to distinguish between *mental retardation* and *mental impairment*. A number of recent investigators have taken a similar position, as, for example, Sarason and Gladwin,[25] and Masland,[26] who attempt to distinguish between *mental deficiency* (intellectual defects attributable to heredity, disease, or injury), and *mental retardation* (intellectually defective functioning present when an individual fails to utilize his native potentials).

As we have said, there is ample evidence that inferior cultural-educational experience can depress the I.Q. Studies of Canal Boat children (who lived in very inferior and socio-economically deprived circumstances),[27] gypsy children (who had little opportunity for formal schooling),[28] Kentucky mountain children (who lived in extreme isolation and at low cultural and economic levels),[29] and Negro children (who moved from inadequate to fairly adequate schooling opportunities),[30] have shown how serious this effect can be. In Chapter Two we examined a num-

---

[25] Sarason, S. B., and Gladwin, T., "Psychological and cultural problems in mental subnormality: a review of research," *Amer. J. ment. Defic.*. 1958, *62*, 1115–1307.

[26] Masland, R. L., "The prevention of mental retardation: a survey of research," *Amer. J. ment. Defic.*, 1958, *62*, 994–1012.

[27] Gordon, H., "Mental and scholastic tests among retarded children . . . An enquiry into the effects of schooling on the various tests." London: *Bull. Educ. Pamphl.* No. 44, 1924.

[28] *Ibid.*

[29] Asher, E. J., "The inadequacy of current intelligence tests for testing Kentucky Mountain Children," *J. genet. Psychol.*, 1935, *46*, 480–486.

[30] Klineberg, O., *Negro Intelligence and Selective Migration.* New York: Columbia University Press, 1935.

ber of other studies bearing on this same problem and indicating, generally, the same kind of findings: namely, that prolonged exposure to inferior cultural experiences serves to depress the I.Q. as measured on standardized tests.

There are other studies which indicate the reverse trend is possible when children are exposed to superior educational or cultural opportunities, especially if this is done at an early age. We shall refer only to two important studies.

Burks studied more than 200 foster children who were adopted *before 12 months of age.*[31] On the basis of their known sociological backgrounds, she assumed that these children, who were tested when they were from 5 to 14 years of age, should have measured, on the average, about 100 in I.Q. However, she found that they actually tested, on the average, at 107.4 in I.Q., a gain which she attributed to the relatively superior foster environments which they had had. She also found that the maximal shift which the difference from a very poor home environment to a very superior environment might make was about 40 points in I.Q., a not insignificant shift! Moreover, she also found that the correlation coefficient between the social status of the true parents and the I.Q. of the children who had been living with foster parents was .07, whereas if inheritance played a major role in determining I.Q., one would have inferred from the social status of the true parents that the correlation would have been substantial.

Even more revealing is the study by Wellman on two groups of nursery school children.[32] One group came from homes of low incomes and the other from homes of middle-class incomes. In both groups, there was a gain over a year's time of 6.6 points in I.Q. That this accompaniment of attendance in nursery school was not an artifact of the effect of practice on the tests, nor was it simply an accumulation of "knowledge" that unduly affected the test results temporarily, was indicated by the fact that, in follow-up studies, these children tended to retain their improved position on I.Q. scores.

Thus far we have seen that variations in environmental experience can affect the assessed evaluation on standardized intelligence tests. Now, we shall turn our attention to studies specifically directed to the relative influence of heredity.

[31] Burks, B. S., "The relative influence of nature and nurture upon mental development: a comparative study . . . ," in *27th Yearb., No. Soc. Stud. Educ.,* 1928, *1,* 219–316.
[32] Wellman, B. L., "Iowa studies on the effects of schooling," in *39th Yearb., Nat. Ass. Stud. Educ.,* Vol. II, 1940, 377–399.

Perhaps the outstanding classic in this field is the series of studies done by Newmann, Freeman, and Holzinger.[33] They analyzed the results of intelligence tests, personality questionnaires, and achievement tests on identical twins and fraternal twins. Particular attention was given to comparisons of the identical twins who were reared together with those who were reared apart. Assuming that all of the identical twins were in fact identical (and authorities now indicate that evaluation of this fact is not as simple as it was formerly thought to be), and that they therefore came from identical heredity, an analysis of differences associated with differences in environmental experience could be crucial in determining the limits which heredity imposes on intellectual functioning.

These researchers found that, in general, the correlation coefficient in measured intelligence for all of their identical twins was .88, a relationship that is quite high. For fraternal twins the correlation coefficient was .63, thus suggesting, on the one hand, that heredity plays an important role, and yet indicating, on the other hand, that environmental factors are not insignificant.

When their data are analyzed more fully, the relative effect of environment becomes more significant! For instance, they found that the correlation coefficient on intelligence of identical twins *who were reared apart* dropped from .88 to .77. Further, when the relatively small population of identical twins is studied even more, it appears that the twins who were reared apart were placed in different homes at varying ages, that the *differences in the home environments* to which they were exposed were not maximal, and that the differences in intelligence tended to be closely related to the degree of difference in environment. Intrapair differences in I.Q. ranged from 1 point to 24 points. Thus, taken together these data indicate the considerable effect of environmental factors.

We should also like to cite the evidence from a more recent study by Skodak and Skeels.[34] In this study the intelligence of 100 adopted children was correlated with the intelligence of their biological mothers, from whom they had been separated. The correlation was found to be .44, a still considerable relationship. However, in a later study by Skodak,[35] it was found that when *unrelated children* were adopted into

[33] Newmann, H. H., Freeman, F. F., and Holzinger, K. J., *Twins: A Study of Heredity and Environment*. Chicago: University of Chicago Press, 1937.

[34] Skodak, M., and Skeels, H. M., "A final follow-up study of 100 adopted children," *J. genet. Psychol.*, 1949, *75*, 85–125.

[35] Skodak, M., "Mental growth of adopted children in the same family," *J. genet. Psychol.*, 1950, *77*, 3–9.

the same home, their intelligence correlated to the extent of .65, a figure comparable to the correlation of siblings reared together, and close to that of *fraternal twins!*

In some previous studies, Skeels found that, in some cases, when foster children were placed in homes that were superior in socio-economic status to that of their true parents, not only was there a rise in I.Q. but the correlation of the I.Q.'s of the foster children with those of their true parents dropped to about .00.[36]

All of this evidence, taken together, indicates that tested intelligence and educational functioning can be significantly modified, *upward or downward*, by appropriate modifications in cultural and educational opportunities. *Tested intelligence is not fixed and stable from birth onward.* Heredity plays a part in determining the limits within which fluctuation in I.Q. occurs, but culture plays a significant part, too. Not only differences in objective environmental conditions, but emotional stimulation or deprivation and other emotional factors play a role in intellectual growth or retardation!

In short, we must conclude that intellectual functioning is the complex end-result of many interacting internal and external factors, and heredity is only one of these. Perhaps, in extreme cases when there is associated severe disease or organic deficit, the upper limits of heredity are more rigidly fixed, but even here we must be careful to appraise the possible contribution of other concurrent factors before ascribing all of the end-result to hereditary forces alone.

TRENDS IN RESEARCH ON ETIOLOGICAL FACTORS

Many groups are attempting to advance knowledge of the etiology of mental retardation. The National Association for Retarded Children, an association of parents, is sponsoring an extensive program of research. The National Institute for Mental Health is also devoting considerable attention to this area. Numerous institutions and universities are also mapping research activities.

It might be well to summarize some of the directions that recent research on etiological factors is taking. Attention has been devoted to difficulties during pregnancy in relation to mental retardation.[37] The relations of disturbances in the enzyme system to retardation are also

---

[36] Skeels, H. M., "Mental development of children in foster homes," *J. genet. Psychol.*, 1938, *2*, 33–43.

[37] Pasamanick, B., and Lilienfeld, A. M., "The association of maternal and fetal factors with development of mental deficiency: 1. Abnormalities in the prenatal and paranatal periods," *J. Amer. Med. Ass.*, 1955, *159*, 155–160.

being investigated.[38] Much interest is being shown in exploring its etiology at a molecular level through study of changed protein molecules, viruses, and genes.[39]

There also has been renewed interest in *psychological* stresses on the mother during pregnancy in terms of possible importance as an etiological factor.[40] For example, Hepner reviewed a number of studies dealing with the relationship between nutrition of the mother and characteristics of the child.[41] He found that protein depletion of the mother was associated with a lowered conception rate, and that if the depletion occurred after conception, the child tended to be small at birth. Hepner states that neurological defects, some convulsive disorders, cerebral palsies, and mental deficiency may be the results of nutritional defects in the mother.

Masland has reviewed methodological approaches to research in etiology.[42] His position, like ours, is that *mental retardation is not a disease entity in itself, but, rather, it is a symptom which may result from any one of numerous different diseases or other causes.* These diseases have quite different etiologies. This conclusion may serve as the starting point for more intensive research into mental retardation. Masland feels that the basis of clinical research is an improved ability to differentiate and categorize the various forms of retardation, but that such a differentiation must also be related to the basic etiological factors. He stresses the importance of detailed prenatal and postnatal records in extending knowledge of these factors.

Various group research activities relating to the etiology of mental retardation are currently being conducted in many diverse areas. These include studies in: anthropology, neuropathology, biochemistry, histochemistry of brain tissue, immunologic genetics, cytological characteristics of chromosomes, and neurophysiology. Studies such as these are necessarily concerned only with the basic disease processes, of which mental retardation is but one byproduct.

Tarjan reflects the complexity and confusion in regard to the etiology of mental retardation when he points out that even though at least 50

[38] Armstrong, M. D., and Tyler, F. H., "Studies on phenylketonuria: 1. Restricted phenylalanine intake in phenylketonuria," *J. clin. Invest.*, 1955, *34*, 565–580.

[39] Pauling, L., "The molecular basis of genetics," in a paper presented at a meeting of the American Psychiatric Association, Chicago, May 2, 1956.

[40] Bronsted, H. V., "Warning and promise of experimental embryology," *Bull. of Atom. Sci.*, 1956, *12*, 66–75.

[41] Hepner, R., "Maternal nutrition and the foetus," *J. Amer. Med. Ass.*, 1958, *168*, 1774–1777.

[42] Masland, R. L., "Methodological approaches to research in etiology," *Amer. J. ment. Defic.*, 1960, *64*, 305–310.

different agents have been identified as being associated with retardation, the specific etiology of the condition is, in most instances, unknown.[43] He hypothesizes that there are essentially two major groups of retardates: the *physiological* group, where the extent of the mental deficiency is to be expected on the basis of the predicted ratios from the curve of normal distribution (see p. 41); and the *pathological* group, which includes those cases that occur in excess of the number to be expected from the curve of normal distribution. The physiological retardates outnumber the pathological retardates by a ratio of 16 to 1.

The physiologically mentally retarded individuals, according to Tarjan, show a relatively mild degree of retardation, and rarely show any stigmata. They are frequently termed *familial* or *psychogenic* types. They may be capable of making a fairly adequate adjustment, provided they are not faced with difficult situations, but critical stresses increase the probability of maladjustment. Tarjan states that examples of such stresses are: school enrollment, marriage, sexual maturity, adolescence, or job finding. All of these stress situations have in common the fact that they require the individual to compete with others on an intellectual basis. The psychogenic retardates tend to come from below-average socio-cultural backgrounds.

The pathological retardate shows a more severe degree of retardation, and usually has an I.Q. of below 50. Concomittant somatic involvements and stigmata are common, and the brain usually manifests either gross or histological abnormalities. Tarjan states that there are no significant differences between the socio-economic background of the pathological retardate and that of more normal children. The mortality rate in this group is high, and it is very difficult for such an individual to assume an indepedent existence.

One very promising area of research into the etiology of mental retardates, according to Tarjan, is that concerned with metabolic disturbances. He cites Pauling's *molecular concept of disease,* which regards the healthy organism as an aggregation of normal molecules, and the sick organism as being afflicted with abnormal molecules. Tarjan states that the enzyme production is controlled by genetic factors, which are themselves organizations of complex molecular structures. If the gene structure (molecular structure) is defective, then the enzyme production is either absent or abnormal. Four major types of abnormality in enzyme production have been categorized and related to various specific forms of

[43] Tarjan, G., "Research in mental deficiency with emphasis on etiology," *Bull. Menninger Clin.,* 1960, *24,* 57–69.

retardation. These are: (1) defects in protein synthesis (resulting in phenylketonuria) ; (2) defects in carbohydrate synthesis (resulting in galactosemia) ; (3) defects in lipoid metabolism (resulting in Tay-Sachs disease) ; and defects in hormone synthesis (resulting in nonendemic goitrous cretinism). Further research in this area is rapidly expanding.

Tarjan offers a biological concept which he believes might be of value in explaining the lowered mental functioning in the physiological group of retardates. He points out that a person who is heterozygous for a particular biochemical trait will manufacture only one-half of the required dosage of a particular enzyme. In ordinary circumstances, such an individual will function well, but in a stress situation he will be taxed beyond his capacity. Either psychological or biological stresses may produce demands upon the individual which the available enzymes are unable to meet. Consequently, toxic substances may be produced which in turn lead to states of imbalance.

In addition to the group research that is being conducted, many individual researchers are carrying out numerous studies in the area of etiological factors in mental retardation. All of their activities in the field should help clarify some of the obscure issues involved. We are not yet in a position to assess the specific values of current research, but we can predict, with confidence, that considerable advance will be made in the period directly ahead of us.

ch. 5

DEVELOPMENT OF

THE PERSONALITY

Wᴇ SHALL NOW FOCUS OUR ATTENTION ON THE PROBLEMS OF personality development, organization and functioning. In understanding and dealing with individuals, we wish to know something of "what makes them tick." This is no less true for retarded individuals than for normals. If we wish to motivate people to achieve their full potential, we must "be in tune with them," as the popular saying has it, and we must provide them with optimal opportunities to satisfy their basic needs. Anything less than this is likely to be frustrating and result in less efficient functioning than might otherwise be the case. Hence we must understand *the person*; that is, we must know something of how he came to be where he is and why he now behaves as he does. It seems to us, therefore, that we should become familiar with the major aspects of personality development (in the present chapter), the dynamics of behavior (in Chapter Six), and the "structure" of the personality (in Chapter Seven).

PERSONALITY CONCEPTS IN RELATION TO THE RETARDED

As we shall see, a great deal has been learned about the general nature of personality development and functioning, although there is still much more to be discovered. The nature of these phenomena in the mentally retarded is far less understood, since systematic research in this domain has only recently been given any consistent or intense interest. What little knowledge we have about personality problems of the retarded is already proving to be of great theoretical and practical value, and in time we shall undoubtedly learn much more.

However, the retarded pupil is, after all, a human being like all human beings, and we should not expect to find the nature of his personality development to be far different from that of other individuals. It may therefore be expected that most of the general principles of such development will apply with equal accuracy to the mentally retarded.

Although we shall discuss the general findings concerning the nature of personality and its development, we shall try to apply them whenever relevant to the retarded individual, and whenever possible we shall point up exceptions and special considerations as they apply to him. The individual who is retarded in his development, for whatever reason, faces unique problems and special stresses. Life, on the whole, is geared to the average person, and its demands and requirements are therefore intended for this person. The individual who develops more slowly, in all or in most respects, can therefore be expected to encounter more stress in the very process of living. In comparison with others of like age, he may be slower in acquiring understanding and achievement, he is likely to be deprecated more often, and he is likely to be rewarded less frequently. Even within his own family, especially if he has siblings who are, in general, superior to him, there will inevitably be invidious comparisons, spoken or implied. Although his parents may attempt to accept him as he is, they, too, may reject him unwittingly at times. The very pace of life may impose its undue hardships upon the retarded person and cause him to recognize that he is different in some respects. In short, he will be subjected to certain kinds of stress which will be less frequent or less stringent for another individual. And if he has special disabilities, such as gross motor coordination problems, or sensory deficiencies, these may impose even further hardships. It will be our task to examine these special conditions to see how they affect the development and adjustment of the retarded person.

Finally, as we stress throughout this book, the personality and adjustment problems of the individual are central to the whole domain of educational planning and guidance. We must always be concerned not only with whether Johnny learns to read or how well he learns, but with what effect it has upon his over-all functioning. To teach reading, for example, at the possible expense of producing a very frustrated and unhappy child, would benefit him and us very little. The end product of all training, at least in a democracy, is to enable the individual to maximize his potentialities to the end that his life may be more satisfying to him and those around him.

THE GLOBAL PERSON

It is particularly important, at the outset, to keep clearly in mind that we are basically trying to understand how *the person* develops in his personality functions. Whether we are concerned with the average or retarded person, it is always the total human being whom we are considering. In this chapter, we attempt to focus on the personality development of the individual, and in the process we may lose sight of the whole person whose personality attributes are being discussed. Although we are forced to do this for the sake of analysis, we tend to distort the very phenomenon we are considering because of our need to abstract and categorize some aspect, even a broad one, of the global person.

Thus, it is the *whole* person whose personality development we are considering. That this orientation makes a significant difference may be illustrated if we analyze some aspect of personality development more carefully. Suppose, for instance, that we wish to study the development of, or the expression of, aggression in children. In order to do so, we compare two groups of children (group A and group B) at a given age in terms of some characteristic manifestations of aggression, such as bullying behavior, fist fights, and verbal name calling. We may then find that group A shows a considerable amount of what we have termed aggressive behavior, while group B shows little or none of this behavior. We might conclude, then, that group A is more aggressive than group B. But, is such a conclusion valid? We can only say that group A is more aggressive than group B on those behaviors that were measured!

There is a vast difference between the two statements. For if group A consisted of children who came from a very low socio-economic, urban area, and if group B consisted of children who came from a high middle-class urban area, the apparent difference in aggression, *as measured*, might only mean that children from lower socio-economic levels *express* their aggression in these overt ways more frequently than do the other children. It might even turn out that group B has, in fact, more aggression, but expresses it less in physical and direct, overt terms, and more in such other forms of behavior as sarcasm, snubbing, social rejection, failure to cooperate in group activities, and withdrawal. There is ample evidence to indicate that children of different socio-economic levels express their drives and develop defenses in very different ways.[1]

[1] Honigmann, J. J., *Culture and Personality.* New York: Harper & Row, Publishers, 1954; Sears, R. R., Macoby, E. F., and Levin, H., *Patterns of Child Rearing.* New York: Harper & Row, Publishers, 1957; and Miller, D. R., Swanson, G. E., et al., *Inner Conflict and Defense.* New York: Holt, Rinehart & Winston, Inc., 1960.

There are two lessons to be learned from this illustration. The first, and more obvious, is that different people express their drives in different ways, depending on such factors as their stage of general maturation (for example, compare anger in a two-year-old child with that of an eleven-year-old child), the cultural conditions under which they have lived and are now living (compare the expression of aggression in the "wild and woolly west" with that of polite Boston society), and the capacities which they are able to employ (compare the expression of aggression in a highly verbal group of boys with that of a group of mute boys of similar age). The second lesson is that we can understand the specific aspect of behavior in which we are interested only if we relate it to the *whole person* who manifested that behavior.

Even quite specific aspects of behavior have meaning only in terms of the global person. Suppose, for instance, that we were considering the basal metabolism of a patient in order to evaluate his general rate of metabolic activities. If the person who comes in for his basal metabolic test is highly anxious at the time, or if he has not had any food for a number of hours, or if he is severely fatigued, the effects on the test are likely to be quite marked. Without knowledge of these antecedent conditions, one could not properly evaluate the results of the test. In other words, their meaning is dependent on the *whole person* who is taking the test!

Another example is furnished by Cobb.[2] He reports the case of an individual who suffered damage to an area of the brain which often results in disturbed vision. This patient was unaware of any disturbance in his visual functions until after he learned that he had suffered from a particular form of brain damage that affected vision. He then developed severe anxiety and other forms of disturbed behavior as a consequence of the knowledge of his pathology. Thus, brain damage can manifest itself in quite different ways depending upon the condition of the *whole person,* and should not be regarded as being solely responsible for the behavior that develops.

During this century research and clinical evidence have revealed that the way a person feels about himself can drastically influence his physical functioning. This relatively new field of *psychosomatic medicine* has demonstrated that emotional states can, over a period of time, influence gastrointestinal functions, heart functions, blood pressure, skin reactions, and the like. Illnesses may then result, such as ulcers, cardiac failure, hypertension, and allergies.

[2] Cobb, S., "Personality as affected by lesions of the brain," in *Personality and the Behavior Disorders* (J. McV. Hunt, ed.), Vol. 1. New York: The Ronald Press Company, 1944.

Since the person operates as a whole organism, any specific behavioral response is determined by his "total" physical and psychological state, and every "total" response is influenced by any specific response he may make. Only in the abstract sense can we think, then, of an arm movement, or an eye blink, or an aggressive "bit" of behavior. Each of these responses has meaning only in terms of the global person who makes it. And any specific response exerts its effect, in turn, upon the whole organism.

The concept of the global person has special significance in terms of the mentally retarded child and his personality development. As we shall see, the personality functions of the individual may, in some instances, be the central feature determining his retardation. It is also true that an individual's retarded capacities influence his personality manifestations. Even when we speak of the child as having retarded intelligence, we are referring, perhaps, to his retarded functioning on an intelligence test or in school achievement; yet these features of his functioning do not, by themselves, determine that *he* is retarded. He may turn out to be superior in artistic ability, or in physical prowess, or in mechanical skill, or in social relationships!

It may even turn out that the very concept of *the retarded child* is, in the end, a myth. We may mean, in fact, retarded in terms of academic accomplishment, or retarded in terms of academic achievement plus intellectual functioning, or retarded in terms of both of these plus social incompetence. The retardation is the abstraction we may be referring to, but the child as a whole may be very different in many other respects. And since retarded intellectual functioning may be related closely to personality disturbances in some cases, our understanding of the child will profit greatly if we are constantly alert to the fact that assessment of him in some delimited areas does not adequately categorize him in toto.

THE INFANT'S PERSONALITY

Thus far we have been using the term *personality* without specifying precisely what it means. Although many attempts have been made to define personality, few have received wide acceptance. In part, such a confused state of affairs is a result of insufficient clinical and research evidence. Nevertheless, the majority of workers in the field today would find the recent definition proffered by Gordon Allport reasonably acceptable. He states:

"Personality is the dynamic organization within the individual of those psychophysical systems that determine his characteristic behavior and thought."[3]

[3] Allport, G. W., *Pattern and Growth in Personality*. New York: Holt, Rinehart & Winston, Inc., 1961.

Note that the *inner* determinants are specified to be *psychophysical*, and not merely physical or psychological. This implies that, whatever may be the constitutional characteristics with which an individual is born, it is the interplay of these factors with the experiences that he undergoes that finally determines the outcomes. It is also important to note that the resultants (or the personality) may be thought of as *characteristic* or relatively persistent and stable qualities.

As we shall see, the characteristic ways in which an individual behaves are crystallized during the first few years of his life, even though later experience may modify these characteristics through further development or change. But it is the early years of life that are most crucial in determining basic trends in behavioral characteristics, and this is why we wish to examine carefully what is now known of these experiences in childhood. We shall do this, first, by examining the general nature of the maturational process (in the next section on the Unfolding Process), and then by looking at the evidence concerning the birth process and the effects of early experiences (in the two following sections).

The unfolding process

All of us have "grown up." If we observe children around us we can readily see that growth has occurred in a large number of human characteristics, including physical, social, and mental. Growth in physical characteristics is the type most easily observed. A very good example of such a growth process is the "unfolding" of the infant's ability to walk. Another example is the development of teeth at various age levels. A more accurate name for this particular type of growth or "unfolding" process is *maturation.*

Through the mechanism of heredity each infant obtains the potentialities for many personal characteristics. Examples of such bodily characteristics are color of hair and color of eyes. In addition to such specific physical phenomena as these, there are inherent within the organism other potentialities which are not immediately evident at birth. For example, the newborn child cannot talk, walk, or exercise sexual functions, yet these potentialities are already present. They are *latent,* and later, at the appropriate time, will gradually come to fruition and become manifest. This process of development is implied when we speak of the *maturation* of a particular function. Both physical and psychological characteristics are subject to maturational processes.

Perhaps one of the most striking examples of the maturational process is the development of physical sexual characteristics. In the female there are the developments of menstrual activities and mammary glands at puberty. In the male there are corresponding changes in sexual anatomical and physiological characteristics. There is nothing in the appearance of the young child to suggest that these vast biological changes will occur at a later time, but the *potentialities* for these developments are present at birth and, of course, in the foetus prior to birth.

The maturational process can be greatly influenced by either internal or external environmental conditions. For example, sexual functions may be greatly accelerated in warmer climates, and inadequate nutrition can greatly impair or retard general physical maturation. The maturational process is the result of interactions of biologically inherent characteristics and postnatal internal and external environmental conditions.

A child cannot be taught any activity or function until the particular processes involved have reached an adequate maturational level. We cannot teach a new-born child, for example, to walk, to speak, to read, to climb, or to engage in any intricate or coordinated muscular activity until he is physically mature enough to do so.

There have been many experiments concerned with the maturational process. As an example of such studies, one twin was given a great deal of training in climbing and other similar activities while the other was not given such practice.[4] The experiment was continued for three years. The child given the training learned to climb better than the other, yet when the other twin was later given an opportunity to climb, his rate of learning was rapid and he soon approached the level of the twin given the practice.

Poulsen conducted an interesting experiment with newborn chicks.[5] They were kept in darkness for four days. When they were placed in the light, they pecked at all sorts of objects. However, after only four hours of such random pecking activity, they then pecked only at food.

Many other experiments indicate that restriction of activity of an individual does not necessarily inhibit the maturational process and the future exercise of that activity. An example of such a study is the experiment of Dennis upon Hopi children.[6] Immediately following birth the Hopi child is bound to a board, hindering the movement of both his arms and legs. Dennis compared the average age of walking of 63 children treated in this manner with 42 other Hopi children who were

[4] McGraw, M. B., *Growth: A Study of Johnny and Jimmy.* New York: Appleton-Century-Crofts, Inc., 1935.

[5] Poulsen, H., "Maturation and learning in the improvement of some instinctive activities," *Medd. Dansk. Naturh. Foren.,* 1951, *113,* 155-170.

[6] Dennis, W., "The effect of cradling practices upon the onset of walking in Hopi children," *J. genet. Psychol.,* 1940, *56,* 77-86.

not bound. He found no significant difference in the age at which each group started to walk.

Growth and maturation occur in all areas, both physical and psychological. In the present chapter we are particularly concerned with the maturation of psychological functions. An example of such behavior is the maturation of emotional responses. If we studied a group of children we would find that such activities as crying, smiling, and laughing appear at approximately the same age in all children. These occur even when opportunities for the children to observe such reactions in other people are severely restricted. They occur at the same ages in blind and deaf children, where the opportunities for observation are minimal.[7]

In a similar manner maturation or growth occurs in other psychological functions. It may be conceived of basically as a process of interaction of latent inherent characteristics and environmental conditions. The intellectual capacities of an individual are also influenced by the maturational process. At first, the child's growth in measured mental abilities is rapid, then as he grows older the rate of increase starts to decline, until a leveling-off point is reached. The rate of maturation of intellectual functions varies for different individuals.

Let us look at Figure 7, which portrays the rates of development for three groups of children: group A, composed of normal children; group B, children who are mentally retarded; and group C, children who originally were normal in intelligence but due to some brain pathology suffered impairment in their intellectual functions.

The vertical dimension represents intellectual capacity, and the horizontal dimension represents chronological age. The curve for group A shows a rapid increase during the early years, and a gradual leveling-off between the ages of 14 and 18. The curve for group B shows a similar rapid increase during the early years, but the rate of increase is *slower* than for group A. It also reaches its maximum at a point *below* that of group A. The curve for group C, on the other hand, increases at the same rate as for group A but shows a sudden stop due to some pathological factor.

Each individual follows the general curve of maturation but has his own unique maturational rate. Some children mature intellectually at a slower rate than others, and some mature at a much faster rate.

---

[7] See Munn, N. L., *Psychological Development*. Boston: Houghton Mifflin Company, 1938, pp. 451–454.

The maturational process is also related to the development of various thought processes. Piaget has studied the unfolding of specific intellectual functions in the child.[8] He found that the very young child explored the world through the various senses—by touching, looking, smelling, tasting, hearing, and feeling. This he called *sensori-motor* intelligence. The child proceeds developmentally through stages of symbolic thought, instinctive thought, concrete operations, and finally reaches the mature level of abstract and conceptual thought.

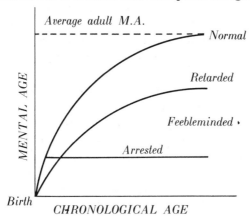

FIGURE 7. Normal, Retarded, and Arrested Mental Development

The birth process

Before the baby's potentialities begin to "unfold" he has to be born! And we are concerned with the nature and the effects of the birth process on the subsequent personality. Even before birth begins many factors in the prenatal life of the neonate may influence the course of his development and may even adversely affect his intellectual development. (See the section of Chapter Four dealing with *etiological considerations* for a discussion of these factors.) The process of being born is not merely a matter of biological development, however. The mother's attitudes toward the birth process and toward becoming a mother, and particularly her anxieties, may have significant effects upon this process.

To quote from Margaret Mead, who noted that a particular group of primitive people were aware of another factor influencing the birth

[8] Piaget, J., *The Language and Thought of the Child,* 2nd ed. London: Routledge and Kegan Paul, Ltd., 1932.

process: "The birth is hard, said the Tchambuli, because the mother has not gathered enough firewood."[9] Many other factors influence the birth process, such as the effects of the cultural attitudes toward birth, the contemporary medical philosophy which may "bend" medical practice in one direction rather than another, and the food intake of the mother.

Our special interest is the effects of the birth process upon the infant. There is little doubt that extreme conditions of birth, such as prolonged labor, excessive or insufficient supply of oxygen to the infant during birth, prematurity or postmaturity, and abnormal birth position may have deleterious effects upon the infant's subsequent development. *Anoxia*, or an insufficient supply of oxygen to the organism, may produce retardation in mental development and prolonged infantile behavior.[10] But normal birth conditions may also be significant!

Otto Rank, an early psychoanalyst, postulated the position that the shock of birth, even normal birth, was so great for the infant that it created a reservoir of anxiety.[11] He believed that the sudden impact of new stimuli (such as changes in light, temperature, pressure, and the like) suffused the infant with anxiety, and that this, plus the separation of the child from its mother, produced relatively persistent anxiety reactions which differed significantly among children. Later, Greenacre summarized the clinical and research evidence on this question and cautiously concluded: "Variations in the birth process may . . . increase the (organic) anxiety response and heightens the anxiety potential, causing a more severe reaction to later (psychological) dangers in life."[12]

There is not much doubt that the trauma (or shock experience) of birth varies among children. And it is equally clear that increased trauma can produce increased irritability, hyperactivity, and other unfavorable effects, as Wile and Davis have shown.[13] It is not as certain how "permanent" these effects and their consequences may be. Nevertheless, any unfavorable effects at birth are likely to make it more difficult for both mother and child in the management of the baby's behavior and the ease with which he begins to learn to cope with his early life problems.

[9] Mead, M., *Male and Female*. New York: William Morrow & Co., Inc., 1949.

[10] Beraron, H. B. W., *et al.*, "Effect of anoxia during labor and immediately after birth on the subsequent development of the child," *Amer. J. Obstet. & Gynec.*, 1960, *80*, 1129–1142.

[11] Rank, O., *The Trauma of Birth*. New York: Harcourt, Brace & World, Inc., 1929.

[12] Greenacre, P., "The predisposition to anxiety," in Tompkins, S. S. (ed.), *Contemporary Psychopathology*. Cambridge: Harvard University Press, 1943.

[13] Wile, I. S., and Davis, R., "The relation of birth to behavior," *Amer. J. Orthopsychiat.*, 1951, *11*, 320–334.

The first years of life

Babies differ at birth in physical characteristics. They also differ in general qualities of temperament, such as irritability or excitability.[14] And they may differ in other general dispositions, such as proneness to anxiety and ability to tolerate stress. What happens to babies during the months following birth—that is, the nature of their early satisfactions and frustrations—may profoundly affect the subsequent course of their lives. We shall now review the theoretical and empirical evidence on this proposition.

Freud proposed that babies had sexual needs which were important to their normal development.[15] This proposition was shocking to Freud's contemporaries and it is still unacceptable to many clinical workers today, although evidence to substantiate this theory is quite extensive.[16] In brief, his position was that the sexual drives are with us from birth to death, that they include the drives for affectional gratification and affiliation, that they take different forms during the several stages of life, acquiring their adult form only after puberty, and—most important of all—that their satisfaction produces more pleasure and favorable effects upon development than any of the other biological drives.

Freud stated that the first phase of sexual (or more accurately, psychosexual) development, which he termed the oral period, normally lasted for about one and a half years. During this time the infant is chiefly concerned with the "taking in" of nourishment and other forms of gratification. This process is centered around the mouth—around the *oral* region. The oral region includes the mouth itself, the immediately surrounding areas, and the upper portion of the gastrointestinal tract.

At first the child takes in nourishment through a process of rather passive sucking. His very life depends upon such an activity, for the intake of food is vital to his existence, but more than nourishment itself is involved. Along with the taking in of the food, the child also "takes in" some of the characteristics of the mother, or mother substitute. Studies have shown that if the mother is, for example, a compulsive person, the child will tend to become somewhat compulsive. A study made by Fries is interesting in this regard.[17] It revealed that when

[14] Gesell, A., and Ilg, F. L., *Child Development*. New York: Harper & Row, Publishers, 1949.

[15] Freud, S., *A General Introduction to Psychoanalysis*. Garden City, N.Y.: Doubleday & Company, Inc., 1943.

[16] Hutt, M. L., and Gibby, R. G., *The Child: Development and Adjustment*. Boston: Allyn and Bacon, Inc., 1959.

[17] Fries, M. E., "The child's ego development and the training of adults in his development," in *The Psychoanalytic Study of the Child*, Vol. II. New York: International Universities Press, Inc., 1946.

infants are taken care of by compulsive nurses there is somehow transmitted to them some of the nurses' tension, and that these babies show
more "startle" reactions (reactions to noise or any other sudden stimuli)
than those taken care of by "quiet" or more composed nurses.

Much more than the mouth and surrounding areas is involved in the
oral development of the child. As the baby sucks on the mother's
breast, or upon the nipple of the bottle, he begins to look at the person
who is feeding him. He begins to grasp at the bottle or breast, and so
he begins to learn to "feel." The gratification of the oral needs of the
child thus means much more than the intake of sufficient and proper
kind of nourishment. There is ample experimental evidence to substantiate this point of view. When a baby gets insufficient opportunity
to suck at the breast of the mother or at the nipple of the bottle, due
perhaps to insufficient time to engage in this activity or to some inappropriate condition of the nipple (when the nipple of the breast is
inverted or when the hole in the nipple of the bottle is too large, for
example) he will seek to gratify his need to suck by excessive sucking
of his fingers or of his toes or of some other object. If, when the child
is ready to give up the mouth as the primary zone of pleasure and move
on to another, he is not encouraged to do so but, rather, is encouraged
to remain at the oral level through some form of excessive gratification,
he will tend to remain *fixated* at that level. Fixation, as we may recall
from our earlier discussion, may occur when the child receives either too
little or too much gratification *at the time that it is the primary mode of
satisfaction* in the maturational development of the child.

In addition to the psychological needs perpetuated by the way in
which the child is treated by the mother, children appear also to vary
in regard to their inborn needs. Some require a greater amount of oral
gratification than others.[18] Some persons believe that prenatal conditions
may set up particular predispositions. Whether or not the differences
are due in large measure to the innate constitution of the child, all
authorities agree that variation in oral "needs" exists. Nevertheless,
the way in which a child develops depends greatly upon the conditions
of his training and weaning.

It appears that when a child has become "fixated" at a particular
maturational level, he will tend to retain the psychological characteristics
of the modes of that period to an excessive degree even when they are not
appropriate. (By *fixated* is meant the tendency to retain modes of be-

[18] Sterba, R., "Introduction to the psychoanalytic theory of the libido," *Nerv.
and Ment. Dis. Monogr.*, No. 68, 1942.

havior or to "overlearn" them due to excessive or insufficient gratification of relevant needs when these are primary.) During this first oral level of development, the outstanding mode is that of passivity, and the primary method of gratification of needs by the child is through passive sucking. Fixation at this level leads to overemphasis of passivity in the personality of the child.

Thus the infant continues in the first few months to use the oral zones and satisfies needs to passively "take in." This gradually begins to change, and the oral zones then begin to be used for new purposes. The child begins to put objects into his mouth, and to bite and chew upon them. During this period his teeth and his jaw muscles develop. He now has a more active means of coping with his environment—he has a weapon with which he can, for instance, inflict pain or irritation upon the mother. He can also expel food that he has taken in—to "spit it out." This new phase in the oral period, the so-called "biting" period, is important in that it marks the beginning of real interaction between the child and the mother. The child is now capable of playing a more active part—he is now not as passive as formerly and can begin to show both *positive* and *negative* feelings toward objects.* Just as the first stage of the oral level, that of sucking, may be regarded as one of *passive* "taking in," the second may be regarded as one of *active* "taking in." The child often experiences conflict over the use of these two methods, and this adds to his ambivalent feelings. The way in which the mother responds to the child's needs for biting, to the pain that he may inflict upon her during the process of feeding, as well as to his ambivalence toward her, may have much to do with whether or not the child is fixated at this level.

Fixation at this "oral biting" level is important in determining the personality traits later shown by the child. For example, one character trait associated with fixation at this point is *sarcasm*. Even in popular language we speak of a person with a "biting tongue," or a "sharp tongue," or as using "biting sarcasm."

It is believed that the retarded child, like all other children, goes through these phases of emotional growth. However, clinical evidence suggests that he experiences greater difficulty than the "average" child in giving up one mode for another. His maturational process is slower, and there is a tendency for such a child to retain his pleasurable modes of gratification for longer periods of time. Such behavior is further reinforced by the attitudes of society in general, and by the mother in partic-

---

* The term *object* includes both inanimate (things) and animate objects (animals and people).

ular. Weaning presents problems, and is a source of irritation to the mother. She feels perhaps that the neighbor's boy has already given up his bottle, so "why shouldn't my Bill?" Her irritation thus serves to induce further anxieties in the child. Premature weaning attempts may create severe frustrations and conflicts in the child. These serve to reinforce the fixations of the retarded child at the oral levels. Such fixation tends to perpetuate oral traits. It also means that the child is less able to proceed to the next developmental level and to renounce his needs for oral satisfaction.

We shall cite two lines of evidence bearing on this general theoretical position of Freud's. One line of evidence comes from research studies on the effects of early experiences upon children's personality development. A study done by Brody at the Menninger Foundation in Topeka, Kansas, showed that the nature of the infant's feeding experience (that is, the way he was handled, responded to, and the like) was clearly related to his pattern of behavioral development.[19] An accepting and warm relationship seemed to produce the most favorable outcomes.

Another study by Escalona indicated that when mothers were "high-strung" their babies also tended to be high-strung and were disturbed in the total food intake process.[20] These studies are indicative of the kinds of relationships which have generally been established in relatively recent research. In general, such evidence may be taken to indicate that the nature of "oral" experiences is relevant and important, at least in terms of the immediate effects upon the infant's personality development.

The other line of evidence deals with the effects of unfavorable or traumatic experiences during the first year or early period of life. Again, workers are not entirely agreed on the implications of these findings, but it now seems reasonably clear that separation from the mother, or placement in an institution in which the infant receives inadequate affectional and physical stimulation and gratification, may have very serious consequences in terms of adverse personality development. Spitz was able to show, for instance, that separation from the mother and insufficient fondling and affection could not only retard development but could actually lead to the infant's death, or at least to severe depression.[21] In fact, a recent review of the literature on maternal deprivation has led

[19] Brody, S., *Patterns of Mothering.* New York: International Universities Press, Inc., 1956.

[20] Escalona, S. K., "Feeding disturbances in very young children," *Amer. J. Orthopsychiat.*, 1945, *15*, 76–80.

[21] Spitz, R. A., "The importance of the mother-child relationship during the first years of life: a symposium in five sketches," *Ment. Hlth. Today*, 1948, 7.

one author to conclude that this condition is quite deleterious and should be avoided if at all possible.[22]

Enlightened policy today indicates that when infants have to be separated from their mothers, a good substitute mother in the form of a foster mother should be obtained, and if institutionalization is required for some period of time, careful attention should be given to providing a suitable "mother substitute" and substantial physical stimulation and psychological interaction for the infant.

The importance of this problem for mental retardation can, perhaps, best be stated in the words of the report of the President's Panel on Mental Retardation:

"The effects on infants of institutional placement in early life has been studied more intensively than any other similar environmental experience. As a result of these findings, more infants are placed in foster homes in preference to institutions . . . The separation of infants from their mothers or substitute mothers may affect the former adversely. Infants who react negatively to separation live a depressed existence with low physical and intellectual achievement."[23]

As we shall see in later chapters, it is quite possible that a considerable percentage of cases of mental retardation result, at least in part, from unsatisfactory emotional experiences during the first year or two of life. This hypothesis has been given far too little emphasis in previous books and treatises on mental retardation, in our opinion, with the result that study of the specific mechanisms by which many cases of retardation may be induced has been delayed and ameliorative methods have not been instituted.

THE DEVELOPMENT OF BASIC TRUST

The previous section dealing with the possible effects of deprivation upon personality development highlighted a problem of great importance. As the President's Panel on Mental Retardation reported:

"The majority of the mentally retarded are children of the more disadvantaged classes of our society. This *extraordinarily heavy* [italics ours] prevalence in certain deprived population groups suggests a major causative role, in some way not fully delineated, for adverse social, economic, and cultural factors. . . . De-

[22] Casler, L., "Maternal deprivation: a critical review of the literature." *Monogr. Soc. for Res. in Child. Develpm.*, 1961, *26*, 1–64.

[23] *A Proposed Program for National Action to Combat Mental Retardation*, President's Panel on Mental Retardation. Sup't. of Documents, U.S. Gov't. Printing Office, Oct., 1962.

privation in childhood of opportunities for learning intellectual skills, *childhood emotional disorders* which interfere with learning, or *obscure motivational factors* [italics ours] appear somehow to stunt young people intellectually during their developmental period.[24]

It is quite possible that unsatisfactory early experiences, particularly unsatisfactory emotional experiences, can generate a tendency to: avoid coping with the world and its problems; withdraw from more active participation in dealing with one's problems; and develop far less adequately than would otherwise be the case. *Parents from the more disadvantaged sectors of our society may contribute a disproportionate share of the problems of mental retardation in children not only because they are inferior socially and intellectually, but because their severe problems make it more difficult to provide the consistent emotional warmth and security for their children who are thus stimulated to become curious about their world and to learn about it.*

Some years ago, Erikson formulated a theoretical explanation of what he termed "basic trust," based upon his extensive clinical observations as well as the work of others.[25] He was concerned with the problem of how the infant learns to trust himself, and thereafter the world, so that he is able to express his potentiality rather than to curb it. In more recent years workers have explored the conditions which foster "security" in the self, calling the personality variable that of *security-insecurity,* and generally meaning by this variable the degree of *self-confidence* which the individual develops.[26]

Erikson hypothesized that basic trust develops out of the complex of conditions during infancy and early childhood which afford maximal opportunity for action, thought, and the expression of feeling *without excessive threat or interference.* This requires that the infant's needs be met or anticipated with some degree of regularity. It involves not only the mere satisfaction of biological needs but an appropriate general pattern of satisfaction of early psychological needs for protection and warmth. As the infant is taken care of in this way, he learns to trust the world and gradually develops appropriate self-confidence. The development of this basic trust in oneself makes possible the utilization

[24] *Ibid.,* p. 8.

[25] Erikson, E. H., *Childhood and Society.* New York: W. W. Norton & Company, Inc., 1950.

[26] Bayley, N., and Schaefer, E. S., "Maternal Behavior and Personality Development from the Berkeley Growth Study." (Presented at Regional Res. Council, Child Develpm. and Child Psychiat., Iowa City, Iowa, April, 1960.)

of inner potentials and prevents the blocking of emotional and intellectual development.

A study by Sears and his colleagues, based on intensive interviews with mothers, throws some light on this process.[27] This study showed that one of the two patterns that was most important in determining child-parent relationships and the development of the child's personality was the *warmth* of the mother-child relationship. In homes where the relationship was warm the child tended to be secure, while in homes where the relationship was *cold* the child tended to be aggressive, had feeding problems and, in general, was quite insecure.

In the critical review of the literature on maternal deprivation by Casler, cited previously, it is suggested that a factor termed *perceptual deprivation* which results from inadequate stimulation, especially tactile stimulation, early in life may account for retarded personality development.[28] One of the authors of the present volume has been conducting a series of studies on what he terms *perceptual adience-abience* (or perceptual approach versus avoidance behavior). It seems likely that a basic perceptual style of relative adience or abience is developed quite early in life and subsequently influences the relative ease or difficulty with which one can profit from a wide variety of experiences. For example, in one study with deaf-retarded individuals, those who were high in perceptual adience were less impaired in intellectual functioning, showed less psychopathology, and had experienced less institutionalization than the others.[29]

THE INFLUENCE OF THE FAMILY DURING THE FORMATIVE YEARS

The major influence acting upon the child during his preschool years is that of his family. In the beginning it is the mother who is most important in this constellation. Later, the influence of the father becomes more significant, and the interactions of the other children in the family, the siblings, also contribute their share to the developing child's personality. It should be remembered that the ways in which the members of a family deal with the young child is not only a function of the particular personalities of the members of that family, but is also a function of the culture in which the family lives. Child rearing practices differ

[27] Sears, Macoby and Levin, *op. cit.*

[28] Casler, *op. cit.*

[29] Hutt, M. L., and Feuerfile, D., "The clinical meanings and predictions of a measure of perceptual adience-abience for a deaf-retarded group," Paper presented at Amer. Psychol. Ass. Convention, Phila., Pa., Sept., 1963.

markedly in different cultures. It seems self-evident to state that a good family climate may affect the child's development favorably and that the converse is also true. But what is a good family climate? And what specifically are its effects? These are some of the questions to which we shall now turn our attention.

The psychoanalytic position—anal period

The most explicit theoretical treatment of the influences of the home upon the child's development during his early life has been that of the psychoanalytic school. Its formulations were derived, in the main, from clinical observations of neurotic adults and was constructed from the data they furnished in the course of their own treatment. Later, psychoanalysis of children furnished additional data. Some of these adults were mentally retarded, and it was observed that, in some cases, resolution of severe emotional conflicts produced significant improvement in intellectual capabilities as well as improved functioning in other areas. We shall examine this theoretical formulation because of its historical importance as well as because of the salience of the hypotheses which it offers. We should keep in mind that the direct application of the theory to retarded individuals has certain dangers. Later, we shall examine some of the research evidence which seeks to test, amplify, or revise the theoretical formulations.

Of course, psychological factors in mental retardation do not always account for the impaired mental condition, as we amply document in Chapter Four. However, when such factors are relevant they are of profound significance. Many careful case studies have demonstrated how dramatic the improvement may be in such cases when these factors are relevant.

For example, Goodnick presents a well documented case study in which the patient's retardation could be ascribed, not to organic injury or inferior "original" intellectual equipment, but to specific and unfavorable psychological conditions in prior years.[30] We agree with the position of Eisenberg, who states, in reviewing cases of emotional factors affecting intellectual development: "We should no longer wonder at the evidence of dysfunction in either (intelligence or emotion), in the presence of disorder in the other, but rather ask: By what mechanism has it occurred in the particular case, and by what means may it be remedied . . ."[31]

---

[30] Goodnick, B., "A case of pseudoretardation," *Psychol. Newsltr.*, 1959, *10*, 331–335.

[31] Eisenberg, L., "Emotional determinants of mental deficiency," *A. M. A. Arch. Neurol. Psychiat.*, 1958, *80*, 119–121.

Now let us look at the first part of the psychoanalytic position as it describes development following the period of infancy.

As the child continues to mature, he begins to give up the mouth as the primary source through which satisfactions are achieved and moves on to utilization of another bodily area for such purposes. Usually, starting at about the eighth month of life, and ending at about the fourth year of life, the *anal* region assumes primary importance. The anal region includes the anus, the buttocks, and the surrounding regions of the lower end of the intestinal canal. It is capable of offering highly intense emotional satisfaction to the child as soon as his biological development has made it possible.

In general, during the second year of life, the *anal expulsive period,* expulsion of feces is pleasurable to the child. This pleasure is reinforced in many ways. Perhaps the chief of these are the reactions of the mother who conveys her own pleasure in observing her child's healthy bowel movements. When too great concern or excessive pleasure is expressed by the mother over this act, it becomes even more important to the child. However, the act of expulsion of the stool may be painful at times, so the child develops some ambivalence toward it. This ambivalence may be greatly increased by the mother's insistence that the baby have a bowel movement upon demand, especially if his voluntary control over the act is not adequately developed. In the case of a mentally retarded child this is an even more serious problem since his control is likely to develop at a slower rate.

In the problem of anal training, cultural factors must be considered. In those cultures that insist upon rapid, rigid, and harsh toilet training practices, the psychological damage to the child and the consequent fixations that develop around this anal phase are likely to be marked.

During the first stage of the anal level of development, then, the child secures gratification through the passage of stools. This gratification is not only physical, but is psychologically reinforced or diminished by the feelings expressed by the mother. During the second stage of anal development, the child attains more gratification by retaining or withholding the stool rather than by passing it. Unless their parents stop them, children will usually play with their stools. If strong prohibitions against such explorative activities have been invoked, the child (and later the adult) may develop excessively negative reactions to fecal matter.

Fixation at the anal level will tend to occur if there has been either *over-* or *under*gratification of the child's anal modes of behavior. Such fixation has an effect upon the future personality structure and characteristics of the child. It tends to produce three major personality characteristics: (1) miserliness or excessive thrift—*parsimony;* (2) obstinacy or excessive stubbornness—*petulance;* (3) meticulousness or excessive orderliness—*pedantry*. Although these traits may arise from other sources, their primary source is fixation at the anal level of development.

Toilet training is thus just as important in the psychological development of the child at this level as weaning at the oral level. However, no matter how careful the mother is in initiating toilet training at the appropriate time, it still involves some degree of frustration to the child. The child must give up his freedom to expel or retain his feces whenever he wishes—he now has to learn, for example, to do this at the pleasure of the mother. In summary, the dynamics of this conflict are: (1) the child feels hostile toward the adult (the mother) who is forcing him to give up his freedom; (2) he is afraid to express this hostility since he may be deprived of the love he needs and wants from her; (3) he projects his hostile wishes on the mother—that is, he tends to see her, rather than himself, as hostile; (4) since he wants to be loved he *identifies* with her— that is, he *interiorizes* the mother's wishes in regard to his toilet training (he makes them his own wishes), and therefore develops some control over his bowel movements.

The anal phase has often been called the period of *socialization*. It is the time when the child is more able to communicate with the world, when he is expected to learn for the first time the prohibitions of his culture, to develop some moral habits, and to develop some personal habits of cleanliness.

The mentally retarded child experiences great difficulties in coping with the problems of the anal period. In the first place, he tends to be rather strongly fixated at oral levels, and so has less psychic energy available to proceed to this next higher level. In addition, his frustrations during the anal period tend to be greater than those of other children and adjustment is more difficult. His slowness in developing verbal skills further retards his socialization. His general slowness in maturation often means that he is subjected to toilet training activities long before he is ready for such a program. Many times he is not even physiologically ready to establish controls over bowel and bladder functions when such training is initiated.

A fairly common problem in the relationship of the retarded child to his mother during this period is that of *overprotection* by the mother. Too often she is overly solicitous about his welfare. (This frequently has been called "Momism" in popular literature.) One reason for such a reaction on her part is the guilt she feels over her child's retardation.

She wrongly feels responsible for his condition. (This problem is discussed in Chapter Ten.) When this condition of overprotection exists, the retarded child has too little stimulation to mature to the level that it is possible for him to attain, or to give up his more infantile modes of behaving, and in many instances he becomes very passive, dependent, demanding, and very often even hostile and aggressive.[32]

Walker[33] points out that with the mentally retarded child toilet training is a delayed process, and sometimes an unaccomplished goal. He states:

Can we be certain that the defective does not find some degree of emotional fixation in his untidiness? If we take a defective who has accomplished toilet training and attempt to engage him in play demanding his becoming dirty we often meet with resistance. Parental concern over the prolonged toilet training may have developed a compulsive atttiude for both parent and child. Perhaps the child finds activity so closely allied to what has been a difficult developmental problem, an emotionally undesirable form of endeavor.

The psychoanalytic position—phallic period

The *phallic* period extends from three to seven years. The primary zone through which gratifications are received and drives discharged during this period is the genital organs. Since the maturation of the personality characteristics of the boy is different from that of the girl during this period, we shall discuss the process in each separately.

MATURATION IN BOYS. The primary zone in the boy during this period is the penis and the area surrounding it. It is now well established that boys engage in an increased amount of masturbatory behavior during this phase. When disappointments, frustrations, or failures are strong, such activities increase even more. If masturbation is severely prohibited by the parent, it is likely to be engaged in "on the sly." If there are strong guilt feelings about masturbatory activities, as is frequently the case, regression to either oral (like thumb-sucking) or anal (like becoming constipated) modes of behavior may result. Sometimes, children who are very severely disturbed masturbate almost con-

---

[32] For a full discussion of maternal overprotection see:
    (a) Levy, D. M., *Maternal Overprotection.* New York: Columbia University Press, 1943.
    (b) Symonds, P. M., *The Dynamics of Parent-Child Relationships.* New York: Columbia University Press, 1949.
[33] Walker, G. H., "Social and emotional problems of the mentally retarded child," *Amer. J. ment. Defic.*, 1950, *55*, 132–138.

stantly, and they handle and fondle the penis continually even though no orgasm is experienced.

There are important psychological changes during the phallic period. Under normal circumstances, previous to entering this level, the boy has already developed a very strong emotional attachment to his mother. He has become dependent upon her, since almost all of his physical, social, and emotional needs have been met by her. During this same period the boy has also learned to love his father, but the intensity of his relationships with his father is much less than with his mother. There are many reasons for this: the father had a significantly less important role to the boy in previous years; the father caressed and fondled the boy less than the mother; the father did not meet all the needs of the boy in the same manner as the mother.

The boy's relationships with both parents during this period are ambivalent. Although the boy loves his mother he is also often irritated and frustrated by her. At times he feels very hostile and has other negative feeling toward her. His relationship with his father also contains hostile elements.

On the whole life would be fairly satisfactory in the home, despite the boy's frustrations and ambivalences, if it were not for the development of a "triangle"—a three-way relationship between the boy, his mother, and his father. This triangular relationship has been termed the *oedipal situation*. This is the primary conflict faced by the child during this period, and it usually causes difficulty. Prior to this the boy encountered three major crises: the trauma of birth, the trauma of weaning, and the trauma of toilet training. The fourth—the oedipal trauma—is probably the most crucial of all.

The little boy is quite content to be with mother during the day—to play with her, to receive her attention and affection, and, in short, to be in the very center of things. But in the evening, when the father comes home, things become quite different. Usually the mother devotes much of her attention to her husband, she may hug and kiss him, and in general spends a lot of her time with him. To a large extent she temporarily rejects her little boy, and he is told eventually to go to bed and "go to sleep." The father thus becomes an object of special hostility since he appears, to the boy, to be depriving him of the intense emotional satisfactions he expects from his mother. Also, and this is of great importance, the father is feared for many reasons: he is the boy's rival for the mother; he is much bigger and can harm the boy; and he becomes the outward representation of the little boy's own guilt and fears concerning the situation.

This is the central core of the oedipal conflict in the boy. It is complicated by many other factors, however. In the first place, the boy has many "female" as well as "male" characteristics, partly because of his identifications with his mother. In the second place, all children are bisexual to some extent (the proportion of male and female hormones is never 100 per cent of one to 0 per cent of the other in any person, and the physical characteristics are never entirely male or female). In addition, the mother herself may have many "masculine" qualities, and the father may have many "feminine" qualities.

The normal boy, after a period of considerable stress and conflict, finally learns to identify with the father and give up much of his identification with the mother. In other words, he manages to repress his oedipal wishes for his mother and finally to assume a more masculine role. His behavior toward the mother changes markedly at this time; he often becomes negativistic toward her or appears to be "distant" or removed from her. In taking on his masculine role he usually places a great deal of importance upon the physical "signs" of his masculinity.

In this way the "normal" boy learns to give up his infantile ways of behaving and to progress toward puberty. This period is marked by intensive growth in many directions, for both the boy and the girl. It is characterized by an increasing amount of exploration and curiosity. Physical abilities of many kinds have become well established, and locomotion is used in the process of establishing better contact with a larger world. The eyes, ears, and other sense organs have assumed more mature functions, and have become more important in discovering the widening world of reality. Intellectual development has also gone on apace, and enables the child adequately to integrate his new knowledge and to use it more effectively.

MATURATION IN GIRLS. Progress through the phallic level and resolution of the oedipal conflict is more complicated for girls than for boys. Like the boy, the girl identifies first with the mother, and obtains similar attention and emotional gratifications from her. Also like the boy, the primary zone through which her satisfactions are achieved is the genital region. During this period the girl, like the boy, learns to identify with her father, but here we find important complexities in the process of feminine maturation. The girl now has one additional phase through which she must pass—she must give up her identification with her father and re-establish her identity with her mother. Only in this way she can assume and accept the role of a female. This brief précis of the oedipal situation for girls is an over-simplified statement of a very complex process. The interested reader who wishes to obtain a full discussion is referred to the works of Helene Deutsch for a more adequate presentation.[34]

DIFFICULTIES OF THE RETARDED CHILD.   The mentally retarded child has an unusual amount of difficulty in dealing with the problems of the phallic period. He brings to it a reduced amount of energy to apply to its resolution, since he has not adequately resolved the problems of the oral and the anal levels. His strong fixation during these periods make it more easily possible for him to regress to these levels when he is faced with oedipal conflicts. There is then a basic "unreadiness" to be able to cope with the traumatic experiences of this level, and many resultant disturbances in behavior are shown.

The attitudes of the mother in her relationship to the retarded child, furthermore, are not conducive to an easy solution of oedipal conflicts. Her relationship to such a child is likely to be emotionally complex and oversolicitous because of the child's difficulties and hence effective changes on the child's part are more difficult to achieve.

The process is further hampered by the numerous disabilities of the retarded child. Intellectual development is such that new knowledge cannot be integrated or used effectively. The growing world of reality is still not adequately comprehended, and there are problems in adequate perception of external events.

The retarded child often does not adequately resolve his oedipal conflicts. The boy continues to be dependent upon his mother, and he does not become able to assume an adequate masculine role. The girl, too, retains her primary identification with the mother. This has significant implications for her later emotional behavior.

The solution of oedipal conflicts can be greatly influenced by the emotional adjustment and psychological sophistication of the parents, and, depending upon the capacities of the child, by psychotherapy.

Some experimental evidence

The general theory of personality development cannot be tested *in toto*. Rather, specific subdivisions of the theory have to be evaluated after first being formulated in some testable form. Then the inter-relationships of the various elements affecting development have to be considered.

[34] Deutsch, H., *The Psychology of Women*. New York: Grune & Stratton, Inc., Vol. 1, 1944; Vol. 2, 1945.

Many studies have dealt with the effects of the climate of the home, and we have already referred to some of these. In a series of well-designed studies at the Fels Research Institute, in Yellow Springs, Ohio, it has been demonstrated that the experiences of children during the formative years greatly affect their personality development. For instance, it has been shown that "accepted children" tend to be more alert mentally, as well as more friendly and more responsive.[35] In contrast, rejected children are less alert mentally, do more poorly in school work, are more unstable emotionally, and more frequently tend to be apathetic or rebellious.

In one of the more recent studies, Kagan and Moss were able to show that emotional disturbance had a significantly depressive effect upon intellectual functioning.[36] Another group of research workers has demonstrated that the patterns of relationships between mother and child are generally quite consistent with the predictions derived from psychoanalytic theory. Blum has shown that there is a large and significant relationship between the combined rigidities of mother and father and that of their four- and five-year-old children, the correlation being .50.[37] And, in an intensive longitudinal study which extended into the adolescent phase of the children who were evaluated, it was found that ego strength (see Chapter Ten) and friendliness, absence of unnecessary guilt and hostility, and spontaneity in behavior were related to home climate which was lenient, democratic and relatively consistent.[38]

The effects of severe toilet training and of correlated suppressive training procedures in the home have been well documented in the book by Symonds.[39] In addition he has offered his own research evidence to indicate that such types of experience lead to personality maladjustment, various forms of inhibition in mental and emotional expressiveness, and withdrawal or compensatorily aggressive behavior.

In what is regarded by the writers as a classic study, Watson evaluated the effects of strict versus permissive home discipline upon children coming from "good" homes.[40] Among other things that make this study

[35] Baldwin, A. L., "The effect of home environment on nursery school behavior," *Child Develpm.*, 1949, *20*, 49–61.

[36] Kagan, J., and Moss, H. A., "Maternal influences on early I.Q. scores," *Psychol. Reps.*, 1958, *4*, 655–661.

[37] Blum, A., "The relationship between rigidity-flexibility in children and their parents," *Child Develpm.*, 1959, *30*, 297–304.

[38] Peck, R. F., "Family patterns correlated with adolescent personality structure," *J. abnorm. soc. Psychol.*, 1958, *57*, 347–350.

[39] Symonds, P. M., *The Psychology of Parent-Child Relationships*. New York: Appleton-Century-Crofts, Inc., 1938.

[40] Watson, G., "Some personality differences in children related to strict or permissive parental discipline," *J. Psychol.*, 1957, *44*, 227–249.

impressive is the fact that it dealt with home situations that were not abnormal in the usual sense; *i.e.*, economically abnormal or emotionally abnormal. And yet, the evidence from this research is quite clear in indicating that, while permissive homes do not have a monopoly in producing all of the favorable effects upon personality development, they clearly excel in the production of the following kinds of behaviors: friendliness, low hostility, independence, spontaneity, creativity, and originality. Watson adds, ". . . no clear personality advantages were associated in general with strict discipline in a good home."

We have cited the previous studies to illustrate the kinds of findings which have accumulated from empirical research. Not all studies report similar confirmations of the general psychoanalytic position, and certainly not all workers interpret their findings in terms of this theoretical framework. Nevertheless, the preponderance of evidence is certainly not in disagreement with the basic propositions offered by Freud, although many extensions and modifications of his theory are evidently needed.

Some recent evidence seems to be particularly intriguing. Hall and Domhoff have made an extensive study of 3874 dreams reported in 11 separate investigations.[41] The study of dreams tells us something of what is going on within the recesses of personality and throws light on unconscious components of the personality. (See Chapter Six for further discussion of such phenomena.) They found ubiquitous sex differences in the dreams of males and females. Moreover, these differences are consistent with the Freudian position in that the content of the dreams and the types of conflict which were represented indicated that both the nature of the oedipal conflict, in general, and of the delayed resolution of this conflict in girls, in particular, were confirmed by the data.

We should like to close this section by citing some work done at the George Peabody College for Teachers. This series of studies has led to a learning theory interpretation of the personality development of retarded individuals. In a review of this work, Cromwell has suggested seven principles to account for this development.[42] The emphasis is upon the value of positive reinforcement in encouraging effective learning. (See Chapter Eight for a detailed discussion of these principles.)

We have no quarrel with this type of formulation, and in fact commend it as highly valuable and relevant. But it leaves far more unexplained than it explains, especially as regards complex aspects of per-

[41] Hall, C., and Domhoff, B., "A ubiquitous sex difference in dreams," *J. abnorm. soc. Psychol.*, 1963, *66*, 278-280.
[42] Cromwell, R. L., "Selected aspects of personality development in mentally retarded children," *Except. Child.*, 1961, *28*, 44-51.

sonality development. It is most helpful in showing how serious is the adverse effect upon learning of failure experiences,[43] and how much less stimulation is provided by a failure experience for mentally retarded individuals than for normal individuals,[44] as examples. The general principle of positive reinforcement of behavior in a social setting, as valuable in stimulating more effective growth in learning than negative reinforcement, seems to have relevance for all individuals even though it may have special significance for retarded persons.

FURTHER PSYCHOSEXUAL DEVELOPMENT

The period in the life of the child that is perhaps most marked by visible signs of the inner turmoil which emotional conflict engenders is that of adolescence. This is the period so frequently attacked bitterly in popular journals and newspapers because it is attended by delinquent behavior and by other forms of aggression and defiance of cultural conventions. It is a period when most children are required to begin making some prevocational decisions and to take appropriate steps to assure themselves of relevant education, training, and experience. For the retarded child, the difficulties of this period are inordinate, and may be crucial in determining the kind of adjustment he makes in later years. In the present section we shall discuss only briefly the general features of personality development during this period, and in later chapters we shall deal specifically with problems of adjustment (Chapter Eight), problems of education and training (Chapters Eleven and Twelve), and problems which society needs to resolve (Chapter Thirteen).

Puberty

In the "normal" child, puberty ushers in the beginnings of adult sexuality, although there may be a long delay before society permits the individual full gratification of such sexuality. The period is marked by intense upsets in all spheres, both physiological and psychological, and these "storms and stresses" are particularly pronounced in the mentally retarded child. With the biological development of the child there is a resulting intensification of the sexual drives; there are rapid physiological changes such as secretion of sex hormones, increase in the size and

[43] Gardner, W. I., "Reactions of intellectually normal and retarded boys after experimentally induced failure, a social learning theory interpretation." Unpublished doctoral dissertation, George Peabody College for Teachers, 1958.

[44] Gardner, W. I., "Effects of interpolated success and failure on motor task performance in mental defectives." (Paper read at S. E. Psychol. Ass., Nashville, Tenn., 1960.)

sensitivity of sexual organs, and the development of secondary sex characteristics. In the psychological development there is the reemergence of intense sexual feelings, and the presence of many contradictory impulses within the child, such as, for example, the need for independence and the need for dependence, or the need for sensuality and that for asceticism.

There are also other complications. During this period there is a reactivation of older conflicts that may have been adequately controlled by the child's defense mechanisms up to this point. Further, our society does not permit gratifications of the child's increased sexual drives: intercourse before marriage is strongly discouraged.

The child strives toward two major goals during this period. In the first place he tries to achieve sexual gratification, either directly or symbolically. In the second, he strives for a sense of independence and self-esteem. The number of avenues open to him, however, is limited by the customs and practices of his society. His intense needs continue to exert pressure, and his guilt feelings and anxieties are pronounced. These problems may often overwhelm the ego, and the child may react to them by either excessive withdrawal or excessive aggression or other forms of rebellion against the parents and society in general. It is often difficult for the parents to understand and tolerate all the upheavals going on within the child. Sensitive handling of the adolescent is necessary in order that the child's older problems not be reactivated or new ones created.

The adolescent wants a job, he wants to be self-sufficient, he wants a "hot rod" so that he can feel a sense of power and masculinity. He likes to dance, to have heterosexual relationships, and to relieve his sexual tensions to some extent. He is in a constant state of turmoil. Superego* forces alternate between being excessively harsh and punitive on the one hand and excessively permissive on the other. Finally some degree of harmony is achieved, and the superego demands are not so excessive in either direction.

This period is an excessively difficult one for the mentally retarded child. He has the accumulations of fixations at oral, anal, and phallic levels, and the constant pressure of conflicts that have remained unsolved throughout his entire life history. The added problems of adolescence impose a further burden and additional conflicts upon him (and his parents).

The mentally retarded child is not adequately equipped to assume the independent role that society sometimes demands of him. He tends

---

* The superego is that part of the person which is concerned with "right and wrong." It may be termed the "conscience" of the individual. For a full discussion see Chapter Seven.

to continue to be dependent, although at the same time he is aware of his growing needs for independence. Both the pressures of society as well as those within his family situation make it exceedingly difficult for him to adjust successfully to the demands of puberty and adolescence.

FACTORS INFLUENCING THE PERSONALITY DEVELOPMENT OF RETARDED INDIVIDUALS

We shall now summarize those factors that present evidence indicates significantly influence the course of personality development of retarded individuals. Most of these factors also are relevant for so-called normal individuals, but their salience for retarded ones may be somewhat different.

The biological equipment with which an individual comes into this world determines the *initial* tendencies which are manifest in his behavior. Whether he is inferior or superior, whether he is excitable or lethargic, and whether he is prone to stress reactions or can tolerate stress quite well are "givens" in the organism at birth. Some individuals develop and "unfold" more slowly than others. Hence they need more time and more specific and detailed instruction to enable them to master what may be simple adaptive problems for others. The retarded person tends to become more frustrated more easily than does his more superior contemporaries. He may need more prolonged care, protection, and warmth than others. He may be adversely affected by the expectancies of his parents and his older siblings who are frustrated by his relatively slow development. Consistency in training procedures and great tolerance for his slowness in developing and mastering adaptive behaviors are especially important for him.

It has been demonstrated by both clinical studies and research investigations that some individuals, with potentially normal or even superior intellectual capacities, are thwarted severely in the early experiences they have in meeting their biosocial needs. Experiences involving parental rejection, separation from parents, rigidity in training schedules, and a repressive home climate may separately or in combination produce avoidance reactions, and, in the extreme, may produce severe psychological withdrawal, low drive for accomplishment, and other forms of emotional disturbance. These forms of behavior may then form part of the pattern which involves intellectual retardation. The child may learn, as Gardner has put it, to have a "low expectation level that his efforts will lead to success in problem solving."[45]

[45] Gardner, W. I., "Personality concomitants of mental retardation," in Wilcox, R. K. (ed.), *Strategies for Behavioral Research in Mental Retardation*. Madison: University of Wisconsin Press, 1961.

Moreover, the child's early lack of success in coping with the problems of adaptation to the expectancies of his environment may produce further abasement of his self-regard, which in turn may lead to further loss of drive in successful adaptation. This early lack of success may be attributable to constitutional inferiority in some, to slow developmental rates in others, and to frustrating experiences in still others.

Since society is geared to the "normal child" the retarded child may experience a disproportionate share of failures and frustrations in early life at home and later in school. He may experience such failures in the psychosexual sphere as well as in the other emotional and intellectual spheres of interaction. The retarded child needs ample time for growth and detailed and supervised learning experiences that will encourage a self-regard that is trustful and optimistic.[46] He needs special encouragement and positive reinforcement in his attempts to cope with new learning situations, and unwitting rejection must be avoided by not expecting of him more than he can reasonably accomplish.

The vast majority of retarded children come from culturally deprived homes and suffer further deprivation of favorable emotional, cultural, and intellectual experiences as a consequence. For such children, massive preventative programs need to be instituted in order to compensate for such deficiencies—at the community level and in special educational agencies. As we shall see in later chapters, special guidance is needed in both home and school. (See Chapter Ten). The "community" needs to learn how to deal with the retarded individual, regardless, whether there is a constitutional deficiency or some severe emotional impairment. Recent research has pointed up the difficulties such individuals experience in attending to relevant stimuli, and the improvement demonstrated when tasks are properly graded or when special learning procedures are applied.[47]

There seem to be critical periods in the adjustment of the retardate. Although it is impossible to divide the life span into artificially separate periods, it is helpful to think of the first year of life as being especially important, both in assessing the individual and in providing appropriate and therefore emotionally satisfying experiences. This is followed by

[46] *Ibid.*

[47] See, as examples: Ware, J. R., Baker, R. A., and Sipowics, R. R., "Performance of mental deficients on a simple vigilance task," *Amer. J. ment. Defic.*, 1962, *66*, 647–650; and, Zigler, E., and Unell, E., "Concept-switching in normal and feebleminded children as a function of reinforcement," *Amer. J. ment. Defic.*, 1962, *66*, 651–657.

the preschool years when early patterns of interpersonal relationships are learned, and then by the early adolescent period when there is a resurgence of old problems as well as new ones for the retardate. These are all critical periods when the several factors—biological, psychological, and cultural—may have their greatest impact.

ch. 6

CONFLICT AND ANXIETY

I N THE PREVIOUS CHAPTER WE LEARNED THAT THE DEVELOPMENT OF the personality depends upon the interaction of the organism with experience. We can no longer naively hold the view that the development of an individual merely "unfolds" independently of experience. Development of intellectual capacities, in particular, as well as of personality, in general, are crucially dependent on the *kind, amount,* and *timing* of such experiences. For the sake of convenience, we may distinguish two major types of general experience which have an impact upon personality development: (1) *deprivation* of relevant stimulation when needed to foster development; and, (2) *conflict* in satisfying needs which motivate behavior.

J. McV. Hunt marshals evidence which dramatically supports the proposition that intellectual development may be grossly retarded (as well as facilitated) by variation in relevant sensorimotor stimulation.[1] Deprivation of such stimulation, particularly in the early periods of development, may retard intellectual development by as much as 50 per cent. We shall refer to such evidence from time to time to point up the fact that retarded functioning is not a matter only of inferior genetic inheritance, as is so commonly believed. Such evidence is especially important in view of the fact that the majority of mentally retarded individuals come from inferior cultural environments in which some deprivation is most likely to occur.

[1] Hunt, J. McV., *Intelligence and Experience.* New York: The Ronald Press Company, 1961.

The effect of conflict, especially when severe or protracted, upon personality development and intellectual functioning has been given relatively little research attention in discussions of the retarded individual. Not only has it often been assumed that such individuals are born as retardates and "stay that way," but it has also been assumed that conflict plays only a minor role in the development of retarded functioning. Only in recent years, and usually only in connection with exceptional cases, has attention been pointed toward the severely debilitating effect of severe or prolonged conflict, with its consequences, upon intellectual development and functioning .

Our major purpose in this chapter is to examine the concepts of conflict, and its major consequence—anxiety—and to consider the probable relevance of such phenomena upon the development of retarded individuals. Although evidence that is specifically relevant to retardation has been rapidly accumulating within the past few years, most of what we know at present applies to relatively normal populations, and we shall have to extrapolate these findings to the population of retardates to a considerable degree. Our conclusions must, therefore, be regarded as only tentative, but we believe that they are so important that we shall not temporize incessantly, but instead shall rely upon the reader to exercise caution in evaluating our implications. We feel we can do this without undue danger, for the pendulum of opinion has for so long held steadfastly to the untested and unopposed conclusion that inferior intellectual development is necessarily the result of inferior genetic background and is therefore incapable of any correction (see Chapter Eight).

THE NATURE OF PSYCHOLOGICAL CONFLICT

Conflict may be defined as the simultaneous arousal of two or more sets of motives which are antagonistic to each other. As an example, we may cite the case of an individual who simultaneously wishes to attend a party and go to the theater. If both motives are strong and the satisfaction of one means that the other cannot be satisfied, then conflict may become quite intense. In this example, we assume that the individual is fully aware of both sets of motives and that he can make a deliberate choice between them. He may also decide to satisfy one set of motives now and try to satisfy the other set at another time. In any case, the stronger set of motives will usually prevail and some degree of reduction in tension then results.

However, even in this relatively simple type of conflict situation, inability to make some choice will result in continuing tension until some other act of behavior tends to reduce it. And continuing tension, if severe, may reduce intellectual judgment temporarily, divert attention from relevant "facts of the situation," and have other disabling effects. On the other hand, *moderate* degrees of conflict and ensuing *moderate* tension may sharpen intellectual judgment, increase attention to relevant stimuli, and the reduction of the tension state by choice and gratification of one set of motives may be experienced as pleasurable. Such kinds of conflict situations are common in life generally and in school situations as well, and the evidence which has been derived from research studies indicates that moderate degrees of tension, accompanied by relatively accurate awareness of its source, usually improves performance, especially on simple tasks.[2]

Conflict may, however, involve motives which are unconscious. The concept of "unconscious" will be discussed fully in the next chapter, but at this point we can conceptualize it as a state of lack of awareness of the motivation which is operating. The reader may be able to think of many commonplace examples of unconsciously motivated behavior. "Forgetting" to make an unpleasant telephone call or to do something else which one dislikes is the kind of unconsciously motivated behavior with which all of us are familiar. Getting a headache before a party which one imagines one would like to attend, but of which one is unconsciously fearful, is another example. Becoming afraid in a situation which, from a rational viewpoint, should not lead to such fear is still another example of the operation of unconscious motives.

In conflicts either or both of the sets of motives may be unconscious. An individual may have tendencies to behave in a certain way of which he is totally unaware, and when these tendencies are unopposed by external barriers to their gratification or by other internal tendencies of which he is unaware, they may be acted upon impulsively. Many cases of antisocial behavior and many cases of such impulse-driven behavior as "fire-setting" may be explained on the basis of unconsciously motivated behavior that is unopposed by other internalized motives. On the other hand, many "guilt-ridden" individuals are unable to function effectively because they are experiencing conflict between two sets of antagonistic and unconscious motives.

Unconscious conflicts, it is believed, are extremely important in the development of disturbed states of behavior.[3] Since the source of the

[2] Spence, K. W., "A theory of emotionally based drive (D) and its relation to performance in simple learning situations," *Amer. J. Psychol.*, 1958, *13*, 131–141.

[3] Hutt, M. L., and Gibby, R. G., *Patterns of Abnormal Behavior*. Boston: Allyn and Bacon, Inc., 1957.

conflict (or sources) is unknown to the person, he is unable to deal with it effectively. And since he has difficulty in resolving the conflict, much psychological energy must be devoted to keeping the soure of the conflict unconscious, since all motives seek expression and the very fact of their being unconscious indicates that, for some reason, they are intolerable to the individual, and therefore have to be "guarded against" (see Chapter Seven for further discussion of this point).

One of the major motives of all human beings is to seek affection and acceptance (to gain love). In the case of retarded individuals, this psychosexual set of motives is often in conflict with other motives involving fear of criticism, fear of rejection, and fear of ridicule. In the school situation, in particular, when the retarded individual has come to learn that he cannot live up to the standards expected of him, and when he has learned to anticipate not only failure but rejection, there may be a sharp and intense conflict between striving to perform to gain acceptance and fear of performing in order to avoid rejection. The whole school situation may become unconsciously threatening, and the conflict which is experienced may become so severe that withdrawal (at a psychological level) may be the only apparent solution. Inattention, lack of interest, and constant lethargy and fatigue may be the observable symptoms of this kind of intense conflict. Or, in a distorted manner, the retarded pupil may unconsciously pit his strength against the school (teacher), by refusing to learn as his main means of defiance and self-assertion. His behavior says, then, in effect, "See how strong I am. No matter how hard you may try, you cannot make me learn." In clinical practice, one finds that this kind of disturbed reaction occurs fairly frequently as the pupil's *passive oppositional* "solution" to his conflict between wishing to be loved and his fear of being deprecated.

Unresolved, unconscious conflicts produce persistent tension or anxiety (see next section). The effects of this anxiety may not only produce the immediate effect of increased anxiety and diminished effectiveness, but may have crippling effects upon the development of the person's *ego.* (See Chapter Seven for a discussion of this concept.) There may also be the cyclical effect of: persistent, unconscious anxiety which leads to reduced energy and effectiveness, which leads to decreased intellectual functioning, which leads to increased conflict, which leads to still additional anxiety, and so on. In the case of the retarded pupil who is already handicapped in his ability to deal with the complex demands of the social and intellectual environment of his school situation, these effects may be devastating indeed. When a pupil's previous experience has been culturally deprived, and when his capacity to cope with conflict has already been impaired, as is the case with most retarded individuals, these effects are more likely as well as more significant.

Other theories of conflict have been developed by various workers in the fields of personality development. By way of contrast with the psychoanalytic viewpoint we have presented, it may be fruitful to consider one of these. Shaffer and Shoben, in a very clear exposition of conflict theory, following Lewin's position in many respects, offer the following type of explanation.[4]

First a distinction is made between the concepts of *frustration* and *conflict*. The former is defined as a condition in which external factors (a person, a person's behavior, or a situation) prevent the reduction of an aroused drive. Such blocking of a drive leads to varied behavior, increased drive (at least frequently), aggression (often), or regression "from better organized to more primitive behavior."[5] Conflict is defined as the simultaneous arousal of two or more "antagonistic patterns of motivation" which cannot be satisfied at the same time. These authors maintain that frustration may lead to conflict under the following conditions: When the frustrating object is feared, and love by this object is needed (note that this already implies conflict), the frustration leads to aggression, and this learned fear acts as a thwarting motive to the aggressive drives.

They suggest that there are three types of conflicts. They propose first (following Lewin) that all conflict may be understood as "an interaction between an individual and the events of his environment."[6] It is believed that every object or person in an individual's psychological environment either attracts (has *positive valence*) or repels (has *negative valence*). The degree of attraction or repulsion (or strength of the valences) may vary. The three types of conflict may then be conceptualized as those arising when there is: (1) *approach-approach* conflict (two positive valences that cannot be satisfied simultaneously), (2) *avoidance-avoidance* conflict, or (3) *approach-avoidance* conflict. They believe that the most severe or most disturbing type of conflict is of the approach-avoidance type when the avoidance motive is based on fear.

A theory such as this serves to clarify many of the phenomena of emotional disturbance. It is not incompatible with the psychoanalytic theory discussed previously. However, one may question how well it accounts for the genesis of many kinds of conflicts.

---

[4] Shaffer, L. F., and Shoben, E. J., *The Psychology of Adjustment* (2nd Ed.). Boston: Houghton Mifflin Company, 1956.

[5] *Ibid.*, p. 103.

[6] *Ibid.*, p. 104.

THE NATURE OF ANXIETY

Anxiety is a common experience that we have all shared. We have undoubtedly felt anxious from time to time, and have been aware of fluctuations in the intensity of our anxiety. If we analyze our experiences when we are anxious we will note that we probably feel somewhat "disorganized." We may feel that something "bad" is going to happen to us. We dread something, and yet we are not quite sure what it is we dread.

Anxiety is not the same thing as fear. For example, we fear to cross a railroad crossing when a train is approaching, or we are afraid of walking in front of an oncoming car, or of remaining in a building that is on fire. *We fear something specific that is consciously known to us.* In an anxiety reaction we have somewhat similar feelings but *we do not know exactly what it is that arouses these feelings within us.* In anxiety the specific object or situation that induces the anxiety reaction is not known at a conscious level.

All human beings experience numerous anxieties. An example of a common anxiety situation is the birth process, which induces severe anxieties in the newborn individual. Freud emphasized the importance of the fact that the newborn infant at birth emerges into an environment that is very different from that of his prenatal existence.[7] He stated that the child is suddenly exposed to a flood of stimulation that he is totally unable to handle. According to Freud, this is the first significant danger situation to which we are all exposed, and it serves as the model for all future anxieties that we experience.

Other authorities have differed with this viewpoint. Rank feels that birth not only strongly shocks the individual, both physiologically and psychologically, but that it also creates a reservoir of anxiety which is released throughout his life.[8] Freud views the birth process as the physiological model of later anxiety; Rank views it as the source of the anxiety itself. Greenacre takes a position somewhat between Freud and Rank.[9] She feels that constitutional factors, prenatal experiences, the birth process, and the situation immediately after birth all play a part in creating within the child a predisposition to anxiety. Greenacre states that this basic anxiety differs from later anxiety in that it operates on a reflex level, and has no psychological content. Fodor feels that birth is

[7] Freud, S., *The Problem of Anxiety*. New York: W. W. Norton & Company, Inc., 1936.

[8] Rank, O., *The Trauma of Birth*. New York: Harcourt, Brace & World, Inc., 1929.

[9] Greenacre, P., "The biological economy of birth," in *The Psychoanalytic Study of the Child,* Vol. I. New York: International Universities Press, Inc., 1945, pp. 31–51.

traumatic in almost every instance.[10] It is not our purpose at this point to relate the birth process to future personality traits, but rather to offer the birth process as an example of an anxiety-producing situation to which all humans are exposed.[11]

The very young child has basic needs that he is totally unable to gratify or satisfy by his own efforts. An example is the infant's need for food. The infant cannot satisfy his hunger needs until he is fed by another person, usually the mother. No action of his can satisfy these needs; they must be satisfied by outside sources. A tension automatically results in the child whenever these needs are present. If his hunger needs are not satisfied immediately, he experiences pain and discomfort. The chief point with which we need to be concerned here is that the child experiences impulses and needs that are not gratified immediately. This may create very strong anxieties, which may be overwhelming.

Since the ego structure of the very young child is weak, he experiences his anxieties in a very passive manner and is unable to control them.[12] As the ego matures, however, the child learns to anticipate dangers. When this occurs the individual experiences a reaction similar to the earlier, more primitive states of anxiety, but at a much less intensive level. This reaction may be regarded as being similar in *quality* but not in *quantity* to the earlier and more primary anxiety which is centered around the need for nourishment. The new type of anxiety, brought about by the ego's anticipation of a future danger, may be regarded as a warning signal. This signal initiates some sort of defensive reaction in order to guard against the anticipated threats to the person. When we experience this type of anxiety, it means that something is automatically and unconsciously perceived by us as threatening, and then we try to do something about it in order to allay the anxiety aroused by this anticipation.

We may regard all anxieties, in the last analysis, as unconscious fears of experiencing a threatening and damaging state. Anxiety may be regarded as being a fear that the ego structure will be overwhelmed by some sort of a situation that it cannot master. Basically, anxiety stems from the apprehension that id impulses cannot be controlled. If, how-

---

[10] Fodor, N., *The Search for the Beloved*. New York: Hermitage Press, 1949.

[11] Representative studies of the relationship of the birth process to future personality traits may be found in: Cattell, R. B., *Personality*. New York: McGraw-Hill, Inc., 1950.

[12] This discussion is based upon the psychoanalytic theory as developed in: Fenichel, O., *The Psychoanalytic Theory of Neurosis*. New York: W. W. Norton & Company, Inc., 1945.

ever, there have been no serious disturbances in ego development and it has matured sufficiently, id urges are usually not perceived as threatening by the ego and so no overpowering anxieties are aroused.

At times the ego of the child is totally unable to handle the anxieties that are present, and the signal that initiated activities to lessen the threat actually serves to precipitate a threatening state. If a child has many repressions that have resulted from previously threatening situations, the slight anxiety that is added by an additional threat of danger is enough to "blow the whole situation apart," and overwhelming anxiety results. The ego's signal of a possible approaching danger in this instance not only fails to avoid a threatening situation but actually precipitates an exceedingly serious situation.

In the newborn child the anxiety that is experienced due to the immediate nonsatisfaction of needs is rather automatic and is specific to certain situations. This is a usual reaction. As the ego develops, anxiety functions more in the service of the ego. Normally the anxiety reaction is controlled and is used by the child as a warning signal to avoid further disorganization. When ego control fails and anxiety becomes overwhelming, the child reverts to the original primary anxiety stage, and ego controls are lost. This is an abnormal reaction.

A special type of anxiety is known as *guilt*. We have all had the experience of feeling very guilty about some things without knowing why we feel that way. Feelings of guilt are centered around such thoughts as —"I have done wrong," or "It was not right." The core of the special anxiety we know as guilt is the ego's warning. "Do not do that or something terrible will happen to you." The guilt feelings that a child experiences arise primarily from his fear of abandonment by his parents because of something bad he has done or wishes to do. These feelings are quite specific. What is really feared in a guilt reaction is that there will be a loss of those pleasant feelings of well-being, security, and protection that all children desire. We may summarize all of these reactions under the general term "self-esteem." In guilt the child fears the loss of self-esteem. Anxiety, in general, warns the child not to undertake a particular course of action, but guilt feeling is an actual materialization of this particular threat. The core of the child's guilt reaction is anxiety over the possible loss of love of the parents.

Anxiety, then, may be regarded as a danger signal which is felt and perceived consciously by the child, although the origin of the anxiety or the underlying cause is always unconscious. The basic origin of anxiety is always a threat from within the personality. This internal threat, however, may be initiated or modified by the external situations in which the child finds himself. The symptoms of the child's internal conflicts are expressions of the defensive forces through which he attempts to control his anxieties.

As a result of anxiety the functions of the ego are inhibited, since the energy of the ego is consumed in the defensive struggle. The retarded child already has an impoverished or inadequate ego, and thus his ego functions tend to be disturbed even more.

Thus far we have presented the traditional psychoanalytic viewpoint on the problem of anxiety. This theory helps us to understand many aspects of this phenomenon, and especially the relationship of anxiety to behavioral disturbances in the retarded child. However (as Freud himself and many psychoanalysts since have acknowledged), this theory still leaves many crucial questions unanswered. In the following pages we shall present some of the recent experimental and clinical data on this subject, and propose some extensions and modifications of the psychoanalytic theory of anxiety.

A review of much of the experimental evidence is presented in two books: one by May[13] in which a general theory of anxiety is developed; the other by Hoch and Zubin[14] in which several authorities present summaries of their positions. There are already considerably more data than these volumes present, since the experimental work in this area is in a state of active ferment. Cattell, for example, has prepared another volume which summarizes some of his recent evidence and speculations.[15]

One could say that there are at least two basic questions that remain to be answered in regard to the conceptualization of anxiety. The first of these asks whether or not anxiety is a unitary phenomenon. In other words, is there simply one kind of anxiety that may vary in intensity but not in its quality or characteristics? The second question is whether or not the amount of anxiety and the stage of the child's life at which it is manifested have differential effects upon behavior. This latter fundamental problem includes such subsidiary questions as: Under what conditions does anxiety result in psychopathological behavior? May anxiety serve to facilitate learning and effect adjustment favorably? Is there a relative degree of anxiety, which may vary for the individual during different stages of his life, which is optimal for adjustment? This whole problem area is an intriguing one and is of vital significance to an under-

[13] May, R., *The Meaning of Anxiety*. New York: The Ronald Press Company, 1950.
[14] Hoch, P. A., and Zubin, J., *Anxiety*. New York: Grune & Stratton, Inc., 1950.
[15] Cattell, R. B., *Anxiety, Motivation and Measurement*. New York: Harcourt, Brace & World, Inc., 1957.

standing of personality in general as well as to the psychopathology of the mentally retarded child.

Various investigators have taken the position that there are several, or indeed an infinite variety of, anxieties. Evidences for this position rests on the demonstration that various kinds of stress may separately induce anxiety reactions.[16] Nevertheless, reaction to stress may not be quite the same thing as basic anxiety. In both there may be increased activity of the autonomic nervous system, disorganized responses and *hyperactivity* (more than normal activity) at the motor level, and feelings of tenseness or panic, and the like. However, there may be a significant difference between such reactions to specific stress (or *trauma*) and to anxiety as we are using the term. In the latter, we have postulated an unconscious element, so that the child is unaware of the real danger factor, whereas in the former the danger is known and may be perceived or dealt with more or less directly. Again, in anxiety, the whole ego appears to the child to be threatened, whereas in stress the ego may be only partially involved or not involved at all.[17]

This leads to another and perhaps even more basic difference between anxiety and disturbed reactions to stress. In basic anxiety, the child behaves as if there is a built-in anxiety "structure"; that is, he is unable to deal with the situation realistically, he is unable to modify his ways of coping with the difficulty and he continues to respond with relatively *stereotyped* behavior and with anxiety when the stress situation (objectively) is no longer present. Thus, he behaves as if he had a reservoir of anxiety which tends to be discharged whether the objective reality calls for it or not. This discharge may be direct, in which case the anxiety is directly expressed, or it may be indirect, in which case inner equivalents or symptomatic derivatives may be substituted for the emotional part of the reaction.

Stress reactions may gradually give way to anxiety if a child meets repeated stress situations that he cannot master, if the intensity of the stress becomes sufficiently great, or if he is insufficiently mature to cope with the stress. In such a case, perception of the real danger becomes more and more distorted, more repression occurs, the ego becomes less adequate and more rigid and fear is finally replaced by anxiety; there is then an "unknown factor." Conversely, a child who already has much anxiety is likely to be disproportionately affected by stressful situations

[16] Hoch and Zubin, *op. cit.*

[17] See, for example, the studies by Sarason, S. B., and Mandler, G., of which "A study of anxiety and learning," *J. abnorm. soc. Psychol.*, 1952, *47*, 166-173, is an illustration.

to the degree that the stress involves the security of his ego. Hence, stress is more "stressful" when the subject is younger, is less competent and experienced in dealing with it, and when the ego is more likely to be overwhelmed, as in the case of the mentally retarded child.

It can be understood readily that stress or shock to a child may result in increased anxiety. It may be more difficult to conceptualize the effects of actual or anticipated separation from or rejection by an important loved object, such as the mother, although common knowledge tells us that such experiences may result in at least severe depression. The psychological meaning of separation as a vital threat to the ego, particularly as it affects young children, is highlighted by a number of studies. Anna Freud and Burlingham, who studied the effects of such separation in England during World War II, point out that with young children, particularly those between the ages of two and four years, separation from the parents may produce severe and persisting anxiety reactions and neurotic behavior.[18] This, rather than the fear of being hurt physically, was more often than not the decisive factor in the development of such reactions. Studies by others have not only confirmed this conclusion but have shown that severe depression, sometimes called *anaclitic depression*, and other clinical conditions tend to result from such separation during the first year of life. The reaction tends to be more severe when a good or fairly good relationship had already existed between mother and child. Similar, but usually milder, reactions have been reported in soldiers who became anxious, depressed, and disorganized when they were simply removed from their homes or home towns and their families, long before they were subjected to actual threat of physical injury or to more threatening battle conditions.[19] In such studies, separation may easily be seen as a threat to the ego, in conflict with drives for security, affection, and the preservation of the status quo. When such stress is introduced early in the life of the child, when the ego is still weak, the effects upon the ego tend to be proportionately more severe, producing disorganization to such a degree that persistent psychotic tendencies (*processes*) may be induced. In early life, when the ego is relatively weak and cannot institute appropriate defensive measures, the effects are far-reaching because the basic security of the individual is threatened, and anxiety and its derivatives mount to high levels.

[18] Freud, A., and Burlingham, D. T., *War and Children*. New York: Medical War Books, 1943.

[19] See, for example, Grinker, R. R., and Spiegel, J. P., *Men under Stress*. New York: McGraw-Hill, Inc., 1945; and Mira, E., *Psychiatry in War*. New York: W. W. Norton & Company, Inc., 1943.

We have highlighted the effects of severe stress and the resultant induction of high degrees of anxiety, but we have not given much attention to the effects of milder degrees of these phenomena. This is not because these conditions are unimportant, but because they are more significant for an understanding of normal reactions and for theories of learning than for psychopathology. Various investigators have been experimenting with reactions of essentially normal subjects to milder forms of stress. The studies by Sarason and Mandler have shown that, with an "unselected" population of college students, those students who have a low level of anxiety tend to do better in test situations in which unanticipated stress is introduced, whereas those who are higher in anxiety level do better on the regular scholastic or course examination for which they were able to prepare.[20] These studies point up the differential effects of degrees of anxiety. The effects of different kinds of defense mechanisms in handling anxiety have also been explored.[21] Additional studies by Eriksen,[22] Lazarus,[23] and others have contributed further to our understanding of the differential effects of anxiety and have shown, in addition, that there may be different kinds of anxiety for different kinds of situations (which we would prefer to call objective anxiety or fear, in contrast to basic anxiety).*

Cattell has been working intensively on the problem of the measurement of anxiety for a number of years, using factor analytic methods of investigation.[24] He has developed a questionnaire method of measuring anxiety (called the *I.P.A.T. Anxiety Scale*), as well as methods of measuring anxiety by laboratory methods. He summarized much of his thinking in a speech prepared for delivery in January, 1957, which the authors were privileged to hear and permitted to quote. He believes: "that there is indeed a single factor in the realm of anxiety manifestations. . . . This functional unity called the *general anxiety factor* is also shown to be distinct from neuroticism, and from the stress reaction though it tends to be significantly correlated with the former." Cattell has also shown that what he calls anxiety states (and what we have called objective anxiety

---

[20] Sarason, S. B., and Mandler, G., "Some correlates of test anxiety," *J. abnorm. soc. Psychol.*, 1952, *47*, 810–817.

[21] Waterhouse, I. K., and Child, I. L., "Frustration and the quality of performance. III: An experimental study," *J. Pers.*, 1953, *21*, 298–311.

[22] Eriksen, C. W., "Psychological defenses and 'ego strength' in the recall of completed and incompleted tasks," *J. abnorm. soc. Psychol.*, 1954, *45*, 45–50.

[23] See the review: Lazarus, R. S., *et al.*, "The effects of psychological stress upon performance," *Psychol. Bull.* 1952, *49*, 293–317.

* See our previous discussion of this issue in this chapter.

[24] Cattell, *op. cit.*

or reaction to stress) are subject to specific stress situations, whereas general anxiety is a persistent characteristic of the individual, operating at a continuous level within that individual. Cattell's position is, in general, consistent with our own. We differ from him mainly in our specific analysis of the cause of anxiety (he postulates five or six possible sources of anxiety), and in our conclusions that anxiety at the latent or symbolic level may not be measurable by the same means as other manifestations of anxiety (especially overt anxiety). Nevertheless his experimental studies have extremely important implications which will stimulate considerable research in the future.

We may now pull all this material together and summarize our own present position. In doing this we wish to remind the reader that our summary is essentially intended to provide a frame of reference and to stimulate further critical thinking.

We have defined anxiety as a condition in which the child is unaware of the source of his intense emotional reaction, his apprehension or dread. In any given response, however, there may be an admixture of this type of objectless anxiety and "objective" anxiety (or fear). Each child has a persisting anxiety level which tends to remain more or less constant over a period of time, unless increased by severe trauma or decreased by some benign or favorable factor (such as psychotherapy). Anxiety of the objectless variety has a highly significant effect upon the ego, depending upon the age and condition of the child when it is developed, and upon the intensity level of the anxiety, among other conditions. Small amounts of anxiety that can be dealt with successfully lead to strengthening of the ego's functions. Large amounts of anxiety tend to overwhelm the ego, produce some persistent damage to its functioning, create the need for certain defensive maneuvers to reduce the tension level somewhat, and produce symptomatic derivatives. There is probably an optimal level of anxiety for effective functioning and effective learning.

Thus we may conceptualize three ranges of anxiety level: a normal level, which facilitates learning and adjustment; a lower than normal level, which has little or no effect upon adjustment; and a pathological level, which produces more or less persistent maladjustment and rigid and stereotyped behaviors, poor learning and adaptation, and the use of pathological defenses and symptoms. In addition to its resultants upon the emotions (the *affective* behavior), pathological amounts of anxiety disturb the *cognitive* (intellectual) processes and interfere with smooth and effective motor behavior.

In addition to the individual's characteristic or chronic level of anxiety, we must consider two other general factors. One of these is the relative and sudden increase or decrease in anxiety (particularly the former), which may be produced by some ego-involving stress (which is subjectively perceived as threatening). Such rapid changes in anxiety level tend to produce the effects that we attribute to pathological anxiety. The other is the nature of the defenses that have been developed to deal with anxiety. The more immature these are, the less satisfactorily will the anxiety be controlled.

Basic or objectless anxiety may be characterized as either security anxiety or separation (or *rejection*) anxiety. As noted above, either type of basic anxiety, in intense amounts, is conducive to some degree of maladjustment. We may think of separation anxiety as being a prior psychological model of basic anxiety, in which anticipation of losing support or being rejected by an important love object tends to bring on feelings of catastrophe. Security anxiety, or apprehension over being mutilated or destroyed, can be conceived of as a second model of anxiety, associated with later forms of interpersonal experience. These two basic forms of anxiety proliferate, as the individual matures and differentiates, into many subsidiary forms, the characteristics of which may be greatly influenced by cultural factors.

THE RETARDED PERSONALITY AND ANXIETY

It can be assumed that, like all other human beings, the retarded child experiences anxiety for the same basic reasons that we have discussed above. It can be expected that problems of *security* and *separation* will be especially important for such children, and we have some evidence to support this expectation, as we shall see as we review some of the research literature. It is our contention that retarded children are, in general, more prone to develop intense anxieties than other children, although the manifestations of such anxieties at the behavior level may take different forms than with children of normal and superior intellectual development. For example, tendencies to *characterological* (that is, persistent life styles) behavior which involves loss of attention and interest in the intellectual world, loss of interest in many forms of social interaction, relatively decreased use of intellectual capacities in abstract thinking and in fantasy creation, decreased use of verbal skills in interpersonal communication and increased use of motoric skills, and passive-oppositional orientation to the world may be more common manifestations of continuing, intense anxiety in the retardates.

The proposition that retarded children experience more anxiety than other children is supported generally by the research evidence which has accumulated in recent years. This is certainly the case for overt or manifest anxiety, or, in other words, in anxiety which is consciously visible to others and which is experienced by the individual as apprehension of an immediate situation. Anxiety concerning tests is an example of this kind. Consciously experienced anxiety in relation to immediate learning situations of other kinds constitutes another type of example. Two studies, dealt with in greater detail in Chapter Eight, document the proposition that mentally retarded children show more manifest anxiety than do normal children.[25] In these and related studies, manifest anxiety is usually measured by a questionnaire in which the respondent states how he "feels" at a given time in his life. Thus the evidence is indicative that retarded individuals experience and are aware of anxiety in greater amounts than members of other, more superior, populations.

The evidence is not as clear-cut or convincing with respect to covert and basic anxiety. In fact, there is some evidence that the latter type of anxiety, sometimes termed *general anxiety* to distinguish it from more specific anxiety (like test anxiety), is not greater in retardates than in normals.[26] However, it is evident from the research that has been published that it is both more difficult to measure covert than overt anxiety, in general, and that the application of the usual tests of covert anxiety to retarded groups leads to doubtful validity in such cases.[27]

That covert anxiety may, nevertheless, be directly related to mental retardation, or that there may even be a significant causal relationship, may be inferred from an intensive study of 172 children referred for evaluation because of suspected mental retardation.[28] In 15 per cent of the cases, even after intensive study by relevant clinical techniques, no conclusive diagnosis could be reached. Moreover, of the total population, 18 per cent were evaluated as not being mentally retarded although they were referred because of this probable problem.

The authors are careful to point out that the interplay of diverse factors, especially of emotional factors that may affect behavior and performance, makes the diagnosis of mental retardation in young children

[25] Cochran, I. L., and Cleland, C., "Manifest anxiety of retardates and normals matched as to academic achievement," *Amer. J. ment. Defic.*, 1963, *67*, 539–542; Malpass, L., Mark, S., and Palerma, D., "Responses of retarded children to the Children's Manifest Anxiety Scale," *J. educ. Psychol.*, 1960, *51*, 305–308.

[26] Sarason, I. G., "Intellectual and personality correlates of test anxiety," *J. abnorm. soc. Psychol.*, 1959, *59*, 272–275.

[27] Sarason, I. G., "Empirical findings and theoretical problems in the use of anxiety scales," *Psychol. Bull.*, 1960, *57*, 403–415.

[28] Garfield, S. L., Wilcott, J. B., and Milgram, N. A., "Emotional disturbances and mental deficiency," *Amer. J. ment. Defic.*, 1961, *66*, 23–29.

an especially difficult task. Judging from the evidence which is presented in this study, one could infer that a significant proportion of this population was suffering from emotional problems in which a major factor was covert anxiety, although the authors do not specify this as a probable condition. As we have noted earlier, if intense and continuing anxiety is present, and if it takes the form of characterological withdrawal and reduced participation interacting with the environment, one of the major consequences may be apparent mental retardation.

One of the recent workers in the field of mental retardation has suggested that impairment in learning capacity may be attributed to psychological stresses associated with disturbed parent-child relationships.[29] In his study, Davis suggests this thesis with evidence from learning theory experiments by Liddell and others and by a review of the clinical literature. Other workers urge the abandonment of the term "mental retardation" in favor of the term "culturally different" for children who do not have any known brain damage.[30] The evidence and arguments amassed in this article suggest to the present writers that not only may cultural deprivation contribute to retardation but it may contribute as well to covert and basic anxiety, affecting the basic security system of the individual, and thus lead to persistent impairment in the use of mental abilities.

Another type of evidence, admittedly indirect, bears upon the effects of anxiety on the development of mentally retarded behaviors. This evidence comes mainly from experiments on the learning characteristics of mentally retarded individuals. We shall discuss some aspects of this evidence in a later section of this chapter (see Anxiety and Learning), but we shall refer to three kinds of evidence at this point.

Zeamon and House have focussed interest on what they call an "attention theory" in relation to the learning of discriminations in simple perceptual tasks.[31] They have found that when retarded individuals are helped by some experimental procedures to maximize their attention (and they have shown that retardates tend to be deficient in this regard), they are able to learn much more effectively even difficult perceptual discriminations. Their studies raise the question, "What causes the

[29] Davis, D. R., "A disorder theory of mental retardation," *J. ment. Subnorm.*, 1961, 7 (1, Whole No. 12), 13–21.

[30] Olshansky, S., Schonfeld, J., and Sternfeld, L., "Mentally retarded or culturally different?" *Train. Sch. Bull.*, 1962, *59*, 18–21.

[31] Zeamon, D., and House, B. J., "An attention theory of retardate discrimination learning," *Progr. Rep. No. 3, Res. Grant M-1099*, Nat. Inst. Ment. Hlth, Bethesda, Md., Nov. 1962.

attention difficulties in the first place?" Was the attention difficulty a result of the mental retardation, was it caused by the same factors that led to both retardation and poor attention, or was some other factor at work? In our view, it is possible to understand the decrease in attention as a function of persistent anxiety (although other factors may also be causative agents). Hence, training in attending, while effective, may be regarded as treatment of the symptom directly. It might be possible, also, to relieve the anxiety which produces inattention, and thus effect an even more significant improvement. In any case, Zeamon's findings are consistent with such a view.

A second aspect of this type of evidence comes from studies of the learning of abstract concepts by retarded individuals. It has been found repeatedly that such individuals do much more poorly than normals, even when matched for mental age. Even more striking is the finding that this ability becomes progressively and relatively worse when such individuals are placed and continued in institutions for mental retardates.[32] One may speculate as to why this condition develops. Is it because such individuals are innately less accomplished in verbal, and particularly in abstract, thinking? This should not be the case when they are matched with other individuals for mental age. In fact, the reverse should be found under such conditions, for when they are matched with other individuals in mental age, they have lived longer and should therefore have had more learning opportunity to acquire abstract concepts. We suggest, instead, that cultural deprivation and the general withdrawal which persistent anxiety breeds, in many instances, leads to decreased need for the use of verbal communication and abstract thinking.

This last line of research is supported by studies which open still another line of relevant evidence. As Jordan has shown, mentally retarded individuals have lower needs to achieve than do normal children.[33] This finding continues to be manifested even when mental age is held constant. Here again, decreased need to achieve may be the resultant of persistent anxiety, which is so often accompanied by lack of cultural stimulation.

All of these lines of evidence need confirmation and clarification. But the total impact of the evidence is at least suggestive that the effects of anxiety upon personality and performance are highly significant.

[32] Badt, M. I., "Levels of abstraction in vocabulary definitions of mentally retarded school children," *Amer. J. ment. Defic.*, 1958, *63*, 241-246.

[33] Jordan, T. E., *The Mentally Retarded.* Columbus: Charles E. Merrill Books, Inc., 1961.

We should point out that our own clinical experience with retarded children has led us to give special emphasis to relevant emotional factors in such cases. One of the writers (MLH) has recently been able to observe the behavior of a deaf-retarded group in an institutional setting, in which intensive habilitation and therapeutic measures are being employed to improve the adjustment and skills of this severely handicapped population.

ANXIETY AND DEFENSIVE BEHAVIOR

It has been learned that an individual is unable to tolerate intense degrees of anxiety. He attempts to achieve some degree of reduction in anxiety (*homeostasis**) by expressing his needs, if necessary, in some indirect or compromise fashion. There are two general ways in which anxiety can be reduced. One of these, the more healthy method, is to learn to cope with the conflict directly, making some appropriate, adaptive response to the situation on a realistic basis, and thus resolving the conflict. The other, less efficient and always relatively more pathological, is through the use of *defense mechanisms*. A defense mechanism is an indirect method of dealing with conflict, and does not involve a resolution, but, rather, involves some substitutive method of reducing its severity. All children, so far as we know, employ both *coping behaviors* and *defense mechanisms* (as do all adults), but there is some evidence that retarded individuals rely less on coping behavior and more on defensive behavior than do normal children. Moreover, retarded children probably employ some types of defenses disproportionately more than do normals. We shall discuss defense mechanisms in this section and then turn our attention to coping behavior in the next.

Every person would express his biological drives quite directly if: (a) he were physically capable of executing the behavior necessary for this expression (*i.e.*, if maturation and learning enabled him to do so); (b) there were no conflict with another, opposing drive; and (c) there were no external factors inhibiting their expression (physical reality and cultural prohibition). However, some drives are prevented from direct or immediate expression because the individual has learned to fear their expression through guilt or social value which has been interiorized. The retarded child who has been made to feel guilty because his behavior does not meet familial or cultural standards is less likely to be able to express his drives directly or in some appropriately adaptive manner than

* See Chapter Seven for a full discussion of this concept.

a child who has not experienced such psychological rejection. The retarded child, especially if he has some general lag in biological development, is also less likely to be able to express his drives appropriately in relation to the realistic difficulties which the external reality may involve. This may occur not only because his sensorimotor development is inadequate to the task at hand, but also because he has not acquired the cognitive or intellectual means of interpreting accurately or responding adequately to the complexities of the external reality.

When a child is in conflict, he attempts to produce some compromise solution through the use of various psychological defenses. Both the conflict and the use of defenses consume psychic energy. The greater the intensity of the conflict, the less energy is available for other purposes.

As we have said, in early infancy drives tend to be expressed quite freely. When the ego and superego begin to form, the expression of the drive is changed in accord with their "demands"—it is either blocked or altered in some manner. The reason for both this blocking and alteration of behavior is the *anxiety* that is developed because of the presence of the conflict. Anxiety is, then, the signal of the conflict within the child. The drive can then only be expressed in a modified form. This is the basic function of psychological defenses: to change, in some manner, the way in which a drive is gratified.

The various ways in which drives are expressed, blocked, or modified are graphically represented in Figure 8.

Let us assume, for example, that the drive seeking expression is one of hostility on the part of the child toward the mother. In condition A, neither ego nor superego structures have been established, and hence there is no internal barrier to the free expression of the hostility. It is permitted direct gratification. (For example, the child may bite his mother.) In condition B, ego and superego structures have been established, and so the direct expression of hostility is blocked. (The child might think, in effect: "Mother is bigger than I am, and will punish me if I am hostile toward her"; or, "Mother will not love me if I am hostile.") Since the drive is not permitted direct expression, the child experiences anxiety. In such an instance, even the hostile thought itself may be blocked, and the child may only be aware of the fact that he is anxious. In condition C, the drive is again blocked, but only temporarily. Anxiety is experienced and a psychological defense comes into automatic operation. The drive is then permitted expression in an altered form, and some or all of the anxiety is discharged. An example of behavior like condition C is the expression of hostility toward a substitute person or object in place of the original object of the hostility. A child might throw a doll on the floor instead of biting or injuring the mother. In this way, through the utilization of a defense, the child resolves his conflict and maintains a minimal tension level—that is, he does not become too anxious.

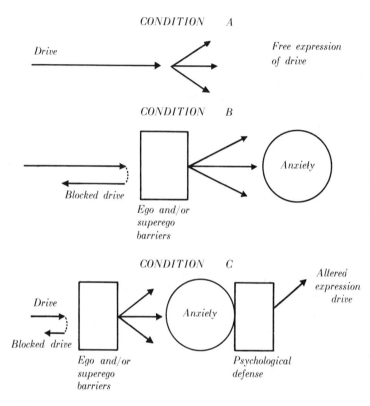

FIGURE 8. Expression of Drives and Operation of Psychological Defenses

Major defense mechanisms

We shall now discuss some of the more common defense mechanisms. Every child employs each of these defenses at some time. However, some children characteristically employ some of these defenses in preference to others. Some defenses, as we shall see, are more likely to produce more serious types of behavioral maladjustment if employed as the preferred pattern.

REPRESSION. Repression is one of the most prevalent and one of the earliest defenses utilized by the child. It represents a sort of "unconscious forgetting," or a becoming unaware of internal drives. Not only may a drive itself be repressed, but events and feelings associated with a drive may also be "shut out" of consciousness and so not remembered. We are all aware of instances in which we were not able to recall a well-known fact or name. These are instances of repression in our own lives. Repression probably occurs as soon as there is even an immature differentiation of the ego from the id.

DENIAL. Denial is another very primitive way of dealing with unpleasant or psychologically painful realities—by denying their very existence. If a situation or object did not exist, then it could not possibly be a threat to the child. If we observe a child closely, we may see the mechanism of denial in operation. He may simply assert that a given situation or present objective does not exist. At a more primitive level, he may close his eyes and not "see" the object or situation that is painful to him. When the ego is poorly developed or when the young child is unable to escape physically from a painful object or situation in the external world, he may use denial or a means of avoiding psychological pain. Repression and denial are closely allied defenses.

ISOLATION. Isolation is another very primitive and infantile defense. It involves the process of separating the emotional components of a drive from their ideational representations in conscious thought. Thoughts may then be experienced because their emotional aspects are stripped away. A child may, for example, experience the thought "I am going to kill you," without any psychological discomfort because the emotional aspects of the wish have been blocked off. The impulse is then no longer threatening to him.

UNDOING. In the mechanism of undoing, the child does something that is *symbolically opposite* of what would be done if the drive were to be directly expressed. Because of its symbolic nature, the act of undoing may appear to be the execution of an act like the drive itself, but its meaning in the unconscious is, nevertheless, the opposite. To ward off the impulse, which is felt as painful, the child tries to "reverse the field," to undo the act that permits expression of the impulse. For example, as an extreme instance, a boy who had an impulse to raise the skirts of girls and examine their genital organs would usually go to bed and sleep, thus *undoing* by this means his impulse to observe sexual objects. If this defense is utilized by the child, he finds it necessary to repeat the undoing act constantly in order to reduce the anxiety that he would otherwise develop.

INTROJECTION. This defense mechanism has its origin in infancy. Its function at this time is the avoidance of undue tension provoked by external prohibitions or frustrations. When the infant's drives are prevented direct expression, the threat of the opposing person (or situation) appears to be very great indeed. Since he depends upon this person (usually his mother) not only for affection but for his very existence, there is an intense conflict between the need to express his drives, on the one hand, and his fear of disapproval by his mother, on the other hand. To solve this dilemma he resorts to introjection of his mother's wishes—that is, he acts as if he, and not his mother, disapproves of the expression of the drive. By this process of internalizing his mother's wishes, he avoids some of the anxiety since it now appears to him as if *he* wants to do, or not to do, what the mother forbids. By means of this mechanism, the mother's prohibitions are introjected or "taken in."

The process of introjection has been preceded by the infant's experience of "taking in" other, more literal, aspects of his environment. For example, in the very act of being nourished, the infant has learned to "take in" food. This is the prototype of the later mechanism of introjection. The infant gradually learns to "take in" not only food but also the prohibitions of his mother—and later of other important adults. He learns to behave as they expect him to do. Although much of this introjection is a process of internalizing prohibitions, it also consists of taking in some of the positive characteristics of the important adults in his life. Through introjection the infant identifies with the important people around him—he feels as they do and behaves as they do, to a certain extent.

REACTION FORMATION. Reaction formation is a defense that produces behavior exactly opposite to that demanded by the unacceptable drive. It always involves repression of the drive seeking expression. For example, an individual with strong hostile drives behaves in a very passive and docile manner by developing a reaction formation against his hostility; or a child with "dirty" impulses (that is, impulses that appear to him to be "dirty"), such as sexual impulses or an impulse to play with his feces, may respond, instead, by being excessively clean, often going to extreme lengths to achieve such a condition.

PROJECTION. In the defense mechanism of projection, the child attributes his own unacceptable traits, impulses, and ideas to another person or to other people. It is one of the early defenses of the child, and may be thought of as opposite to the defense of introjection. In introjection, as we may recall, the child takes into himself certain traits; in projection the child externalizes his unacceptable traits. Such a defense is "normal" only during the period when the ego structure is weak and poorly formed or during periods of extreme stress. When the ego develops to the point where reality is perceived accurately, the use of projection as a defense is usually considered abnormal or psychopathological. As an example of this mechanism, we can consider the impulse of hostility again. The child may deal with this unacceptable impulse by projecting it upon another person and feeling that this person, rather than he, is hostile. He then reacts to this attributed hostility of the other person.

REGRESSION. In all the defenses previously listed, the ego actively participates in the particular defense that is utilized. However, in the defense of regression the ego experiences the phenomenon passively. In regression, the child resumes a previous mode of behavior when conflicts or frustrating situations cannot be resolved by the ego. For example, the child may return to thumb-sucking or enuresis (bedwetting) when conflicts occur. (This often happens to young children when another child is born into a family.) Regression is more likely to occur when the child has previously been *fixated* (or traumatized) and so has overlearned the modes of behavior prevalent at that time and has not been able to mature adequately to higher modes of behavior.

SUBLIMATION. Of all the defense mechanisms, sublimation is the most mature. (In fact, some workers do not classify this behavior as a defense.) In sublimation, in contrast to the other defenses, the drive is fully discharged, but its goal is so changed that it is discharged in a socially acceptable manner. Sublimation therefore makes a change in the *object* of the drive. It is used only when there is no great amount of repression. The ego must be sufficiently well developed to make and accept the change in the object of the drive. For example, as adults, we often sublimate sexual drives through our vocational activities, reading of poetry, dancing, and the like.

To illustrate some of the differences among the various defenses discussed, some of the behavioral reactions to hostility are summarized in Table 7. The behavioral reactions listed are, of course, not the only ones that are possible, but are merely representative types of behavior that *may* be shown by the child in each type of defense.

TABLE 7. Various Defensive Reactions to Hostile Drives

Defense	*Behavioral Reactions*
Repression	Total unawareness of hostile feelings.
Isolation	Expression of "I'd like to kill him" without any emotional reaction.
Undoing	Giving money to a charity.
Introjection	Behaving like the person toward whom the hostilities are directed.
Reaction formation	Showing "love" toward the person toward whom the hostilities are directed.
Projection	Seeing the hostilities as directed toward himself by another person.
Regression	Bed-wetting or thumb-sucking.
Sublimation	Shooting a cap pistol or bow and arrow at a target.
Denial	"I don't feel angry. He doesn't do anything to make me angry. Everything is fine."

Defense mechanisms in mental retardation

We have discussed the major characteristics of defense mechanisms in general, and have pointed out their major attributes. All these considerations are applicable to the defensive reactions developed by the mentally retarded child. However, due to his more severe problems and lesser capacities to tolerate stress, his anxieties are more readily aroused, and he has more need to engage in defensive reactions. He utilizes the *same* defensive mechanisms as do all other children, but there are some points of difference that need to be considered.

In the first place, the retarded child cannot as readily utilize those defenses that depend upon a more mature level of ego development. In general, he tends to use more primitive defenses more readily. Further, not only does the ego fail to reach as high a degree of maturation as that of the more normal child, but it also matures at a slower rate. The extremely primitive defenses of the personality thus persist, and continue to be utilized over a much longer period of time than they are by the more average child. We tend to expect certain forms of behavior from an infant, but are more intolerant of the same behavior when it is shown by an older child. We are not overly concerned by thumb-sucking in a one-year-old child, for example, but are highly concerned when this form of behavior is shown by a ten-year-old youngster. This intolerance and disapproval of his behavior by the adult increases the anxiety level of the mentally retarded child, and this leads to further maladaptive behavior on the part of the child.

Another major point of difference is in the rigidity or persistence of the defensive mechanisms employed by the retarded child. The more average child, provided he does not suffer from an emotional problem, has a relatively fluid defense network. These are employed in accordance with the requirements of the particular situations in which he finds himself. He "switches" from one to another with no great difficulty. The retarded child, however, does not vary his defense as the situation dictates.

This type of child shows a preference for such defenses as denial, introjection, regression, undoing, and repression. To a lesser degree he utilizes such defenses as projection, reaction formation, and isolation. Sublimation is very difficult for him to achieve.

There have been relatively few studies of the defense mechanisms of the mentally retarded child. Stephens, who has studied the defensive reactions of mentally retarded individuals, feels that the primary defense utilized by them is *denial*.[34] He states such persons are unable to accept the reality of their retardation. (But this may be due to the fact that they are not given adequate help to do so.) The concept of his retardation tends to be forced upon the retarded child by society, through the experiences of his early childhood which in effect were "socially alienating" and which served to lower his own self-esteem. In general he perceives himself as odd and queer, and becomes fearful of his own "defectiveness." This is a function of the way in which he is perceived by other persons. There is a tendency upon his part to incorporate the feelings of other persons toward mental retardation, and so he often ends up with a "fear-ridden" image of himself. Stephens points out that such an individual uses the defense of *identification*. (We would prefer to label this *process* "introjection," and call the end-product or resultant of this process "identification.") Stephens points out that the retarded child has strong feelings of inadequacy from which he tries to escape. In order to deal with these feelings of inadequacy, he identifies with and clings closely to other people. He unconsciously selects someone with whom he has contact. This process eventually precipitates him into difficulties, since he identifies (or attempts to incorporate) ego ideals that are far beyond his level of attainment.

We may cite the case of Johnny, discussed in Chapter One, to illus-

---

[34] Stephens, E., "Defensive reactions of mentally retarded adults," *Soc. Casewk.*, 1953, *34*, 119–124.

trate the use of psychological defenses in mental retardation. Johnny used several defenses in attempting to cope with his emotional problems. The most striking of these was regression: Johnny again began to creep and crawl and later to soil and wet himself after the birth of his siblings. There were also indications of Johnny's attempts to deny threatening situations. Johnny would put his head on the desk and withdraw completely from the too-difficult academic work. Such behavior is also suggestive of attempts at isolation and repression. Johnny also appeared to have introjected attributes of his third-grade teacher, with whom he had good interpersonal relationships.

Perhaps our greatest problems in dealing with the defense mechanisms of the mentally retarded child lie in the area of attempting to reduce the *necessity* for the child constantly to employ psychological defenses to such a great extent. This requires an adequate total program for the child himself, an educational program for the public at large, and treatment or guidance for the parents. We shall elaborate on this problem in Chapters Ten and Eleven.

A problem that requires considerable additional research is that of the effect of defensive behavior upon cognitive and intellectual performance. We have maintained that severe and continued anxiety leads to the development and persistent use of undesirable defensive behavior. What is the effect of this behavior on intellectual development? Clinical, as well as research evidence currently available, suggests that there can be considerable distortion of intellectual development under such circumstances, and that withdrawal from intellectual pursuits may be a primary consequence in some cases.

A recent study lends some additional support to this thesis. Silverstein and Mohan[35] evaluated the intellectual behavior of 50 retarded patients in an institution by means of two types of intelligence tasks: the *Object Sorting Test,* and the Similarities subtest of the *Wechsler Intelligence Scale for Children.* (See Chapter Nine for a discussion of such tests.) These were patients who were about 36 years of age, on the average, and whose average length of institutionalization was about 15 years. Their intellectual behavior was analyzed in terms of two dimensions of conceptual behavior: *public-private* (which refers to the relative degree with which the concept employed has communal agreement); and *open-closed* (which refers to the relative degree multiplicity of attributes with which a concept can be defined). These dimensions

[35] Silverstein, A. B., and Mohan, P. J., "Conceptual area analysis of the test performance of mentally retarded adults," *J. abnorm. soc. Psychol.,* 1963, *66,* 255–260.

may be thought of as defining the degree of *concreteness* (or specificity) and *abstractness* (or generality) of thinking. The study showed that the thinking of these retarded individuals was both *private* and *closed*, whereas other studies have shown that the thinking of normal individuals may be characterized as both *public* and *open*.

Unfortunately, all types of retarded individuals were included in the sample of retarded persons. This makes the meaning of the results less clear. Nevertheless, the findings suggest that possibly the retarded individual, at least the one who has experienced lengthy institutionalization, has become relatively more withdrawn and more concrete-minded as a defensive maneuver of the personality. One wonders how these individuals might have developed intellectually had they had different kinds of learning and adjustment experiences!

Coping behavior

Coping behavior may be understood as behavior which enables the individual to master his external world. As the child encounters external obstacles to the satisfaction of his inner needs he is at first frustrated, and then, if successful, he learns to deal with his needs by mastering or appropriately circumventing these obstacles. When coping behavior is successful, internal drives are not blocked, but find relatively direct expression in some appropriate and realistic manner. In the process of learning such behaviors, the child not only builds up a complex array of personality attributes which give him flexibility and adaptibility, but he also gains importantly in *self-regard*. Coping behavior may be employed in combination with defensive behavior, but the healthy personality is relatively rich in coping methods and uses defense mechanisms relatively sparsely.

In a fascinating and detailed account of the development of coping behavior in a group of children, Lois Murphy found that such behaviors were related to some types of early learning experiences.[36] For example, gratification of oral needs in infancy was correlated with accuracy of perception, sense of "self-worth," and ability to control the impact of the environment. On the other hand, unfavorable experiences in infancy were correlated with poor coping behaviors, including criticalness of people, a tendency to become fatigued, and decreased perceptual clarity.

We do not have evidence of the effect of early experiences upon individuals who are born with retarded biological capacities or who

[36] Murphy, L. B., *et al., The Widening World of Childhood.* New York: Basic Books, Inc., 1962.

function retardedly during early phases of their development. We do not know precisely how retarded individuals differ in coping behavior from normal and superior individuals. And we certainly know far too little about the possible inter-relationships of early experiences and the development of coping behaviors in retarded individuals of different kinds. The facts, however, that many retarded individuals experience more than the usual share of reality frustrations, and that the majority of them experience moderate or severe cultural deprivation in early childhood, suggest that retarded individuals are less likely than normals to develop good coping behaviors. In turn, this would lead to more need for defensive behavior, and to less adequate development of inner potentialities.

ANXIETY AND LEARNING

We have noted previously that moderate degrees of anxiety may facilitate simple learning tasks but that severe degrees of anxiety are likely to have disabling effects upon learning, especially upon complex learning activities. In Chapter Eight, we deal extensively with the general adjustment effects of intense and persistent anxiety. In this section, we wish to emphasize the specific effects of anxiety upon learning, and especially upon school achievement.

Studies, such as that by Wiener *et al.*,[37] have shown that there is a negative correlation between level of manifest anxiety and educational achievement as measured by a standardized achievement test. Other studies, such as that by Jordan and De Charms,[38] have suggested that retarded children have proportionately less motivation to achieve (*i.e.,* a lowered aspiration level) than children of average intelligence. These and related studies suggest that one of the important variables producing proportionately less effective learning in retarded individuals, lower even than their mental age level would indicate, is the presence of persistent anxiety. We are not suggesting that other variables may not contribute an even greater amount to their decreased ability to learn, or that high anxiety is necessarily the only or fundamental cause of reduced learning capacity. The problem of impaired learning ability is far more complex than that.

Other studies suggest that retarded individuals have reduced ability

---

[37] Wiener, G., Crawford, E. E., and Snyder, R. T., "Some correlates of anxiety in mildly retarded patients," *Amer. J. ment. Defic.*, 1960, *64*, 735–739.

[38] Jordan, T., and De Charms, R., "The achievement motive in normal and retarded children," *Amer. J. ment. Defic.*, 1960, *65*, 42–45.

to attend and to discriminate—a loss that is disproportionate to mental level.[39] It has also been demonstrated that the performance of both organic and familial cases of retardation is characterized by disproportionately high rigidity.[40] These findings indicate the prior presence of persistently high anxiety levels, which, in turn, may have contributed to the phenomena in question. That some of these factors which adversely affect learning capacity and give the behavioral effect of retardation (sometimes a pseudo-effect) are reversible has also been demonstrated.[41] Training which emphasizes improved attention, improved discrimination, and offers reinforcement for correct performance (especially when carefully graded to the abilities of the subjects) significantly increases learning performance.[42]

Thus, we are able to support the general hypothesis that, for a considerable portion of at least non-organic cases of retardation, high anxiety experienced over a long period of time adversely affects learning performance, learning potential, and other skills such as ability to attend and to perceive accurately. We are also able to support the hypothesis that for cases such as these, techniques and environments designed to reduce anxiety, and to provide compensatory retraining experiences and reinforcement of appropriate responses, may considerably improve both the short-term and long-term learning abilities of retardates. As we shall see in later chapters, schools and institutions which are responsible for the training of retarded individuals have the tasks of carefully evaluating the personality difficulties of such individuals, determining the nature and causative factors in the anxiety reactions when they are present, and of providing specific remedial educational programs and/or therapeutic programs to correct the difficulties. We are appreciative of the complexities of the tasks and of the additional knowledge we need to gain in order to maximize such efforts. Even though, for many retarded individuals, progress and improvement are impossible, sometimes even slight improvement may increase our motivation, and sustain us even when our efforts do not produce appreciable gains.

[39] Zeaman, D., and House, B. J., "An attention theory of retardate discrimination learning," *Progr. Rep. No. 3, Nat. Inst. Ment. Hlth.*, Bethesda, Md., Nov. 1962.

[40] Shepps, R., and Zigler, E., "Social deprivation and rigidity in the performance of organic and familial retardates," *Amer. J. ment. Defic.*, 1962, *67*, 262–268.

[41] Kass, N., and Stevenson, H. W., "The effect of pretraining and reinforcement on learning by normals and retarded children," *Amer. J. ment. Defic.*, 1961, *66*, 76–80.

[42] Clarke, A. D. B., and Cookson, M., "Perceptual-motor transfer in imbeciles: A second series of experiments," *Brit. J. Psychol.*, 1962, *53*, 321–330.

ch. 7

ORGANIZATION OF
THE PERSONALITY

I N THE PREVIOUS CHAPTERS WE DISCUSSED SOME MAJOR ASPECTS OF personality development and some of the characteristic dynamic patterns of adjustment. Now we shall turn our attention to the complicated problem of how to describe this total personality. It is complicated not only by virtue of the difficulties inherent in describing the "organization" of any individual, but also because the "organization" never remains entirely stable or fixed. The term *organization* (or *structure*, as it is often called) refers to the *relatively* consistent relationships among the "parts" of the personality. We shall also be faced with the dilemma that, in order to describe the organization of the whole personality, we shall have to describe its parts, and these parts acquire new meanings and relevances in terms of their interrelationships with each other, as well as in terms of the constant adaptations which the individual has to make.

Thus, we shall begin our discussion with the concept of *homeostasis* (or the "See-Saw," as we call it) to emphasize the dynamic character of the organization of the personality. After this we shall consider the nature of conscious and unconscious processes. Then we shall discuss the nature of "traits" as major components of the personality. And, finally, we shall discuss the Freudian conception of personality organization, the findings of factorial studies of personality structure, and some other pertinent conceptions.

161

THE "SEE-SAW"

Physiologists have been concerned with the various regulatory mechanisms of the body for a considerable period of time. As early as 1859 Claude Bernard published his important research in this area.[1] He described the internal environment of living cells, and pointed out that the body made continual and automatic efforts to remain in a constant condition despite the constantly changing external and internal environmental forces. It became evident that the physiological processes of the human being tended to compensate for any changes in the steady states of the organism caused by the effect of changes in external or internal forces. This point of view led Cannon to the formulation of the principle of *homeostasis*.[2] He described the self-regulating physiologic processes of individual tissues, organs, and organ systems. It was clearly evident to him that the organism tended to maintain its natural organic states. Homeostasis, in Cannon's formulation, referred to compensatory reactions undertaken by the organism after the disturbing stimulus situations came about. This tendency is innate in the organism, and is a function of the autonomic nervous system. Behavior of the person, according to Cannon, is directed either toward getting rid of disturbing forces or toward prolonging or reviving what the person perceives as agreeable stimulation. Homeostasis was seen as referring to the first of these two possible behavioral reactions—toward getting rid of unwanted pressures.

More recent work by Richter[3] has substantiated the earlier hypotheses of Cannon. Of most importance is Richter's finding that even when the simple physiologic regulators of the body are experimentally removed the organism will attempt to maintain homeostasis by changes in the behavior of the *total* organism. The homeostatic tendency is thus a function of the entire organism, and not just of one "part." One of his observations will serve to illustrate this point. An animal living in a region deficient in salt will (1) migrate to a salt lick, or (2) show an increase of activity in the adrenal cortex with a resultant decrease of salt loss in the urine. An animal whose fodder contains too much salt will (1) decrease its total food content, or (2) increase its excretion of salt by

---

[1] Bernard, C., *Leçons sur les Propriétés Physiologiques et les Altérations Pathologiques des Liquides de l'organisme* (2 vols.). Paris: Baillière, 1859.

[2] Cannon, W. B., *The Wisdom of the Body*. New York: W. W. Norton & Company, Inc., 1932.

[3] Richter, D. C., "Biology of drives," *Psychosom. Med. Ann. Rev. Physiol.*, 1942, *4*, 451; "Total self-regulatory functions in animals and human beings," *Harvey Lectures*, 1943, *38*, 63.

drinking large amounts of water, or (3) show a decrease of activity in the adrenal cortex with a resulting increase of salt loss in the urine.

The tendency of the organism to strive continually to preserve its "status quo" has thus been clearly demonstrated insofar as physiological qualities are concerned. It is not surprising, therefore, that we find applications of the homeostatic principle to psychological functions. As Fenichel points out:[4]

Mental functions should be approached from the same angle as the functions of the nervous system in general. They are manifestations of the same basic function of the living organism—irritability. . . . Stimuli from the outside world or from the body initiate a state of tension that seeks for motor or secretory discharge, bringing about relaxation.

The human being learns to tolerate a particular level of psychic tension or irritability. This tension tends to remain at a fairly constant level, and as long as this particular level is maintained, the individual is in a comparatively pleasurable state. However, if for some reason, either from an internal or external stimulus, the tension level is increased, then the individual strives to regain the former level. Activities of the person are therefore constantly directed toward an attempt at the removal of forces that increase tension states within himself. The aim, it is important to note, is *not* to eliminate *all* tension but to *preserve* the level of tension that is characteristic for the particular person.

This homeostatic process is illustrated in Figure 9. This represents schematically the hypothetical anxiety-tolerance (tension-tolerance) level of an individual.

In A, the anxiety-producing forces are dealt with by the defensive reactions of the individual, and the child is quite comfortable in regard to the anxieties he experiences. There are anxieties, but they are not so great that he feels uncomfortable.

In B, the anxiety-provoking factors have been augmented by an additional factor—for example, by a situation in which the child feels rejected. The anxiety level then increases beyond the point of comfort and tolerance. Attempts are then made by the child to defend himself against the pain of this increased anxiety.

In C the defensive reaction (for example, an increase in the hostile and aggressive behavior) has been strengthened so that the anxiety level

[4] Fenichel, O., *The Psychoanalytic Theory of Neurosis*. New York: W. W. Norton & Company, Inc., 1945, p. 11.

is again reduced to one that is comfortable to the child and can be more easily tolerated.

As used in psychology, the homeostatic hypothesis has taken on a much broader meaning than that originally implied in the physiological applications of the concept. It is concerned with the *entire* behavioral reactions of the individual. It applies to both the physiological and the psychological aspects.

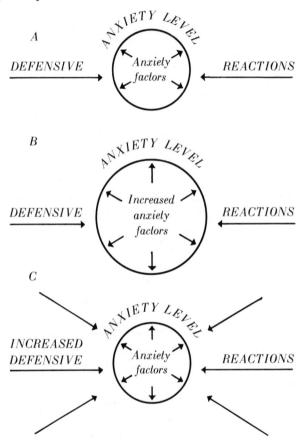

FIGURE 9. THE HOMEOSTATIC PROCESS

There is another important aspect of homeostasis that we should consider. The individual never achieves a complete condition of rest; rather, there is a continuous instability to which the person reacts by striving to return to his "original" condition. He reaches an "almost achieved" state, when there is a further imbalance. The homeostatic reaction, therefore, should be conceived as one of continuously *striving* for maintenance of the most comfortable psychic tension level within the individual. A perfectly stationary condition cannot be achieved during the life of any organism, either from physiological or psychological standpoints.

Maze has emphasized some important points concerning the concept of homeostasis.[5] He stresses the complexity of the process, and deplores the fact that too often we refer to only its steadiness or its restorative aspects. He feels that we do not remember that homeostasis is not the *cause* of balance in various physiological or psychological functions, but is the *effect* of various specific processes.

The mentally retarded child, like all other persons, also strives to maintain his "status quo." He strives to rid himself of unpleasant forces and pressures, and, perhaps more than the normal child, is particularly resistive to changes in his status. This is partly because he perceives change as more threatening—and the unknown as more dangerous. He clings tenaciously to previously learned patterns of behavior and reactions; they have controlled his anxieties in the past and so are comforting and reassuring. This leads to a tendency toward rigidity and persistence of established behavioral reactions. Because of his generally lowered capacities to deal with change and make the necessary adaptations, new situations are approached very cautiously and adapted to only with great difficulty.

LEVELS OF MENTAL LIFE

In order to obtain a better understanding of the over-all psychological characteristics of an individual, normal or retarded, it is essential to have some knowledge of his personality organization. In this way we are better able to characterize him, and, therefore, to predict how he will behave.

We are prone to describe or evaluate a person in terms of his consciously motivated behavior. As we shall see, this aspect of behavior is most visible to others and therefore is likely to impress us most. But the conscious mental life of an individual is only one aspect of his mental functioning. The total mental life of the person comprises much more than his conscious experiences. Most of us are aware of this fact, and we

[5] Maze, S. R., "On some corruptions of the doctrine of homeostasis," *Psychol. Rev.*, 1953, *60*, 405–412.

find that the term "unconscious" (or "subconscious") appears frequently in our daily vocabulary. It has been demonstrated that mental processes take place at different levels within the personality. Freud described three major levels of mental phenomena: (1) the conscious, (2) the preconscious, and (3) the unconscious. The conscious level consists of that mental activity of which we are aware. The preconscious level refers to mental experience that can become known to us when we shift our attention to it. It is the background of conscious mental activity. Thus, if I wish, with a little or great effort, I can recall the author of *Dangerous Corner* —it was in my preconscious thought. Material is at an unconscious level when it cannot be recalled by the individual except by prolonged effort or special techniques, such as psychotherapy. Ordinarily the individual has no conscious awareness of its existence.

The conscious level

We have stated that the conscious level of the personality is that part of mental life of which the individual is aware. It usually offers no serious threat to the person and does not produce severely painful psychological reactions. The content of the conscious mind is those thoughts that form rapidly from moment to moment and from situation to situation within the individual. The conscious aspects of mental life are those that the person has developed to meet the demands of the external world and its realities. However, the total content of our conscious life is not confined to our sensory perceptions of the situations and relationships to the outer world. In addition, it is made up to a large extent of *derivatives* of the unconscious level which force themselves into consciousness in a disguised and often in a symbolic manner.

The way in which we perceive reality is determined in part by unconscious factors. According to this concept, an individual tends to avoid perceiving or distorts in some way those situations that are threatening or unpleasant to him. Research has indicated that an individual may either avoid a threatening situation or be *overly vigilant*. In the latter case he tends to be unduly sensitive to potentially threatening situations.

The conscious level of the personality should be considered as *only one* important aspect of mental life. It is *not* the aspect that is of the greatest importance in the determination of human behavior, however.

We may explore the contents of consciousness through the process of introspection, that process in which we turn our thoughts inward and reflect upon inner events. Not only may the contents of the conscious thus be scrutinized readily, but they also may be easily verbalized, *i.e.*, we can tell them to others.

The preconscious level

There are some aspects of mental life of which we are consciously aware only at certain times. There is a fluctuation in their availability to consciousness. The part of mental experience that can become conscious only through special effort is called the "preconscious." It has more of the characteristics of the conscious than of the unconscious. In fact, the preconscious does not differ markedly from the conscious except that it is not part of our day-to-day awareness.

The unconscious level

The third level of mental life, the unconscious, is of crucial importance.

The unconscious has, of course, no actual physical existence, and cannot be located in either an anatomical or a physiological sense. It is a theoretical construct—a concept. Through the utilization of the concept of the unconscious we are able to integrate and better explain the large masses of apparently unrelated data we may gather about an individual. We cannot "see" the unconscious. It must be *inferred* from the observed behavior of the person. The conscious and preconscious may both be verbalized through introspection by the person himself, but unconscious material is *inferred* by another person from the actions and verbalizations of the individual.

Phenomena of the unconscious level may be readily demonstrated. Freud described some of these methods of demonstrating the operation of unconscious processes.[6] The following are some of the major types of relevant evidence. When a person is *hypnotized,* he may be given the specific suggestion to perform a certain act after he has awakened. He does so without awareness of the fact that he had previously been given instructions to do it. *Dreams* are representatives at a conscious level of unconscious material that is too threatening to be directly accepted by the individual at the conscious level. *Slips of the tongue* are usually manifestations of internal (unconscious) conflicts. Sudden appearance of *ideas* or solutions to problems are indications of unconscious activities. During *psychotherapy* long buried (repressed) conflicts and traumatic episodes emerge.

The unconscious has many unique qualities. Its major characteristics are: (1) there is no awareness of *time* sequence; (2) the unconscious has no understanding of deprivation, and there is complete absence of *nega-*

---

[6] Summarized in Healy, W., Bronner, A. F., and Bowers, A. M., *The Structure and Meaning of Psychoanalysis.* New York: Alfred A. Knopf, Inc., 1930, p. 22.

tion; (3) the unconscious ignores completely all social, moral, and ethical considerations; it is *amoral;* (4) the unconscious may be completely *irrational,* and ideas that are mutually exclusive exist without contradiction; (5) both the manner in which the unconscious functions and its contents are *infantile.*

At this point we may ask what makes up the content of the unconscious level of mental life. Primarily, its content consists of those thoughts, wishes, and needs of the infant and very young child that were never consciously experienced. Many of these remain at an unconscious level and are never known. Secondly, the unconscious is composed of previous conscious experiences that were extremely painful to the child and caused him a great deal of psychological discomfort. In order to protect himself against the pain of these experiences they were "pushed back" to the unconscious level. The process whereby conscious material that is painful is thrust back to an unconscious level is termed "repression" (see Chapter Six).

Factors in the unconscious are not merely passively present but are constantly seeking discharge and are partially responsible for all forms of a child's mental and motor activities. Let us examine a simple illustration from everyday life in which the unconscious determinants are not at a very deep level. An individual comes home following a day's work. He is very irritable, and without any apparent reason becomes involved in an argument with his wife. He criticizes his dinner, the behavior of the children, and in general is quite hostile. If we reviewed his activities throughout the day we might find that he had been severely rebuked by his supervisor. He might have felt the criticism to be quite unwarranted and felt very hostile toward his boss. However, since one usually cannot express hostility directly toward one's boss, this man unconsciously expressed hostility toward his wife and children.

The behavior of young children toward their school teachers also furnishes us with a clear example of the presence of unconscious determinants of behavior. Children often behave toward their teachers in the way they feel inwardly toward their mothers.

Even though a "situation" is repressed it is usually the memory content of the repressed situation that is not consciously experienced. The emotions that were part of the previous situation are constantly striving for expression, and become attached to other situations that may be consciously known to the child. The emotion of the repressed material is thus experienced, but its source is not known to the person.

The mental life of an individual is thus much richer and more extensive than one would infer from investigation of its conscious elements.

It should be emphasized that a tremendous amount of activity is continually going on at an unconscious level and that unconscious reactions exert tremendous pressure for expression at all times. When unconscious drives are discharged they are expressed in distorted and symbolic ways, so that their origins remain hidden from the conscious awareness of the person.

All behavior of the child contains unconscious determinants to some extent. The number of such unconscious determinants varies within the same child from situation to situation and from time to time, as well as from one child to another. Probably the greater part of mental life and activities is at an unconscious level. We may think of the total personality structure as being somewhat similar in nature to an iceberg, with only a small part above the surface (conscious awareness). Most, like the greater part of the iceberg, lies beneath the surface and is hidden. The quantitative relationship between the conscious, preconscious, and unconscious levels is diagrammatically illustrated in Figure 10.

The unconscious plays a highly significant role in our everyday relationships with other people. The unconscious of one child may react upon the unconscious of another, with the children not being consciously aware of the fact that such subtle interactions are occurring. For example, we ourselves may have violent likes or dislikes upon our first encounter with another person. We may feel comfortable with some individuals and very uncomfortable and anxious with others, without knowing just why. These are indications of the influences of unconscious factors in our interpersonal relationships. The concept of the unconscious is one of the cornerstones of our modern system of psychopathology.

Mental processes operate at all three levels in the retarded child. However, due to his impaired functioning, such a child tends to react more to the pressures of unconscious motives than the average child. He

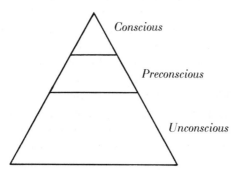

FIGURE 10. THE THREE LEVELS OF MENTAL LIFE

has great difficulty in holding back unconscious drives. His behavior tends, at times, to be largely determined by his unconscious needs. Often he will engage in a form of behavior that is unexplainable to the observer; that is, it apparently is not in accord with the situation in which the child finds himself. The retarded child is thus more prone to engage in impulsive or, at least, insufficiently consciously controlled behavior. However, if we spend enough time with the child and make a determined effort to try to understand his behavior, we can help him make a better adjustment.

Although the unconscious is not essentially different in the mentally retarded child and the non-retarded child, there are differences in the manner in which it is controlled. In the mentally retarded child, unconscious materials tend to emerge more readily in overt behavioral reactions, and they govern much more of his behavior. Much evidence for the conclusions we have offered is derived from data obtained in psychotherapy with retarded children; these data are discussed in Chapter Eleven.

TRAITS AND STRUCTURES

When an individual responds, he behaves in a particular manner to some particular situation. We might attempt to characterize him in terms of all of the particular responses he makes in his lifetime or over a considerable span of time, but of course this would be an almost impossible task, and we would still be left with the problem of *categorizing* the individual in terms of *clusters* of behavior.

One way of dealing with this difficulty is to try to extract some of the characteristic ways in which an individual responds over a number of situations. These relatively characteristic ways of behaving are commonly called *traits*. A trait, then, is a relatively persistent way of behaving across a number of different but related situations. It is a higher order of organization of personality than the specific behavior. But it should also be clear that traits do not exist in reality; rather, they are abstractions that are inferred from selected observations of behavior. For example, we may say, in describing a person, that he is *honest,* or that he is *persistent.* What we really mean, however, is that he has behaved in certain situations in which we or others have observed him so that we may characterize his behavior as that of honesty or persistence. The behavior of the person, and not the person, thus led us to believe that, since he was behaving honestly or persistently, *he* might, by inference, be characterized as honest or persistent.

Generally speaking, there are three major ways in which we may characterize a person by a certain trait. We may do so from *what* he does, *how* he does it (or the manner in which he performs the behavior), and *how well* he does it. In all of these instances, we infer the trait from samples of behavior which we, the observer, note. Of course, it is possible for a person to rate himself on various traits. But whether it is the result of self-ratings, ratings by others, or even a result of scores on a test, the trait is an inference derived from some sample of behavior.

Another problem concerns the number and nature of traits that might be utilized in describing the total personality. Some careful, rigorous workers in the field of personality believe that a very great number of such trait-names is needed. For example, Allport and Odbert found that nearly 18,000 terms used to describe people were insufficient to account for all of the subtleties of human personality.[7] The philosophy of their approach to personality description has been termed *idiographic,* meaning that each person represents a unique constellation of innumerable qualities. At the other extreme are psychologists who prefer to categorize people into *types,* or a few very general clusters. In between are those who believe that a relatively small number of traits may be used in describing adequately each person in the population. Although there are scientific grounds for preferring one system over another, the basic differences in the kinds and number of traits which can be employed is largely a matter of the philosophy one adopts towards personality evaluation rather than of scientific criteria, for one can make out a good scientific case for each of the three major approaches.

In relatively recent years, a number of workers, using the statistical method known as *factor analysis,* have attempted to characterize the personality structure in terms of *factors,* that is, statistically derived clusters of traits or scores which have a great deal in common. The factors which have been suggested, as we shall see in a later section of this chapter, are then organized into what is called the "personality structure." Thus, there is a hierarchical organization from specific responses, to traits, to trait-clusters or factors (sometimes called *primary traits*), to personality structure. The accompanying figure illustrates this scheme.

We shall discuss some of the proposed trait-clusters or factors in a later section, but at this point we wish to comment further on the values and limitations of such an approach to the description of personality organization.

[7] Allport, G. W., and Odbert, H. S., "Trait-names: a psychological study," *Psychol. Monogr.,* 1936, *47,* No. 211.

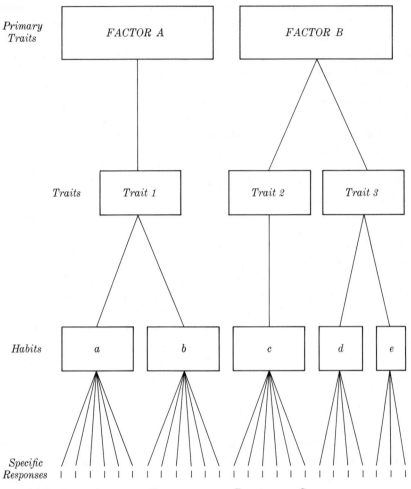

FIGURE 11. SCHEMATIC ILLUSTRATION OF PERSONALITY STRUCTURE

One of the great values of factor-analytically-derived descriptions of personality is that it enables us to assess the personality with an economy of a small number of trait-clusters. Another is that these factors can be objectively derived from test questionnaires or from self-ratings with statistical rigor, and that they can be subjected to further experimental study. Still another advantage to this method is that the generality of the derived factors can be studied in different populations, so that it is possible to tell whether the same or different factors can be used in describing divergent populations.

This last advantage is also a limitation, since recent research has failed to develop a list of factors which most workers will accept. There are many reasons for this, but one of them is that since the factors depend upon the measurement of traits, and since self-rated traits are of doubtful validity in some populations (and this is especially true of retardates), they can hardly be used to make inter-group comparisons. Moreover, ratings of subjects by observers as a basis for deriving factors also has very serious limitations. For example, in one study in which instructors were rated by their students in a variety of instructional situations, these ratings only correlated between the levels of .13 and .19 with ratings obtained in the same situations from other instructors, teacher peers, self-ratings by teachers, and ratings of performance behavior in test situations.[8]

Such low correlations suggest that very different things are being measured by the various sets of ratings and that rating scores are therefore of dubious value. When traits are derived from carefully constructed test questionnaires of personality, the problems of cultural bias, level of intelligence, deliberate falsification by the respondent, and sundry *halo* effects (effects produced by general bias of the respondent) all affect the validity of the findings.

Finally, it has been argued that the meaning of any trait is interdependent upon its place in the total constellation of traits of any given person. At the extreme, this difficulty would mean that the values (or weights) assigned to traits would be as variable as the individuals to be evaluated, and that there could, therefore, be no common consensus. Another way of putting this is to indicate that the dynamic meaning of a trait may vary markedly, depending upon the way it is utilized by an individual. Thus, fantasy can be used constructively by the healthy, creative person. But the same amount of fantasy in a very disturbed person could lead to withdrawal from reality and immersion in pathological or delusional thinking.

Some psychologists have attempted to develop a "structure" of the personality, not from statistically derived trait-clusters, but from clinical observations of maladjusted people in terms of some theoretical model of personality. The data that were employed in reaching such formulations were based upon direct observation of such people over extended periods of time, coupled with inferences by the observers concerning the levels of life which such observations tapped. Such types of derived personality

[8] Borg, W. R., and Hamilton, E. R., "Comparison between a performance test and criteria of instructor effectiveness," *Psychol. Rep.,* 1956, *2,* 111–116.

structures also are limited by the bias of the observer and by the relatively non-rigorous methods which clinical assessment involves. On the other hand, they provide a dynamically derived structure as it is inferred from the total-person-in-operation, and they include all the pertinent levels of personality as they appear to influence behavior. Moreover, elements of the proposed personality structure can be tested in subsequent experimental studies as well as in developmental studies.

We shall now turn our attention to the most widely influential theory of personality structure derived in this manner—that conceived by Sigmund Freud.

FREUD'S CONCEPTION OF PERSONALITY STRUCTURE

Freud suggested that three distinct aspects of the personality could be hypothesized: (1) the *id,* (2) the *ego,* and (3) the *superego.* Each of these "parts" functions in *complete interdependence* with each other, yet each has definite and specific characteristics of its own. This basic conceptualization of Freud's enables us to explain many aspects of the operation of human behavior.

Since knowledge of the structure of the personality is essential to an understanding of both normal and mentally retarded children, we shall consider in detail the characteristics of the id, ego, and superego. We shall then discuss the relationships among them. We shall emphasize that their proper development is essential to the achievement of adequate capacities for functioning as a healthy adult. Regardless of the degree of intellectual potential with which a person has been endowed, it cannot be utilized adequately unless there has been an appropriate maturation in these aspects of the personality.

The id

"Id" is a Latin term, which may be roughly translated into English as "it." The id* is the basic and central core of the personality of the individual. It is the source from which all the psychic energy of the child is derived. It is the basis of all the inborn instinctual forces. For example, all of our sexual drives stem from the id. The instinctual forces of the id constantly strive for expression and gratification.

Id forces, if unopposed, are always pleasurable, and result in gratification of unconscious wishes. Like the unconscious, the id is amoral, and

---

* Although we speak of "the id," and later of "the ego" and "the superego," we do not imply that they are things or entities. "The id" is simply an abbreviated way of saying "the organized system of unconscious drives."

has no sense of right or wrong. It has no concept of time. It is quite illogical, and is not susceptible to the impact of intellectual arguments or processes. However, even though the id shares the characteristics of the unconscious, the id and the unconscious are *not* synonymous. The id is only one part of the total unconscious processes of the individual. We may say that all of the id processes are unconscious, but that the unconscious is not all id.

The personality of the newborn child is motivated primarily by id forces. It has not developed, as yet, those attributes ("structure") which the maturational process will produce. It is from the id that all the other elements of the personality structure later evolve in accordance with maturational processes that are *common to all persons*. These processes will be discussed in terms of the gradual evolution of the ego and superego from the basic core of the id.

The ego

As we noted, the id may be regarded as the central core of the personality. It is the innermost layer. As the child's psychological maturation proceeds there gradually develops out of the basic id core a second type of structure. This new portion of the personality has the function of relating id forces to the outside world. However, the outer world often will not permit id wishes to be gratified. An important example of this is the prohibition by social forces (which, in turn, cause an individual to learn to inhibit) of many of an individual's basic urges, as in the inhibition or modification of sexual wishes. The individual has to learn to mediate the demands of the world and of the id. The structure that does the mediating is known as the *ego*. The ego, therefore, is essentially concerned with all of the relationships demanded of the child by the outer reality. For example, a child may have an extremely strong urge toward a particular activity (such as urinating in the bed). The ego would then evaluate the perceived reality situations, and in terms of its evaluation would mediate between the demands of the id and the demands of the reality situation.

According to psychoanalytic theory, the functions of the ego may be divided into two major cateories:[9] (1) the ego attempts to permit the gratification of id impulses at the best possible times; it decides whether or not such impulses may be gratified at any particular time; and (2) if for some reason the reality situation is such that the basic impulse can-

[9] For a full discussion of this process see Freud, S., *The Ego and the Id*. London: Hogarth, 1927.

not be gratified, then the ego in some way induces the id to modify or inhibit, for the time being, the impulses that are striving for expression. The ego learns (that is, this "part" of the child learns) that it can sometimes modify conditions in the outer world of reality, so as to bring about changes that are favorable enough to permit gratification of the various id impulses striving for discharge.

Even though the ego is developed out of the id, it is never completely separated from the basic id structure. Actually, we may think of the ego as attempting to substitute for the immediate pleasure demands of the id the very real and basic demands of the external world. We may regard the ego as being the representative of the outer world of reality within the person.

Since an appreciation of reality depends upon the various sensory mechanisms (such as vision, audition, and the like), the development of the ego is closely related to their development.

The ego structure of the very young child is rudimentary. It cannot adequately cope with id urges. We find the young child largely dominated by his basic instinctual desires, which therefore tend to be expressed in a rather uncontrolled manner. Emotional reactions are not subject to ego control in younger children (temper tantrums, for example, are common). As the maturational process continues, the ego structure becomes stronger and the perception of reality factors more appropriate. In the mentally retarded child, the slow and inadequate development of ego functions produces poor control over impulses, inaccurate evaluations of reality, and improperly integrated behavior.

A great proportion of the ego functions at the conscious level of the individual's mental life, but the ego never becomes completely separated from the id. Unlike the id, the ego is concerned with time sequences, and is also concerned with external realities. It is concerned to some extent with morality; it differentiates to some extent between "right" and "wrong."

Many pressures are placed upon the ego. It constantly needs to adjust to pressures from three major sources: (1) the basic id forces, (2) the pressures of the external world, and (3) the pressures of a third structure of the personality, the superego (see the next section).

Freud postulated that the ego differentiated from and developed out of the id structure under the influences of the external world. At birth, the newborn child has no ego structure. There are, of course, reactions on the part of the child to various stimuli arising from the outer world, but, with some exceptions, these are not specific, goal-directed responses. As we can readily see if we observe a newborn child, its reactions to stimuli are global in nature, that is, they are carried out as mass responses by the child as a whole, except for some specific types of reflex behavior.

Fenichel describes the archaic or primitive reactions of the infant exhaustively.[10] He points out that his perceptual processes are very hazy. Objects and persons are not sharply distinguished, and visual images tend to be large and inexact. The perceptions of the various sense organs tend to overlap, creating a confused total perception. The most primitive of the perceptual processes is dominant—that of kinesthetic (bodily movement) perceptions. The primitive perceptions of the infant are further modified by two additional factors. First, the child is physically small in relation to his outer world. This modifies, by contrast, what he perceives. Just imagine, for example, what our perceptions would be in a world where we would be surrounded by smoke-spouting giants, by 25-foot chairs, and by towering objects whose summits we could only dimly perceive! Secondly, the child tends to see the world either as a provider, satisfying his wants, or as a terrible threat that constantly seeks to annihilate him. He cannot distinguish between the "self" and "not self." He does not know what is "inside" and what is "outside" himself. Rather, he attempts to differentiate at first between states in which he is in greater tension and states in which his tension is much less.

The ego, then, starts to form and grow toward maturity when the needs of the child are not satisfied. The occurrence of deprivation, in certain areas, is automatic in the lives of all children, and will occur to some extent regardless of the promptness or extent of parental activities. No matter how quickly the need for nourishment is satisfied, there exists a period in which some time elapses between the experiencing of the need by the child and its actual gratification and resultant lessening of tension. Because of this time interval during which heightened tension is experienced, the child gradually becomes aware of the presence of an external source that satisfies his needs. He begins to be aware of external reality—he perceives that he has needs which he cannot gratify by himself. The ego evolves as the child meets partial deprivation or delay in gratification of basic needs. If one could in some automatic way immediately take care of all the needs of the newborn child, and satisfactions were immediately provided, the child would be exceedingly slow in developing an ego structure. Actually, the concept of reality that the child develops is concurrent with the development of the ego structure. To have a strong ego structure he must have a full awareness of outer reality, an awareness of the forces of the outer world as they affect the

---

[10] Fenichel, *op. cit.*

individual. It is only through a long, gradual maturational process that the child finally becomes aware of the fact that there are forces in the outer world that are beyond his control and that do not lie within himself.

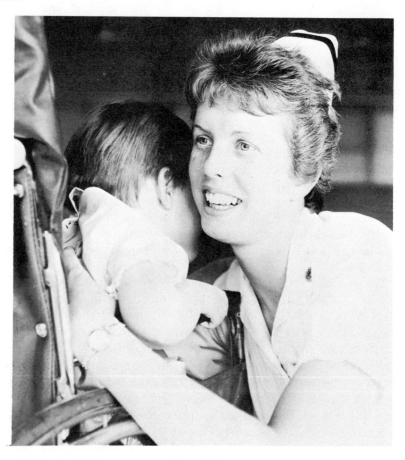

THERE IS NO SUBSTITUTE FOR LOVE (Courtesy of Plymouth State Home and Training School, Northville, Mich.)

At this point some of the implications of the above formulations should be mentioned. The child's first conception of reality is in terms of his mother (or mother substitute) and her behavior—the child and the mother are one as far as he is concerned, and not separate. It is only gradually that he begins to see that the mother is an object who is entirely separate from himself. Sullivan states that during the first year of life the child knows essentially only momentary states of "consciousness." He makes no distinctions in either time or place. Later he begins to perceive the mother.[11] Spitz investigated the first smiles of babies, and found that they were elicited only by human faces or masks of faces. [12] By the age of eight months children began to differentiate new from known faces.

Thus, the infantile ego is extremely weak, both in relationship to its control of the forces of the id and also in its relationship to the external world. The ego itself develops because the needs of the child are not immediately gratified. On the other hand, if the child is too severely deprived then the development of the ego is hindered. Hartman and collaborators feel the best situation is one in which the mother gives the child a great deal of indulgence and a small amount of deprivation.[13] Eventually the child, if he is to become a well adjusted adult, must learn to substitute future for immediate gratifications.

The process of giving up the belief that the universe rests within himself is a long and bitter one. The child hangs on to this belief tenaciously. He must finally face the fact that he is not omnipotent. Many are the devices that he creates to maintain the notion of omnipotence, only to have to give them up one by one as reality forces itself upon his awareness.

If we observe the behavior of young children we can readily find examples of these kinds of longings to control reality by maintaining infantile omnipotence. We can find many additional examples in our folklore and fairy tales (remember "Rumpelstiltskin?").

Many writers have stressed the fact that there must be gradual opportunity for the child to experience a delay in gratifications of his needs.[14] If, however, the frustrations he undergoes are too severe, then an incomplete and immature ego structure may result.[15]

[11] Sullivan, H. S., *Conceptions of Modern Psychiatry*. Washington: William Alanson White Psychiatric Foundation, 1947.

[12] Spitz, R., "The smiling response: A contribution to the ontogenesis of social relations," *Genet. Psychol. Monogr.*, 1946, *34*, 57–125.

[13] Hartman, H., Kris, E., and Lowenstein, R. M., "Comments on the formation of psychic structure," in *The Psychoanalytic Study of the Child*, Vol. II. New York: International Universities Press, Inc., 1947.

[14] For relevant studies see:
    (a) Hartman, H., "Comments on the psychoanalytic formulation of the ego," in *op. cit.*, Vol. V.
    (b) Kris, E., "Notes on the development on some current problems of psychoanalytic child psychology," in *op. cit.*, Vol. V.
    (c) Spitz, R., "Psychiatric therapy in infancy," *Amer. J. Orthopsychiat.*, 1950, *20*, 623–633.

[15] Rank, B., "Aggression," in *The Psychoanalytic Study of the Child*, Vol. III–IV. New York: International Universities Press, Inc., 1949.

The ability to postpone immediate gratifications and to tolerate the resulting tensions is only gradually mastered. In order to achieve this mastery there must first be an adequate control of the muscular and motor components. The child must learn to walk, talk, and control his own bodily functions. In addition, he learns to "test reality." That is, he learns to anticipate the future in his imagination, and to test out in a very small way what might happen in the real world. Bowlby puts this excellently when he states:[16]

As our personality develops we become less and less at the mercy of our immediate surroundings, and the ways in which they affect us, and become more and more able to choose and create our surroundings, and to plan ahead, often over long periods of time, for the things we want. Amongst other things, this means we have to learn to think in an abstract way, to exercise our imagination and to consider things other than just our immediate sensations and desires. Only when he has reached this stage is the individual able to control his wish of the moment in the interests of his own more fundamental long-term needs. One expects the child of three, or even five, to run into the road and seek his ball—at those ages he is still largely at the mercy of the immediate situation. As he grows older, however, he is expected to take more things into account and to think ahead. By ten or eleven he is capable of pursuing goals some months distant in time. At sixteen or eighteen the more developed boy or girl is able to perform great feats of abstraction in time and space. This is the process whereby the individual frees himself from slavery to his instincts and urge for immediate pleasure, and develops mental processes more adapted to the demands of reality.

The development of the ego structure is thus a long, arduous, and gradual process, and an adequate perception of reality depends upon its maturation. However, the primary components of ego structure, although modified to some extent in later years, are usually well established by the time the average child reaches the age of five or six years.

There has been a great deal of experimental study of ego phenomena and ego development in the past two decades, and many extensions of Freud's concepts of the ego have been proposed. A few of the major innovations will be of particular interest to the student of the retarded individual.

It has been learned that the infant's omnipotence has to be subordinated to the tests of reality. How does this come about? Depending upon the culture and the subculture in which the infant lives, he is required to adapt his behavior to the needs of his environment. His parents no longer minister to his helpless needs with complete disregard of their

[16] Bowlby, J., *Child Care and the Growth of Love.* Baltimore: Penguin Books, Inc., 1953, p. 56.

own wishes. Instead, as the infant's motor, emotional, and intellectual growth permits, as well as in terms of the parental expectations in that culture, he is urged, coaxed, cajoled, and taught to begin to behave differently. The parent judges the infant's readiness for these changes by the kinds of behaviors of which he becomes capable. Such behaviors may involve the infant's emotional interest in external objects, his beginning perceptions of other people as being different from himself, and especially his beginning differentiation, in rudimentary language symbols, of himself from others.[17]

The pressures of the culture, as expressed usually through the demands of the parents, cause the infant to become aware of some of the limits of his potency. His ego now begins to experience some traumatic devaluation as his sense of omnipotence diminishes. One of the important early signs of the process of his self-devaluation, and the defense against it, is the emergence of negativistic behavior.[18] In the healthy parent-child relationship some of this negativistic behavior is tolerated, and the child is not overly traumatized by rejection if he does not conform immediately. This beginning mutual process through which the child learns that he is loved for what he is and receives additional affection as he learns to conform to some parental expectations enhances the development of healthy ego functions. It marks the early stages of volitional activity on the part of the young child.

It has been learned that the child's ego can suffer severe, even irreparable damage, if this early series of crises in ego development is not weathered successfully. One of the main requirements of healthy ego development during this phase has already been noted: a mutually satisfying relationship between mother and child, in which the child is fully accepted for what he is and not mainly in terms of how well or how rapidly he incorporates the demands of his culture. This process leads to the child's *identification* with his parent, through which he can share in his parent's power and prestige and thus assuage his loss of infantile omnipotence. Further, as Erikson puts it, "The fate of childhood identification, in turn, depends on the child's satisfactory interaction with a trustworthy and meaningful hierarchy of roles as provided by the generations living together in some form of family."[19]

---

[17] Gesell, A., and Ilg, F. L., *Infant and Child in the Culture of Today*. New York: Harper & Row, Publishers, 1943.

[18] Ausubel, D. P., "Negativism as a phase of ego development," *Amer. J. Orthopsychiat.*, 1950, *20*, 796–805.

[19] Erikson, E. H., "The problem of ego identity," *Amer. Psychoanal. Ass.*, 1956, *4*, 58–121.

For the retarded child, this early period of ego development is especially fraught with perils. Since, to begin with, he is likely to be slower in his motor, mental, and social development, he may be severely frustrated or frustrated unnecessarily early, since his behavior does not conform to the norms expected of him in his culture. The mother may experience frustration, too, as she waits expectantly for her child to begin to learn the things other children of his age have already learned, and finds that he does not. In turn, she may become overprotective or rejecting as her own anxieties mount. As Ausubel points out,[20] the lack of a reciprocal and mutually trusting relationship between mother and child may produce a severe loss in ego deflation and, with it, unnecessary loss of self-regard. In the retarded child, the effect may contribute to withdrawal from adequate interaction with the environment, slowing up of the process of mental growth, and increasing frustration in many or all spheres of interpersonal relationships. Thus, what might have been a mild or even a transitional retardation in development may become a severe and more chronic disturbance.

Traumatization of the ego during early childhood is likely to affect the rate and course of language development, in particular. This may contribute to a loss in ability to develop a sense of personal identity and proper autonomy, since language plays such a large role in these developments. [21] The cumulative effects of this possible course of development may be very great indeed. This kind of phenomenon may also explain why retarded children typically do much more poorly on mental tests involving verbal capacity than on tests not involving this ability. (See Chapter Nine for further discussion of such tests.)

The crises in ego development are particularly striking in infancy and early childhood, but they may also occur during other years, and especially during adolescence when new identity roles are being learned and when matters of sexual identity, vocational goals, and further differentiation from the family become important. Each of these crises is especially difficult for the retardate because of his already lowered ego capacities, as well as society's likelihood of rejecting him (or at least not accepting him) because he does not conform to its standards.

The superego

As the child continues to mature, a further modification of the existing personality structure develops. This development is concerned

---

[20] Ausubel, D. P., *Ego Development and the Personality Disorders*. New York: Grune & Stratton, Inc., 1952.

[21] Erikson, *op. cit.*

with the ethical, social, and cultural values of the individual. It is referred to as the *superego*. Just as the functions of the ego are derived from the id, the functions of the superego are derived from the ego.[22] Moreover, the superego can modify, to some extent, the functions of the ego. It does this chiefly through the creation of a strong sense of guilt within the child.

Popularly, the superego has been termed the "conscience" of the individual. In one way we may regard the superego's function as that of a "watchdog"—constantly warning: "This is not permissible." When its warnings are unheeded, we are automatically punished by feeling guilty. This feeling of guilt is unconscious to the extent that we are often unaware of its true source. Unlike the ego, the superego is to a greater extent unconscious, and is beyond the direct control of conscious and ego activities. The superego is more perceptive of and reactive to the id impulses than is the ego. The mature ego of the human being tends to remain under the domination and control of the superego. The id is "instinctual" in nature, the ego is concerned with reality factors, and the superego is concerned with the social, cultural, and ethical values of the particular society in which the child happens to be reared.

The origins of the superego structure are based on the relationships of the child to the parents.[23] They stem from the corrections, the taboos, and the "don'ts" of the parent. The child is punished by the parents for some activities and is praised for others. The mother may be a very demanding person or the father may be a very dominating person; or, conversely, they may be passive and dependent individuals. These and other personality characteristics of the parents are "absorbed" by the child, that is, he takes into himself (he *interiorizes*) the prohibitions and the general standards and ideals of the parents themselves. Since the child wants to be loved by the parents, he feels that the love of the parents will come as a result of doing what they want him to do. For these reasons he adopts the standards and basic values of the parents for himself. In this way the attitudes of society and the culture are made part of the child, and social adaptation becomes possible.[24]

The basic fear of all young children is that they will lose the love of their parents. When the superego structure is more completely formed, this basic fear becomes, instead, fear of loss of support of the superego.

---

[22] For a different theory concerning the development of the superego, see: Klein, M., *The Psychoanalysis of Children* (2nd Ed.). London: Hogarth, 1937.

[23] See Fenichel, *op. cit.*

[24] For an extended discussion of this process, see Hutt, M. L., and Miller, D., "Social values and personality development," *J. soc. Issues*, 1949, *5*, No. 4, 2–49.

In other words, the older child, and later the adult, is fearful of losing the support and love of the parents who are now symbolically *inside* rather than *outside* of himself. As Freud stressed, the individual will behave toward his superego in exactly the same way that he did toward his parents, whose love he needed as a child. If the parent, for example, was extremely punitive or very harsh and hostile toward the child, then it is probable that the superego of the child will be extremely harsh and punitive. In short, there is a direct relationship between the strictness of the superego and the strictness of the parents. The superego functions in such a way as to permit the expression of some id drives and the suppression of others. Getting along with one's superego as an adult is just as important as getting along with one's parents as a child. Getting along well with our superego and complying with its demands gives us a sense of relief and a feeling of well-being. Refusing to comply with our superego demands makes us feel guilty and remorseful.

Bowlby points out that it is the awareness of things that please and displease the persons around us which gives rise to conscience (superego).[25] He, like Freud, stresses the role of the mother in its formation. She acts *for* the young child, getting his way for him and recognizing for him the claims of other people. She provides for him in all ways, and acts as his personality and conscience. As the child grows older, the mother transfers these roles to him. If the child's relationships with the mother are unhappy the superego will not develop adequately.

Interrelationships of id, ego, and superego

The interrelationships among the id, ego, and superego constantly change during the development through which we all pass. For this reason we must regard the complex interplay among them from the standpoint of several different time levels. What would be true of their interrelationships at age three would not be true at age sixteen.

At birth, as we have stressed, there is only id. During infancy the first-formed ego structure is necessarily weak and is completely overwhelmed by the demands of the id. As the ego matures it becomes stronger, until it succeeds in controlling and modifying the basic id drives. A balance is finally achieved between id and ego forces in the "healthy" young child. At early adolescence, the uneasy "truce" between the two is broken, and first the id then the ego forces prevail in a see-saw sort of fashion. In the normal individual the ego is finally able to deal effectively with the forces of the id.

25 Bowlby, *op. cit.,* p. 57.

The primitive superego at first allies itself strongly with the ego in inhibiting id impulses, and cannot be too clearly distinguished from the ego itself. The developing superego is at first extremely rigid and punitive, but gradually becomes more and more permissive. However, at about puberty in most children, the ego and superego finally become completely differentiated.

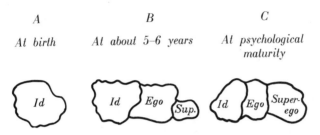

A	B	C
At birth	*At about 5–6 years*	*At psychological maturity*

FIGURE 12. DEVELOPMENT OF ID, EGO, AND SUPEREGO

Figure 12 schematically illustrates the relative strengths of id, ego, and superego at various points in the normal maturational process.

In A, at birth, the id is all-powerful and neither ego nor superego structures have developed to exert any pressures or determine behavioral reactions. In B, at about 5 or 6 years of age, id forces are still powerful, but the ego has developed and exerts considerable control, whereas the superego is still relatively weak. In C, at maturity, ego and superego are fully developed so that all components are in harmony.

The ego and superego are very much alike in that both are based upon the individual's relationships with the external world of reality. However, since the superego is latest in time of development, it stands in closer relationship to the outer world than does the ego—particularly to its social and cultural attributes.

The relationships of the id, ego, and superego to each other, as well as their relationship to the conscious, preconscious, and unconscious aspects of mental life, are diagrammatically represented in Figure 13.

EFFECTS OF RETARDED INTELLIGENCE ON MATURATION OF PERSONALITY STRUCTURES

We shall now turn our attention to the relationship of retarded intelligence to the maturation of the personality.

The mentally retarded child—particularly the child of mild and moderate retardation—does not have *different* id drives from other children. There may be differences in the quantity or amount of psychic energy present, but there has been no demonstration of qualitative differences in basic needs between retarded and non-retarded children.

The general development of the ego in the retarded child probably follows the same general principles of maturation that apply to all children. However, there are highly significant specific differences in ego phenomena between children of inferior and average intellectual potential. In the previous discussion, it was noted that ego development was dependent to some extent upon the development of sensory mechanisms. Consequently, the development of adequate speech patterns, mus-

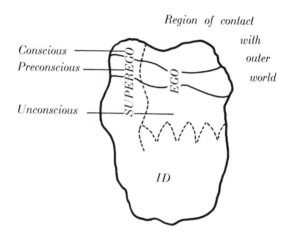

FIGURE 13. TOPOGRAPHICAL RELATIONSHIPS OF ID, EGO, AND SUPEREGO[26]

cular reactions, and the various perceptual processes are of great importance in enabling the child to obtain a valid grasp of reality factors, and to deal with them. Due to the fact that these mechanisms develop more slowly in the mentally retarded child, the development of the ego is also delayed and finally attains a relatively inferior level at maturity. It is, therefore, understandable that the mentally retarded child experiences great difficulties in his ego functions. The retarded child can respond best when he is dealing with immediate and concrete experiences; he has difficulty in responding adequately when the problems are more remote or abstract. Events that are removed from him in either time or space are exceedingly difficult for him to grasp.

The retarded child's relatively immature ego makes it difficult for him

[26] Healy, Bronner and Bowers, *op. cit.*, p. 56.

to control or modify id drives in accordance with the demands of reality. Such drives tend to be expressed in an uninhibited manner, and the controls that are established tend to remain infantile and relatively ineffective. This proves to be a source of considerable difficulty to both the child and those responsible for his behavior. For example, sexual needs tend to be expressed directly, either toward other individuals (as in excessive sexual curiosity) or toward the self (as in excessive mastur-batory behavior). Aggressive drives, similarly, may be expressed with-out adequate control or direction—impulsively or inappropriately. The mentally retarded child does not have excessive drives, but the ex-pression of these drives tends to be uninhibited. The inadequate ego thus proves to be ineffective in two general ways: (1) id drives cannot be controlled adequately; and (2) the demands of the external reality cannot be adequately or realistically assessed.

In addition, the relatively weak ego strength of the mentally retarded child makes it difficult for him to learn to substitute future gratifications for immediate pleasures. He wants things right now—not tomorrow or the day after. Since he cannot plan ahead very well, he remains pretty much at the mercy of the situation in which he finds himself, and is thus unduly influenced by environmental forces which he himself can-not control. His retarded capacity for abstract thought, his retarded capacity for inner creativity and imagination, his inability to take a number of things into consideration simultaneously make him a "slave" to his instinctual drives and wishes. In brief, he has great difficulty in learning to master reality adequately.

The mentally retarded child's inadequate and confused perceptual and intellectual abilities make it very difficult for him to develop a clear self-image and to differentiate his own needs from the demands of reality. He continues, therefore, to be overdependent, and it is only with great difficulty that he succeeds in making even an elementary emotional separation of himself from his parents. Depending in part upon the nature of the early type of home care with which he is pro-vided, he tends (in later life) to see the entire world as either a place that is excessively threatening to himself, or as one that exists primarily to gratify his needs. The first of these defensive alternatives is more probable because most mentally retarded children by their very nature endure excessive deprivations.

There are also severe emotional problems in individuals with an underdeveloped ego structure. Such children often get into severe dif-ficulty with other individuals in various social situations. The resulting conflicts further accentuate their emotional problems. Of particular importance are the reactions of the child's parents (and particularly his mother) to his weak ego functions. (See Chapter Ten.)

The superego of the mentally retarded child, like the ego, also matures at a slow rate. Even when it has developed to its maximum capacity, his superego tends to be quite immature and at times infantile. In such cases, it tends to be structured in terms of absolutes (everything is either all good or all bad, all right or all wrong, and so on). This primitive superego structure tends to be either excessively permissive or excessively severe, as a result of the absence of these finer variations. The mentally retarded child thus tends to respond, to a great extent, in terms of the direct prohibitions of the parents—to the "good" and "bad" valuations that are placed upon his behavioral reactions—or in terms of excessive rebellion against such prohibitions. Parental prohibitions also tend to remain externalized—that is, a particular action is taboo and not undertaken because of the perceived fear of an external person, and not because of internalized and integrated needs. Since growth in the superego is, in part, a result of the awareness of things that please and displease the persons around us, the mentally retarded child, due to his inadequate perception of such results of his behavior, is unable to develop a mature "social conscience"— or a mature superego.

There is another important aspect of superego functions. We all have some desire to achieve—to attain success in some activity. We aspire to a particular level. This aspirational level is, in part, a function of the superego—the inner representations of the parents. The mentally retarded child often aspires to a level that is beyond his ability to achieve. The disparity between the aspirational and achievement levels leads the child to form a poor opinion of himself—he blames himself because he cannot succeed. This results in a generalized lowering of his self-esteem with attendant emotional problems and maladaptive behavior.

Klein points out that the superego of the young child is very much harsher and more cruel than that of the adult, and that it completely dominates the ego:[27]

But in the young child we come across a superego of the most incredible and fantastic character. And the younger the child is, or the deeper the mental level we penetrate to, the more this is the case. We get to look upon the child's fear of being devoured, or cut up, or torn to pieces, or its terror of being surrounded and pursued by menacing figures, as a regular component of its mental life; and

[27] Klein, M., "The development of conscience in the child," in *Psychoanalysis Today*, S. Lorand (ed.). New York: International Universities Press, Inc., 1944, p. 65.

we know that the man-eating wolf, the fire-spewing dragon, and all the evil monsters out of myths and fairy stories flourish and exert their unconscious influence in the fantasy of each individual child, and it feels itself persecuted and threatened by these evil shapes.

This is the type of superego that persists over a longer period of time in the mentally retarded child. In the child of more "average" intellectual functioning, the maturing ego fosters the development of a more benign superego. The mentally retarded child continues, over a much longer span of time, to suffer from the cruel domination of this primitive type of superego.

The individual of inferior intellectual capacities is thus more at the mercy of his id strivings, which are not adequately controlled by either ego or superego forces. He is also more controlled by external forces, to which he reacts in an immature manner. The reactions to his behavior by society and, in particular, by the persons close to him, then further aggravate his emotional problems and the task of adjustment is made more difficult for him.

FACTORIAL STUDY OF PERSONALITY

A number of workers have attempted to develop a conception of personality structure by means of factorial analyses of ratings, test data, or performance. As was indicated in an earlier section, such analyses attempt to extract the least number of trait-clusters, or factors, necessary to account for the intercorrelations among the several traits or test measures which are employed. We cannot go into the technical procedures involved in factor analysis, but a brief summary of some of the main ideas may be helpful to the student.

In factor analysis, the investigator starts out by applying a fairly large number of allegedly well-validated tests to a representative population of subjects. The intercorrelations of these tests are then calculated. Then, by one of a number of statistical techniques, the smallest number of factors necessary to account for these intercorrelations is extracted and the "loadings" (or weights) for each factor are obtained. Usually, these factors do not account for all of the intercorrelations (or, more technically, for all of the *variance* in the data), and the unaccountable data are considered as due to unreliability of the measuring instruments, errors in sampling of the population, and other sources of error.

The final task, once the statistical factors have been selected, is to name them. This is a subjective process, depending, in part, upon the names already given to the tests making up the test battery, the apparent similarity of various tests making up the greatest loadings on each factor, and the investigator's own preference for nomenclature. It should be clearly recognized that the statistically derived factors are abstractions derived from data, and in fact they may even be artifacts of the data—due to cultural bias which predisposes people, for example, to answer tests or to rate others in conventionally approved ways. One investigator has even gone so far as to say, "Factors should be regarded primarily as categories for classifying mental or behavioral performances, rather than as entities in the mind or nervous system."[28]

The vast majority of work done with factor analysis methods has been performed on adults, and within this population the preponderant sampling has been that of college students—a captive audience and so easily tested or rated. This kind of bias limits the generality of trait-clusters which have been proposed, although, in recent years, increasing attention has been given to younger populations and to other kinds of samplings.

As we noted, there is incomplete agreement on the most general factors in personality derived by factor analysis, and many psychologists are completely unwilling to accept even the most agreed-upon findings as relevant or significant. We believe that such an attitude is inappropriate, for, despite their limitations, factor analytic methods remain a powerful tool, and the findings from such methods can still be subjected to experimental and clinical analysis. At least, their findings need to be considered seriously.

Guilford has fairly recently summarized the findings of various factor analytic studies of personality, and we shall follow his summary in sketching some of the most significant findings.[29] He includes findings relating to somatic, aptitude, temperament characteristics, and hormetic disposition (motivational traits) in his compendium of personality structure, but we shall confine our discussion to the dimensions of temperament since this is most relevant to our purposes.

Guilford divided the temperament factors into three major groups: *general, emotional,* and *social.* Then, within each group, he proposed five major sub-categories. Let us consider the *general* group of factors first.

Among the general factors in temperament, a factor that has been very widely studied is that of *inferiority feelings.* Since this is a clearly

[28] Vernon, P. E., *The Structure of Abilities.* New York: John Wiley & Sons, Inc., 1950.

[29] Guilford, J. P., *Personality.* New York: McGraw-Hill, Inc., 1959.

bi-polar factor (not all factors are), Guilford calls it *confidence vs. inferiority feelings*. This factor has been found in populations of normal and abnormal adults as well as in children. The qualities described as belonging to the negative end of this trait-cluster are: is egocentric, feels discontented, has feelings of guilt, and the like. We may be surprised that guilt is an inextricable part of the attitude of inferiority, particularly since the superego aspects of guilt are such a complicated development, as we learned in the preceding section. It is also interesting to note that retarded children rarely exhibit feelings of inferiority, as measured. Whether this is an artifact of the test instruments or is basically true remains to be determined. However, it has been shown that feelings of inferiority are related to the *discrepancy* between the child's home conditions and his attitude toward these conditions.[30]

Another of the widely accepted general factors is that of *objectivity vs. hypersensitivity*. The negative pole of this dimension, hypersensitivity, has often been linked with Jung's concept of *introversion*. This end of the dimension has been found more frequently in the population than the other end. Hypersensitive people recoil from reality. They tend to be egocentric and easily upset. They worry over humiliating experiences. At the extreme, they also have paranoidal thoughts and feelings (such as, "people are watching me," and "they can read my mind").

Still another of the dimensions in the general group which has recently been subjected to much empirical and experimental study is that of *alertness vs. inattentiveness*. Guilford defines this dimension as ". . . a matter of keeping in rapport with the environment versus being inattentive or absentminded." The factor refers to spontaneous attention rather than directed attention. From what we already know concerning the attention difficulties of retarded children (see Chapter Five), we should expect them to cluster at the inattentive pole. It would be interesting to determine how much this factor is a consequence of the condition of retardation and how much it contributes to retarded functioning.

Among the factors noted as belonging in the major grouping of emotional factors, the factor of *cheerfulness vs. depression* is particularly important for our purposes. The negative end of this dimension is characterized by such items as: is emotional, depressed, feels physically depleted, and has periods of loneliness. It has been found that pathological depression is *not* the same thing as extreme depression, as measured by this factor. Nor is *hypomania* (supposedly the opposite of pathological

---

[30] Ackerson, L., "Inferiority attitudes and their correlations among children examined in a behavior clinic," *J. genet. Psychol.*, 1943, *62*, 85–96.

depression) the same as cheerfulness. This finding suggests that there are different levels as well as different attributes to the condition of depression. Indeed, other investigations of depression have indicated that this phenomenon is difficult to evaluate accurately by means of self-ratings or questionnaires because of the intense withdrawal and unwillingness to cooperate which severe depression usually involves. Similarly, depression in retarded children may be a significantly different kind of phenomenon than in normal children. For problems such as these both clinical and experimental study of the phenomenon is needed.

Other factors in the emotional area are: *emotional immaturity vs. maturity; nervousness vs. composure; stability vs. cycloid disposition;* and *poise vs. self-consciousness*. Not all of these factors have been extrapolated in all of the factor studies. The stability vs. cycloid dimension appears extremely well validated and has been demonstrated in both normal and abnormal populations. Again, we should emphasize that little is known concerning the relevance and significance of these factors among retardates. When such findings are available, they will assist us in better understanding this group.

The factors in the social disposition group are most clearly related to specific environmental experiences of the individual. As such we should expect that retarded individuals would rate quite different from children of normal intelligence. Such factors as *ascendance vs. timidity, socialization vs. self-sufficiency, social initiative vs. passivity, friendliness vs. hostility,* and *tolerance vs. criticalness* are clearly dependent upon previous conditioning and learning. The preconditions for the positions on these factors and the consequences of the phenomena should be of great importance in understanding, educating, and guiding retarded children especially. Such questions as, "Is timidity a consequence of retarded intellectual functioning and does it impair still further the retardate's intellectual functioning?" and "Does passivity result from retarded functioning or is it a contributor to such functioning?" are highly important in any adequate psychological approach to the problems of retardation and the education and treatment of such individuals. Unfortunately, there is very little reliable information on such matters, and we must wait for future research to assist us in finding answers.

In commenting on the findings derived from factor analytic studies, we should note that there is as yet no clear picture of what levels of the personality are being tapped, nor do we know what the putative interrelationships of such levels might be. Still less do we know of the possible interaction of the several factors with each other. Although these are still virgin fields for investigation, we must note that studies of personality structure derived from factor analytic research is a fruitful approach, and that there is no essential antagonism between it and clinical methods for the study of personality structure. In time not only a rapprochement of the two approaches may be possible, but a higher order of understanding of people may well emerge.

ch. 8

PROBLEMS OF

ADJUSTMENT

IN THIS CHAPTER WE SHALL BE CONCERNED WITH THE MALADAPTIVE behavior of the mentally retarded child. We shall first discuss some of the general characteristics of his maladaptive behavior, and then some of his specific behavioral disturbances. Our emphasis will be on the emotional trauma to the child and the psychopathological behavior that may result.

MALADAPTIVE BEHAVIOR

Children, as well as adults, often engage in behavior that is in some way disturbing to themselves or to other persons. For example, persons often develop symptoms, such as gastrointestinal reactions, palpitation, and other anxiety reactions, negative and hostile behavior, poor interpersonal relationships, and the like. We call such forms of behavior *maladaptive behavioral reactions,* since they interfere with the adequate adjustment of the individual. They are not the usually accepted ways of behaving. It is important to recognize that the maladaptive behaviors of mentally retarded children *are not the primary result of their retarded intellectual capacities. Rather, they are the result of incomplete or distorted personality functions associated with mental retardation.* It is, of course, true that the inferior intellectual capacities of the mentally retarded child make it much more difficult for him to achieve a high degree of success in many areas (such as academic or vocational areas), but intellectual factors play a *secondary* rather than a *primary* role in the production of maladaptive behavior. Rather than saying: "Billy is a mentally retarded child and therefore shows this or that disturbance in behavior," we should ask instead: "What disturbances in psychological growth, that may be associated with retardation, have led to the production of Billy's maladaptive behavior?" The significance of this point of view cannot be overstressed. It leads to a program of positive action, such as, for example, consideration of possible methods of treatment for the mentally retarded child. Such an approach, of course, is not directed primarily toward "raising" the intellectual capacities of the retardate, but, rather, is oriented toward the removal of his emotional conflicts and the development of more adequate patterns of behavior—in other words, enabling him to live a happier and more productive life.

We should also like to re-emphasize the fact that the mentally retarded child shows *no* behavioral reactions that are not also shown by the child of normal intellectual capacities. The essential difference between the two is that the mentally retarded child is *more prone* to show maladaptive behavioral reactions, and that such behavior tends to *persist* over a much longer period of time than that of the more normal child. This conclusion has been demonstrated by many research studies. McLachlan, for example, who studied the emotional aspects of the backward child, found that the emotional needs of mentally retarded children were the same (qualitatively) as those of normal children.[1] In particular, McLachlan pointed out that the retardate:

(1) Needs recognition. He, like all children, has a self that needs satisfaction.

(2) Needs to be protected from, on the one hand, and prepared for, on the other, those situations whose demands too often exceed his capacities.

(3) Must be given adequate outlets for his tensions.

(4) Must be recognized as having many assets. These should be carefully evaluated so that they can be developed most profitably.

(5) Needs careful explanations of his problems at various maturational stages.

(6) Has a family, and this family as well as the child needs attention.

McLachlan feels that the degree of the retarded child's emotional stability is more dependent on his methods of responding to social situations than on his intellectual level.

---

[1] McLachlan, D. G., "Emotional aspects of the backward child," *Amer. J. ment. Defic.*, 1955, *60*, 323–330.

Gorlow, Butler and Guthrie studied the correlates of the self-attitudes of retarded children.[2] They administered the *Laurelton Self-Attitude Scale* to 164 institutionalized retarded girls. The scores were then related to a number of measures of various traits, such as achievement, intelligence, early experiences, and personality functions. It was found that there were statistically significant correlations between self-acceptance and measures of intelligence, school achievement and success in the institution training program. However, *despite the fact that the correlations reached statistical significance, they were very small indeed, indicating that the child's acceptance of himself was a function of other factors in addition to intellectual level per se.*

This implication is further substantiated by another finding reported by Gorlow and his co-workers. It was found that the girls who were separated from their mothers at an early age had a more negative self-image than did those who were separated at a later age. This finding reinforces our general contention that the emotional characteristics of the retarded child are functions of factors other than intelligence alone, and that they can be primarily, and in large measure, the consequences of early child-parental relationships.

This point of view is supported by evidence derived from studying the productions of mentally retarded children on projective tests.* One example of such a study is that of Beier and his co-workers, who studied the fantasy life of mentally retarded children by means of the Thematic Apperception Test.[3] On this test the child is instructed to make up a story about a picture. They compared the stories of retarded children with those of "normal" children in regard to two major characteristics: (1) the psychological aspects of the themes expressed, and (2) the environmental aspects of the stories they created. Marked similarities between the two groups of children were found in both of these areas. It was the feeling of the investigators that differences in the intellectual capacities of children do not contribute significantly to their emotional needs, although they do affect some other aspects of the child's test functioning (such as the production of a larger number of stories). The themes of the retarded group of children were less aggressive than those of the "normal" group. The retarded group was more preoccupied with themes of self-accusation, rejection, and problems of socialization.

[2] Gorlow, B., Butler, A., and Guthrie, G., "Correlates of self attitudes of retardates, *Amer. J. ment. Defic.,* 1963, *76,* 549–555.
* See discussion of projective tests in Chapter Nine.
[3] Beier, E. G., Gorlow, L., and Stacey, C. L., "The fantasy life of the mental defective," *Amer. J. ment. Defic.,* 1951, *55,* 582–589.

The retardates were more concerned with family relationships than were the normals, and were much more preoccupied with their own perceived "badness."

Beier and his co-workers also observed that the emotional feelings of retarded children came out very directly, almost as "if social learning has not provided the mental defective with techniques for dissembling." It is our judgment that these differences are not the *direct* result of the defective intellectual capacities of the retarded child, but, rather, are the result of his experiences in relating to others—both in his family and in society in general. They are the result of emotional problems stemming indirectly from his inferior level of functioning. They may be changed by ensuring adequate social and learning situations for the child and his family. (See Chapters Ten and Eleven.)

Our approach, therefore, will be to view the maladaptive behavior of the retarded child from the same perspective as that of the more normal child, and as being the result of disturbances in the same developmental processes that are reacted to in the same manner by all children. There are some differences between the two, such as excessive persistence of behavior of the retarded child, and there are some differences in the developmental processes. These special problems will be discussed in detail later in this chapter.

Rather than deal with the maladaptive behavioral responses of mentally retarded children as a single group, we shall divide such children into three subgroups based on chronological age. We shall discuss in turn such reactions in: (1) infancy and early childhood (from birth to about six years of age); (2) late childhood (from six to about puberty); and (3) puberty and adolescence.

PROBLEMS IN INFANCY AND EARLY CHILDHOOD

During the period of infancy the mentally retarded child, like all others, relates primarily to his parents and siblings. Interactions with individuals outside the home are at a minimum, and so the interactions that occur between the child and his immediate family are of primary importance in determining behavioral reactions. Most parents show no great concern about the child's mental retardation during infancy, unless the child is markedly retarded. This is in part due to the fact that the "gap" between the retardate and the more normal child is not yet great enough to be easily perceived. Socio-cultural factors have not yet had an opportunity to make their impact easily evident in the child's behavior, and the personality structures in both the retarded and normal child have not differentiated to the point where marked differences are evident. However, in most cases, the parent *is* somewhat aware that the retarded infant is slower in many aspects of development than is the normal child and may develop some mixed feelings toward the child. When these develop, they usually involve rejection of the child (often unconscious), and frustration because of his limited abilities.

The mentally retarded child usually shows delayed speech and walking. He has difficulty in *visual-motor* functions—that is, he finds it hard to coordinate muscular activities with vision and to manipulate objects accurately. Later, he has great difficulty in feeding himself. He finds it very difficult to tie his shoelaces and to perform similar complex motor activities. The parent often expects too much from the child during this period, and as a consequence the retardate begins to see himself as "inferior" and "inadequate."

Weaning presents many problems, and it is difficult for the mother to get the retarded child "off the bottle." There are many reasons for weaning difficulties. The mentally retarded child has overly strong needs to retain his oral satisfactions, and is not as apt to give them up as readily as is the more normal child. He has many oral conflicts that are not yet adequately resolved, and so is more strongly fixated in this phase. Further, even the physical task of manipulating a spoon often is too difficult for him. When the process of weaning is apparently achieved, the child still shows many residual characteristics of oral behavior. He may continue to suck his fingers, for example, or chew his clothing, put objects into his mouth, or bite himself or other persons. Often he will show marked needs for affection, and will cling tenaciously to other people. Frequently he will want to be held, and will lie quite passively when this need is gratified. In this way he will show his excessive needs for love and support (or for oral, passive gratification).

Toilet training also is a difficult process for the retardate. His fixations at the oral level make it more difficult for him to cope with the problems of the anal level. He has difficulty in understanding what his mother expects of him, and often biologically he is not yet sufficiently mature to establish adequate bowel control. In the earlier phases of this period he is more prone to play with his feces, smear them over himself and objects, and perhaps eat them. This may horrify his mother, and her negative reactions emotionally traumatize him.

As the child approaches school age (kindergarten) his retardation becomes more and more apparent, and the difference between his capacities and those of the more normal child becomes more discernible. In his play activities, for example, he begins to become more and more isolated, and he feels rejected *outside* as well as *inside* the home.

In general, the period of early infancy is one of extreme *biological dependency* for all children. Their very lives depend upon adequate gratification of their biological and physical needs. They are unable to move readily from one place to another, and they are unable to gratify their hunger and thirst needs by themselves. Similarly, they are unable to gratify their psychological needs. Although this is true for *all* children, it is particularly significant for mentally retarded children, since they remain in a condition of biological and psychological helplessness for a longer period of time.

The retardate often develops *depressive reactions*. The development of such reactions is in large measure due to inadequacies in the relationships of mother and child. That a good relationship is of extreme importance in the healthy emotional development of the child has been emphasized by Ribble.[4] Her studies clearly indicate that without adequate "mothering" children lag far behind in both psychological and physical development. This has been demonstrated by many studies of rejected children (such as those placed in institutions). Bakwin, in describing such cases, noted that:[5]

A striking feature is their failure to gain properly despite the injection of diets which in the home are entirely adequate. Infants in hospitals sleep less than infants who are at home, and they rarely smile or babble spontaneously. . . . Infections of the respiratory tract which last only a day or two in a home often persist for months in a hospital. Return home results in a defervescence within a few days and a prompt and striking gain in weight.

He also lists other reactions, such as apathy, poor appetite, or too-frequent bowel movements.

Spitz[6] has perhaps contributed more than others to our understanding of this problem. The children he studied engaged in an excessive amount of autoerotic play which persisted over a relatively long period of time, and were generally emotionally retarded. He noted that they cried a great deal, had immobile faces and expressionless eyes, and that they showed unusual positions of the fingers and hands. Spitz stresses the fact that the absence of maternal care and love may be responsible for severe psychological and physical retardation and illness of the child.

Mohr[7] and his co-workers studied a group of children with *psycho-*

---

[4] Ribble, M., *The Rights of Infants*. New York: Columbia University Press, 1943.

[5] Bakwin, H., "Loneliness in infants," *Amer. J. Dist. Child.*, 1942, *63*, 30–40.

[6] Spitz, R. A., "The importance of the mother-child relationship during the first years of life. A synopsis in five sketches," *Ment. Hlth. Today*, 1948, 7.

[7] Mohr, G. J., Richmond, J. B., Garner, A. M., and Eddy, E. J., "A program for the study of children with psychosomatic disorders," in *Emotional Problems of Early Childhood* (G. Caplan, ed.). New York: Basic Books, Inc., 1955.

somatic involvements (physical symptoms due to psychological factors). On the basis of their results they offered the following as tentative conclusions:

> (1) During the first year of life, any noxious stimulus, physical or psychological, tends to produce a generalized response. It follows that even minimal traumata have a generalized effect and are experienced as traumatic, impending functional growth and integration, during this age period.
> (2) Traumatic experiences of any sort, during this very early age period (under six months), can be responded to only at the level of physiological or somatic response. . . .
> (3) Psychologically, noxious or traumatic stimuli in early infancy evoke reactions of physiological disturbance; only with maturation can these responses become more differentiated and object-directed. Anxiety initially stems from the disintegrative connotations of the noxious stimulus. Later, guilt feelings and fear of retaliation or punishment play their role, e.g., after establishment of object relationships.

It is likely, due to the persisting dependency needs of the mentally retarded child, the lack of understanding of his problems by the mother, and also because of her emotional reactions to the child's deficiencies, that rejection is more apt to occur in the case of a retardate than in one of more normal capacities. Because mothers of retarded children may often unconsciously reject such children (and may even separate themselves physically from their children), they may fail to provide adequate or consistent mothering. When such a situation develops, such children are more likely to become depressed. The retarded child is thus more prone to such depressive reactions.

Occasionally the retarded child develops *convulsive seizures*. Such seizures may result from organic brain damage, but they frequently occur when there is no known organic injury. A convulsive seizure is a symptom of some underlying disturbance and may stem from any one of many causes. For example, it may be the result of some minor infection, or it may result from severe emotional tension. However, apart from specific central nervous system involvements, infants can develop seizures due to their general low threshold for irritability. Such seizures do not necessarily predispose the infant to epilepsy or chorea in later life, nor do they necessarily persist. Only when the condition is severe or prolonged or is complicated by other conditions, especially of an infectious nature of serious proportions, do convulsions have important consequences, by themselves, for the behavioral adjustment of the infant. In this condition, as in all the others, the seizure may be more significant for the subsequent personality development of the infant than the reaction is in itself. Due to the generalized instability of the retarded child, and the increased potency of the emotional trauma to which he is subjected, seizure reactions are more common. When they do occur, careful medical and psychological examinations should be given in order to evaluate the nature of the cause(s). Appropriate guidance can then be offered for *both* mother and child.

Another behavioral reaction of the mentally retarded child is the tendency to *repeat the speech* of an adult. This is a fairly common characteristic of this group. An example of such speech behavior follows:

Mother:	Put the spoon back.
Child:	Spoon back.
Mother:	That's not nice.
Child:	Not nice.
Mother:	Don't talk like that.
Child:	Like that.

This type of repetition of speech is known as *echolalia.* Psychologically, it is similar to other types of *repetitive, imitative behavior.* For example, the child may repeat the actions of his parents, mimicking his behavior in walking or in other physical activities. This type of repetitive behavior is known as *echopraxia.* We often see echolalia and echopraxia in average children during infancy.

Both of these types of reactions are indicative of the fact that the ego of the child is still immature, and that the boundaries between the "self" and the "not-self" have not fully developed. Objects (including persons) are not yet clearly perceived for what they are, and so may appear to be frightening. Retarded children, it will be remembered, develop their ego skills more slowly and less adequately than average children. Hence, they may exhibit these types of repetitive behavior for much longer periods. Moreover, retarded children use such behavior to form a closer relationship with an adult. Both echolalia and echopraxia may be viewed as infantile forms of identification—the retarded child is unconsciously trying to identify with the adult by doing the same things that he does. These behaviors also may be regarded as attempts to master threatening stimuli—another indication of the immature ego strengths of such a child.

The personality development of the retarded child can be significantly influenced by his parents and by those individuals close to him. Cromwell has suggested seven fundamental principles in the behavioral development of the retarded child.[8] Since these are considered to be of importance in providing the best possible growth-stimulating environment for the child, they are presented here in detail. Cromwell believes that the following principles are significant in fostering the personality development of the retardate:

1. Positive reinforcement will increase the possibility of a particular behavioral reaction's occurring. Negative reinforcement will decrease such a possibility. This means that wanted forms of behavior should be praised whenever possible.
2. If the child is to develop a more goal-directed than avoidant form of behavior, then more positive than negative reinforcement should be provided. That is, more "praise" than "punishment" should be meted out.
3. The reinforcement should be as immediate as possible.
4. The parent is, of course, not always able to administer reinforcement whenever it is appropriate. But this does not necessarily mean that its efficiency in maintaining a particular form of desirable behavior is impaired.
5. Whenever possible, the reasons for the positive and the negative reinforcements should be verbalized to the child.
6. It is important that the parent be consistent in the administration of both positive and negative reinforcements. (Do not punish tomorrow what is praised today.)
7. Positive reinforcement should be administered to the child regardless of whether or not it is specific to the behavior that the child is displaying. As a result, the child himself learns to regard himself as a worthwhile person despite his particular behavior. Cromwell feels that this principle is the most important of all.

It is our belief that these seven points made by Cromwell are of importance, and are applicable to the fostering of the development of all children. They are, however, of particular importance in the personality development of the retarded child.

PROBLEMS IN LATER CHILDHOOD

It is during the period of childhood (6 to 15 years of age) that the gap between the mentally retarded child and the child of more average intelligence becomes significantly perceptible. During this period factors in the home situation have a more clearly demonstrable effect on the child; also, and of equal importance, the impact of social and cultural forces outside the home begins to become increasingly important.

---

[8] Cromwell, R. L., "Selected aspects of personality development in mentally retarded children," *Except. Child.*, 1961, *28*, 44–51.

During this period, the parents have an increasing awareness of the deficiencies of the child, and begin to react emotionally to this awareness. Often the parents develop severe conflicts in regard to the retardate, and these, in turn, are reflected in their behavior toward him. These feelings may involve either conscious or unconscious rejection of the child, or both (see Chapter Ten). As many authorities have pointed out, parents of normal intelligence are usually rejecting parents to their mentally retarded child. Since parents usually regard the child as an extension of themselves—indeed, too often *as themselves*—the fact that the child is retarded is a severe blow to their own narcissistic picture. They often feel: "How could I have produced this?" and begin to wonder about their own adequacy. As Foale has pointed out:[9] "(They) regard unconsciously the mental defective as a reflection against their creative forces."

The guilt feelings of the parents over their rejection of the child may rise to serious proportions, and they then tend to react in an overprotective manner toward the child. As a consequence, the retarded child is often not permitted even to learn to do the many things that he could do, and so functions below the level of his already limited abilities. The child is likely to be aware of and sensitive to the feelings of the parents, even though they do not verbalize them; he reacts to *all* the behavioral reactions of his parents, and not only to their verbal expressions. What the parents *do* is often of more importance than what they *say*.

The presence of siblings within the home may greatly complicate the problems of the retarded child. Often siblings develop feelings toward the retarded brother or sister that are similar to those of the parent. They may be overprotective or unwittingly become critical or rejecting of him. They may resent the special attention he is receiving. Like their parents, they, too, may develop feelings of guilt or shame because there is a retarded child in their family.

The parents also are greatly concerned over the sibling relationships. They fear that the younger siblings will "pick up" the characteristics of the older retarded child, or they fear that he will "embarrass" his siblings. Often, of course, these fears are rationalizations or projections of the parents' own feelings.

The interactions of the concern of parents about the effect of their retarded child's behavior upon his siblings, and the defensive behavior and feelings of the siblings, may complicate the problems of adjustment of the retarded child. He is confused, bewildered, and feels rejected. He

[9] Foale, M., "The special difficulties of the high grade mental defective adolescent," *Amer. J. ment. Defic.*, 1956, *60*, 867–877.

is not sure how much he is to blame; he is not sure how to react. Thus, the entire family climate is not conducive to the full development of the capacities that he *does* have. Rather, it has two negative effects: (1) it inhibits psychological maturation in all areas; and (2) it serves to complicate the normal problems that every retardate has.

At the same time, during this period of childhood, social and cultural forces outside the home begin to have important impacts on the retarded child. In school the inevitable, unfavorable comparison between his abilities and those of other children is constantly present. If he is placed in a regular class, he has great difficulty in his academic work, particularly in reading, and he is soon given differential treatment in the classroom. The teacher begins to notice his difficulties and brings the "facts" of his retardation to the attention of his parents. Other children perceive the differences between themselves and the retardate, and are quick to point out his deficiencies to him. The retarded child is likely to become a scapegoat for the jests of other children and the butt of many jokes. Other children displace their own negative feelings upon him since he is weaker than they are, and he often serves as an object of their hostilities, fears, and anxieties.

The retarded child begins to perceive that he is different from other children, and becomes aware of many of his own limitations and disabilities. He therefore tends to perceive himself as someone who is "bad" or "no good." His attempts to relate to other children are often rebuffed; he is the last one chosen for games (if he is even permitted to play at all), and when he is permitted to join a group he is criticized (either explicitly or implicitly) for his ineptness. He is usually aware of and sensitive to the differential classroom treatment that he is given. His self-esteem thus suffers many blows and his security status is constantly threatened.

Neighbors often show irrational attitudes toward the retarded child. Bob is a dull boy, they say, and they fear that if they allow their children to play with him, their children will be affected adversely. They may be afraid that their Billy will become like Bob, or that Bob will lead him into doing "bad" things. They may also fear that Bob will actually harm their Billy physically. They may have such mental stereotypes concerning mentally retarded children as: retarded children are "sex fiends"; retarded children are delinquents; retarded children are sadists. Although, chiefly through the corrective efforts of enlightened parents of retarded children, such attitudes are beginning to die out, they are still far too prevalent.

As a consequence, the entire life activities of the retardate become colored by his inability to achieve success. For example, Jordan and

DeCharms have explored the drive for achievement in retarded children.[10] They compared the achievement motive of 47 mentally retarded special-class children with that of 42 mentally retarded ones who were not special-class children, and with that of 60 children of normal intelligence. It was found that, while the need for achievement was not specifically related to intelligence, in general, the mentally retarded children expressed less need to achieve than did children of more normal intelligence. Jordan and DeCharms attribute this difference to probable differences in child-rearing practices, and, in particular, to the experiences that the retardates are subjected to by their parents.

No specific evidence was offered to support this inference. It may be that the parents of retarded children have a different set of expectations of their offspring than do parents of normal children. In effect, according to Jordan and DeCharms, retarded children receive less training for independent functioning in early childhood, and consequently in later years they are less motivated to strive to achieve than are children of normal intelligence. It is also of importance to note that Jordan and DeCharms found that the special-class retarded children showed less fear of failure than did the non-special-class children, suggesting that the special class may offer many more benefits to the retarded child, in addition to providing for more adequate academic achievement.

The retarded child begins to be exposed to the attitudes that frequently will be shown toward him throughout his whole life—he is rejected and then seen as an *isolate*. These attitudes were, of course, present during his early childhood, but they are far more important during later childhood because the retardate then interacts with more persons, his sphere of activities is enlarged, and social and cultural factors play a more significant role in his life.

Another special problem of the retarded child is that of play activities. All children need play experiences. It is through such activities that their emotional growth is facilitated. Mentally retarded children are in more need of play activities than average children, but they are the ones who are often deprived of such experiences, both at home and elsewhere.

Mentally retarded children are physically able to play with toys during the period of early childhood. Most of the toys that are readily available, however, are inappropriate for their immature emotional and intellectual levels of development. As pointed out by Benoit, the

---

[10] Jordan, T., and DeCharms, R., "The achievement motive in normal and mentally retarded children," *Amer. J. ment. Defic.*, 1960, *65*, 42-45.

toys designed for normal children are usually not suitable for mentally retarded chidren.[11] By the time they are mature enough to use them, they are too large and strong for them and they break the toys too easily—or they use the toys as instruments of destruction. Since they are older and bigger than those children who are their mental equals, they do not care to play with "baby" toys. As Benoit points out, the retarded children want to be like their peers, they wish to be accepted by them and wish to imitate them. They tend to resent "kid stuff," and so reject the toys that are appropriate for their intellectual age but are inappropriate for their chronological age.

Specific intellectual disabilities may make participation in many games and the use of many toys completely out of the question for the retardate. He may not be able to read, and so the usual books of early childhood are "out" as far as he is concerned. Paper and pencil activities tend to be beyond his capacities, and any game that depends upon reading, writing, language abilities, imagination, or complexity is too difficult for him to enjoy. As Benoit stresses, there is apparently an *attitude of helplessness* on the part of many adults toward teaching games to mentally retarded children, but play can be one of the "principal vehicles of stimulation" for such a child. The more such a child is stimulated through his senses, the more his total growth is encouraged. Benoit feels that the mentally retarded child does best in physical games—those that utilize the larger muscular systems. He also believes that such children do best in group games that are essentially realistic in nature; that is, those that do not involve too much fantasy.

Many attempts have been made to provide adequate play experiences for the mentally retarded child. The Play Schools Association has been a pioneer in this area. Cleverdon and Rosenzweig, who have described the program of this association, point out that it has tried for years to develop work-play programs for all children, since *all children have a right to play*.[12] The focus of such programs for retarded children is on the promotion of social adaptability. The conclusions of Cleverdon and Rosenzweig in regard to work-play programs for retardates are summarized below:

(1) A developmental (*not remedial*) work-play program stimulates the mentally retarded child to dramatic expressions and a "playing with somebody" kind of play.

[11] Benoit, E. P., "The play problem of retarded children," *Amer. J. ment. Defic.*, 1955, *60*, 41–55.
[12] Cleverdon, D., and Rosenzweig, L. E., "A work-play program for the trainable mental deficient," *Amer. J. ment. Defic.*, 1955, *60*, 56–70.

(2) Such children must be introduced into group play gradually. Interests of different kinds should be introduced one at a time.

(3) The interests utilized must be especially adapted to meet the retarded child's larger physical size and retarded mental capacities.

(4) There should be extreme repetition in play activities.

(5) There is evidence to indicate that skills and attitudes developed in a work-play program can be maintained by the retarded child.

During childhood the problems of the intellectually retarded child becomes increasingly acute. His conflicts continually grow more severe, and his psychological defenses need to be constantly maintained. The widening gap between himself and other children of his own chronological age leads him to perceive himself as a social outcast and of no worth to his family or society. It is no wonder that profound behavioral disturbances frequently occur. The retarded child is denied the usual childhood experiences—what other children *casually accept* is not for him. Not for him are close childhood friendships, group activities, shared experiences, and successes for which he is praised. Rather, his childhood is one in which he is constantly reminded of his worthlessness and weaknesses; it is full of feelings of futility and rejection. He is truly a Jonah —a social outcast—and rarely has any feelings of belonging to a social group.

Even though this state of affairs does usually occur, it *does not have to occur*. This development is not an inevitable correlate of the child's mental retardation, but is the result of numerous and unfortunate reactions to the retardation—the reactions of the child himself, his family, and those of society and its institutions.

During the period of childhood, the retarded child gradually becomes more socialized. He begins to learn to take care of many of his personal needs, to acquire some skills in communicating with people, and to acquire some information about himself and the world around him. He also manages to learn how to gratify some of his own needs while conforming to the demands of the world of reality. Some of these increments of growth are due to the general maturational process. Many more are dependent upon training and special opportunities for practice. These are referred to as *learning*. Although learning depends upon intellectual capacities and adequate opportunities for acquiring skills, it also requires something more. It also depends upon *the emotional climate* in which the learning takes place. The retardate is thus at a disadvantage in all areas: his mental capacities are at a lower level; appropriate, specialized opportunities with which he is provided are few indeed; and the emotional climate to which he is exposed is not conducive to effective learning (except perhaps in a negative sense).

Retarded children, as a group, are certainly not as happy as they might be. As Morris has pointed out, their need for "contentment, security, and a dignified non-pressure existence is continually disrupted by a demand to achieve and conform."[13] Parents seem always to be

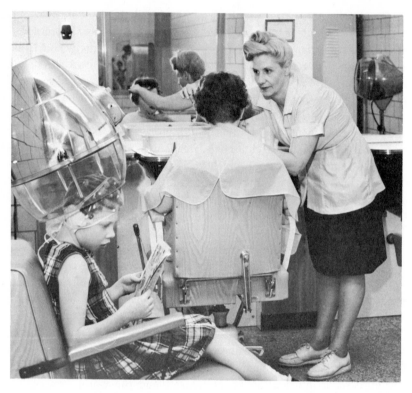

ENHANCING SELF-ESTEEM IS PARTICULARLY IMPORTANT FOR RETARDED CHILDREN
(Courtesy of Plymouth State Home and Training School, Northville, Mich.)

"pushing" the child, and they often resist recognizing the fact of his retardation. Thus he is too often denied the usual experiences of childhood. As Morris states: "Most rights of retarded children as human beings are confiscated, and they are deprived of the respect and mastery of their own simple wishes."

Our general conclusion, from an analysis of this aspect of the prob-

---

[13] Morris, E. F., "Casework training needs for counselling parents of the retarded," *Amer. J. ment. Defic.*, 1955, *59*, 510–516.

lem, is that the retarded child is usually encompassed by a psychological climate, both at home and in society, that predisposes him to maladaptive patterns of adjustment.

Maladaptive behavioral reactions of childhood

The mentally retarded child reacts to the impact of emotional stresses in the same general manner as the more average child, although, as noted previously, he tends to be less able to tolerate anxiety and stress because of his relatively slower maturation. His ego is affected in varying degrees by emotional trauma. In some cases there may be only a slight disturbance in ego function resulting from the emotional stresses he encounters. Such moderate ego disturbances result when there is a relatively mild degree of trauma. The consequent disturbances in the behavior then tend to be of short duration (*transient*) and capable of being remedied (*reversible*).[14] These types of behavior reactions are known as "transient adaptive problems in behavior." If, however, the child experiences more severe trauma, then there may be a disturbance in the growth of the ego, and although the ego may remain essentially intact, the child's total capacity for effective adjustment is impaired. The reactions of a child with such a degree of ego disturbance are termed "persistent, non-adaptive problems in behavior." If the trauma is severe enough to produce disintegration or fragmentation of the ego, then profound disturbances in his behavior may result. The consequent psychopathology in such a case is severe, and the process of recovery, even with intensive psychotherapy, is very difficult and slow. Such reactions are known as "extreme, persistent, non-adaptive problems in behavior." The mentally retarded child may develop behavioral reactions at any one of these levels, depending upon the strength of the emotional trauma to which he is subjected and the stages of development of his ego at the time of the stress. We shall discuss each of these patterns of reactions in turn.

TRANSIENT, ADAPTIVE PROBLEMS IN BEHAVIOR. The mentally retarded child is readily affected, as we have pointed out, by environmental stress. (By "environmental stress" we mean all those factors that are external to the child.) He finds it difficult to adapt to sudden changes in his environment, such as a shift in school, meeting new or strange people, a new sibling, and the like. In addition he finds it very difficult to adapt to the demands of the culture in which he is imbedded. Many transient,

---

[14] For a complete discussion of the classification of behavioral reactions of children that is being presented in this section, see: Hutt, M. L., and Gibby, R. G., *Patterns of Abnormal Behavior*. Boston: Allyn and Bacon, Inc., 1957, pp. 132–136.

adaptive behavioral reactions may result. The more usual of these are discussed in the following paragraphs. It should be emphasized that the retarded child's reactions are similar to those of average children, only they are *more likely* to occur because the world tends to be such a frustrating place for him.

Reactions of *excessive aggression* may be shown. In such reactions the child may bully younger children, and may, at times, hurt them. In this respect, he behaves like an average child with excessive aggression. He may become disobedient and defiant toward his parents, and be cruel to animals. He may break things, even if he harms himself as a result. He may use obscene language. He may lie, cheat, and steal, and be untrustworthy in general. Such reactions are not the result of the mental retardation *per se*, but of the emotional trauma that may be encountered as a result of it.

On the other hand, the retardate may react with patterns of *excessive timidity*. He may be very shy and bury his head in his mother's skirts when he meets strangers, or he may show asocial forms of behavior when in the presence of other children or adults. Such a child tends to react with excessive daydreaming and often seems to be remote and "far away." He may refuse to play games. Often, he will not be interested in other persons and will wander away by himself.

Many *habit* disorders may be shown. The retarded child may react to his emotional stress with *enuresis* (bed-wetting). He may wet or soil his clothing during the day (*diurnal* enuresis), or he may do this only at night (*nocturnal* enuresis). He may show an excessive amount of thumb-sucking or nail-biting. He may also have feeding problems, such as refusal to eat certain foods or even refusal to eat at all (*anorexia*).

Often there is an increase in *masturbatory* activities. Masturbation is often resorted to by the child as a means of *discharging tensions* without any *conscious* sexual connotations. Rather, the act of masturbation provides him with a measure of pleasurable gratification. (Unconsciously, of course, sexual gratification may occur.)

Quite frequently the retarded child will react to stress situations with regressive forms of behavior (see Chapter Six). For instance, it is not uncommon for a teacher to remark that: "Johnny could do really well last month. He knew his letters and could read some words, but he can't do nearly as well now." Or the mother might say: "I thought that Bill had gotten over those tantrums that he used to have, but now they're back again." Complaints of the recurrence of more infantile forms of behavior such as eating problems, soiling of clothes, speech disabilities, and the like are frequently encountered. Such forms of behavior may indicate that the child is reacting to a stress situation through the utiliza-tion of regressive defenses. In such an event a detailed study should be made in order to determine the specific environmental or situational factors that precipitated such a maladaptive behavioral response, since it may result from one of many varied causes.

Barsch studied the regressive behavior of a group of brain injured children.[15] He stated that it is very difficult for the brain damaged child to establish stable perceptions. Consequently, the entire world may be seen as chaotic, and so his tolerance level for stress situations is charac-teristically low. Barsch believes that the child experiences stress when-ever he is forced to restructure or to reorganize a percept, a task which is more difficult for the brain damaged person. He reviewed the stress re-actions of approximately 200 brain damaged children, and constructed a list of the situations which he felt precipitated the stresses. These stress situations included such changes in the child's prevailing structured world as: a new baby in the family, moving to a new home, painting the ex-terior of the home a different color, painting the interior of the house anew, a change in the working shift of the father, new tile in the bath-room, a substitute teacher at school, vacation, illness of family members, new house furniture, omission of a customary story at bedtime, and a dif-ferent classroom at school.

It appears from Barsch's study that any changes in the child's previ-ously structured world which requires that he restructure the old and familiar environment may result in stress and subsequent regressive be-havioral reactions. Further, Barsch found that regressive behavior due to stress may be shown at any age level. But to the mentally retarded child, as Barsch points out, "little things may be very important."

These are merely some of the ways in which the retardate may re-spond to the stresses of the environment. Usually, no serious emotional disturbance is involved. We have not listed all of the forms of temporary disturbance in behavior that may occur. There are so many diverse forms that to list them would be in effect to catalogue almost all types of be-havior of children. We have noted a few of the more common behavioral reactions in order to illustrate transient and adaptive problems. However, in considering these ways of behaving, we should remember that it is not possible to judge the significance or the degree of disturbance on the basis of symptoms alone. Each of the forms of maladaptive behaviors cited may, in fact, also be associated with more severe ego destruction. If it is,

[15] Barsch, R. H., "The concept of regression in the brain injured child," *Except. Child.*, 1960, *27*, 84–89.

then more severe psychopathology is involved. The following sections discuss some of these more severe forms of disturbance. It will be noted in each case that not the symptom, but the severity of ego disturbance, is crucial.

PERSISTENT, NON-ADAPTIVE PROBLEMS IN BEHAVIOR (PRIMARY BE-HAVIOR PROBLEMS). The term "primary behavior problem" has been used traditionally to describe most types of psychoneurotic behavior in children. It is preferable, we believe, to the use of the phrase "psycho-neurotic reaction" for children, because most reactions of children that fall in this category are not as clear-cut or as systematized as are the corresponding reactions of adults. We have suggested, in another context,[16] reasons for a substitute phrase (or category): *persistent*, non-adaptive behavior. This new phrase seems, to us, to help differentiate such reactions more easily from the "transient adaptive," and from the "extreme, persistent, and non-adaptive" reactions.

Mentally retarded children may react to the emotional stresses that impinge upon them with the development of a *psychoneurosis*. A psychoneurosis is a continuing reaction to a basic conflict between the unconscious wishes of the person (the id strivings) on the one hand, and the forces that attempt to prevent such gratifications (ego and superego) on the other. In this type of *solution* to a conflict there is no essential destruction of the child's ego structure. As we have stated elsewhere:[17] ". . . a psychoneurosis is a *continuing* disturbance in the integration of the personality resulting from the conflict of drives within the individual and manifesting itself in tension states, impaired functioning, and symptomatology." The psychoneurotic reactions shown by the retarded child are similar to those shown by nonretarded children, except that they are not as well delineated and are more diffuse in nature. They also tend to be more *directly* shown in his behavioral reactions. (It is in these ways also that the psychoneurotic reactions of the child of "normal" intelligence differ from those of the adult.)

A frequent problem in mentally retarded children is that of *reading disability*, which is *likely* to be part of a psychoneurosis or primary behavior problem. The act of reading is so complex that it is sensitive to the impact of many factors. In discussing reading disability as a persistent, non-adaptive behavior, we should like to make absolutely clear what we mean by "reading disability." We should distinguish between

[16] *Ibid.*, p. 150.
[17] *Ibid.*, p. 199.

two forms of reading difficulties, *reading retardation* and *reading disability,* which are often confused with each other. Reading retardation means that a particular child's level of reading is below that expected of an average child of the same chronological age. An eight-year-old child who reads at a seven-year level is said to have a reading *retardation.* He may or may not have a reading *disability,* however. We are using the term "reading disability" to indicate something else—that the child's ability to read is *below his mental age level.* A ten-year-old child with a mental age of eight years and a reading level of six years has a reading *disability.* Unless there is a discrepancy between mental age and reading age, in which the latter is lower, the condition would not be called a reading disability. It would be a *retardation* if the reading age were below the chronological age, but it would become a *disability* if it were below the mental age level, regardless of whether or not it were below the chronological age level.

Reading disability is thus a phenomenon in which the *actual* reading level is below the child's *potential* reading level as determined by his mental capacity. This is a relatively new concept. The more modern concept of reading emphasizes the discrepancy between *potential* and *actual* reading skills, and, in so doing, also emphasizes the great number of causes that may be responsible for this difference.

Since *reading capacity* is a function of the intellectual level of the child, all mentally retarded children are retarded in reading. However, not all such children *need* to show reading disabilities, although far too many do. Reading disability is *not* a function of intellectual level, but rather it is the result of many factors, including physical defects or diseases, inadequacies in the learning experiences, and disturbances in the social and emotional adjustment of the child. We are particularly concerned with this last category, since we are at this point considering reading disability as a psychoneurotic reaction of the retardate.

If the underlying cause of the mental retardation is a neurological condition, and this has involved sensory mechanisms (such as hearing or sight), then, of course, we may expect a reading disability in addition to the generalized reading retardation. Children of more average intelligence learn to adapt more readily to sensory deficiencies, and so may often show no significant reading disability, particularly if given special attention. The retarded child cannot meet his deficiencies as readily, however, and the disability is more apt to occur, to persist, and to be more serious.

That factors in the emotional and social adjustment of the child are important in the etiology of reading disabilities has been established by many studies.[18] It appears that when the act of reading arouses certain symbolic reactions (such as fear of looking, repression of the impulses involved in curiosity, feelings of guilt, repressed aggression, and the like), blocking in the area of reading may be very severe.

Any one of a number of emotional problems may cause a reading disability. Examples of these would be: fear of competition from classmates, strong sibling rivalries, fear of social situations, repressed hostile feelings toward authority figures, ambivalent reactions toward the teacher, fear of rejection, anticipation of failure, greatly lowered self-esteem, and the like. Any factor that affects the social and emotional adjustment of the child might produce or enhance a reading disability.

The mentally retarded child is particularly prone to such a condition. He generally has a markedly low estimate of himself, and fears competition with the more average children in his schoolroom. Furthermore, attempts are often made to teach him to read long before he is ready to profit from exposure to such a process. This leads him to react negatively to the entire reading process, and makes learning to read much more difficult. Indeed, at times, it is necessary to devote considerable effort to a re-educative attempt in order to undo the harm that such premature attempts usually cause. Reading, to the retarded child, is a tangible indication of his retardation. It interferes with almost all of his other school activities, and is a "badge" of his inferiority. Reading becomes emotionally laden with displaced conflicts, and so in many cases is overvalued and is regarded with too great importance by the retarded child —and also by his parents.

In addition, difficulties in reading act in a circular fashion. They further serve to increase the feelings of inadequacy and lowered self-esteem of the retardate, and so serve to increase his emotional maladjustments. This, in turn, further hinders the development of reading abilities. It is true, of course, as pointed out earlier, that all retarded children have serious reading retardation, depending upon the extent of their mental retardation, but such children may not learn to read at even the level at which they are capable, due to their high susceptibility to emotional involvements which interfere with the learning process.

The mentally retarded child is also prone to other types of psychoneurotic involvements. He may often develop *acute anxiety states*. Usually these are accompanied by feelings of depression or some physical complaints (stomach ache, pains in the side, etc.). These anxiety states

[18] See: Strachey, J., "Some unconscious factors in reading," *Int. J. Psychoanal.*, 1930, *11*, 322–331; and Blanchard, P., "Reading disabilities in relation to difficulties of personality and emotional development," *Ment. Hyg., N.Y.*, 1936, *20*, 384–413.

usually center around the child's feelings of rejection—by his parents, teachers, or some significant adult in his life. He is fearful that he will lose the love of the person who is important to him (usually the mother). He may experience nightmares, horrible dreams in which he is being pursued by a giant, or being run over by a car, or being hurt or mutilated in some way. The basic core of the anxieties of the retarded child is his fear of rejection—and there are many instances in reality to support such feelings.

An important study by Malpass, Mark and Palerma[19] confirms our clinical impression that the child of lowered intellectual capacities may develop strong anxiety reactions. These investigators administered the *Taylor Manifest Anxiety Reactions Scale* (as revised for 10- to 12-year-old children) to 41 children in an educable mentally handicapped group, to 53 children institutionalized in a state school, and to 63 normal children in the same schools as the group of educable children.

It was concluded that the *Manifest Anxiety Scale* differentiated between the educable mentally retarded children and the institutionalized children. The educable retardates were less anxious than the institutionalized children. But, in addition, it was found that both groups of retarded children were significantly more anxious (as measured by the *Taylor Manifest Anxiety Scale*) than were the normal children.

The presence of severe anxiety inhibits the adjustment of the retarded child in many significant ways. For example, it has negative effects upon the child's relationships with his parents, siblings, peers, and other persons. In addition, anxieties may hinder the adequate progress of the child in his academic work. A recent study by Wiener and his co-workers bears upon this latter point.[20] In this research the correlates of anxiety were studied in a group of 52 mildly retarded teenage boys. It was found that poor academic achievement was significantly related to high test anxiety, and that a high level of anxiety prevented the mildly retarded child from achieving academic success at a level commensurate with his ability. It was felt that psychotherapeutic measures designed to reduce severe anxiety might be effective in promoting the academic progress of the child.

EXTREME, PERSISTENT, NON-ADAPTIVE PROBLEMS IN BEHAVIOR. The emotional maladjustment of the mentally retarded child may be so severe

---

[19] Malpass, L., Mark, S., and Palerma, D., "Responses of retarded children to the Children's Manifest Anxiety Scale," *J. educ. Psychol.,* 1960, *51,* 305–308.

[20] Wiener, G., Crawford, E., and Snyder, R., "Some correlates of overt anxiety in mildly retarded patients," *Amer. J. ment. Defic.,* 1960, *64,* 735–739.

as to result in considerable disintegration of the ego. If this occurs, then his already lowered capacities for dealing with reality suffer further impairment. He "loses touch" with reality, and shows even more social inadequacies. There are even further reductions in his outside interest, which in any event are limited, and his abilities to relate to other persons decrease. He may show many forms of pathological behavior, such as hearing voices or seeing people who are not actually present (auditory or visual hallucinations).

Such forms of extremely disturbed behavioral reaction in children have been termed *psychoses*. The most common form that they take is known as *childhood schizophrenia*. Fortunately, however, it is a relatively infrequent condition. We do not understand it too well, and it is very difficult to treat. It is also known by other names. Kanner has termed one form of childhood schizophrenia *early infantile autism*.[21] In this form the individual seems withdrawn and unable to relate to other individuals from the beginning of infancy. As early as 1866 Seguin pointed out that children sometimes developed a psychotic-like reaction.[22] Other investigators since that time have devoted attention to such reactions of mentally retarded children, and have made many attempts both to describe and to understand their behavior. The term "pfropfschizophrenia" has been applied to ego disintegrative reactions in mentally retarded individuals, but it is not commonly used.

Schizophrenia is also one of the most common forms of mental "illness" in adults. In this disorder, the balance among the id, ego, and superego forces is upset. The several components of the personality do not work together in harmony. Thought processes are illogical and not well integrated, and the person's moods and emotions are often inappropriate to the situation in which he finds himself. There are acute disturbances in the total integration of thinking, feeling, and behaving. Perceptions of reality are distorted and often contact with reality is lost. True schizophrenia is usually a long-lasting chronic disorder, assuming many forms, and difficult to treat.[23]

Childhood schizophrenia differs in many respects from the schizophrenic reaction shown by adults. There are many reasons for this. Because the ego of the child is not as well developed as that of the adult, and because his language and speech functions are not as complex, the

[21] Kanner, L., *Child Psychiatry* (2nd Ed.). Springfield, Ill.: Charles C. Thomas, Publisher, 1948.
[22] Seguin, E., *Idiocy and its Treatment by the Physiological Method.* New York: Columbia University Press, 1907.
[23] For a full discussion of schizophrenia, see: Hutt and Gibby, *op. cit.*

manifestations of his "breakdown" are very different. However, despite these differences children do show severe behavioral reactions, characterized by chronic and severe loss or impairment of ego functions.

Whether or not it is really correct to call these severe ego disturbances of the child "schizophrenic," such disturbances involve his whole way of life. Such a child has many unique characteristics. There is typically a withdrawal of interest from the outside world, often accompanied by an increasing seclusiveness; that is, a tendency on the part of the child to want to be alone and not be "bothered" by people. There is a decrease in his emotional reactions. Such emotions as he does show tend to be rigid in expression, and often are not appropriate to the situation. (For example, he may laugh in a situation in which tears would be more appropriate.) There are many severe disturbances in his thinking processes. These may be bizarre, and *hallucinations* (faulty perceptions, such as "seeing things") and *delusions* (faulty and morbid thinking, as, for example, a belief that people "are going to kill me") may be shown. There may be many disturbances in the vegetative nervous system, resulting in such reactions as "cold" extremities, excessive perspiration, or insensitivity to severe changes in temperature.

The specific cause of childhood schizophrenia is still a perplexing question. It is also questionable whether all of these types of reactions constitute one or many types of disorder. Some people believe that the reaction is inherited, or is due to internal physiological causes. Others believe that environmental conditions surrounding the child are primarily responsible. In any case, the evidence does *not* indicate that any significant changes in the brain tissue cause this condition.

There is considerable evidence to indicate that the nature of the child's experience in *interpersonal relationships* is important. The child who develops a schizophrenic pattern of behavior has not developed an *adequate* and *consistent* relationship with other people. This difficulty is clearly related to the home situation, in which *inconsistent* and *pronounced maternal* rejection are commonly found. The mother of such a child is usually overprotective, oversolicitous, aggressive, and—most important—is highly *ambivalent* toward the child. (That is, she unconsciously vacillates in her attitudes toward the child, being overly punitive at one time, overly permissive at another, and the like.) Nevertheless, the specific cause of the disorder is still undetermined.[24] Many attempts have been made to treat such children. At one time it was thought they would not respond to treatment, but today the attitude is one of

[24] Bradley, C., *Schizophrenia in Childhood*. New York: The Macmillan Co., 1941.

cautious hopefulness. There appears to be a difference in the extent of recovery that is related to the type of onset of the disorder. Those children who develop the condition more suddenly, as, for example, directly after an acute psychological trauma or after a severe infectious disease, respond better and more rapidly to treatment than those children in whom the onset is slower and more gradual.[25]

RETARDATES NEED AMPLE OPPORTUNITIES FOR GROWTH IN GROUP INTERACTION
(Courtesy of Plymouth State Home and Training School, Northville, Mich.)

When children of average or superior intelligence develop childhood schizophrenia, infantile autism, or some other form of psychotic disturbance, they may behave in such a way that they are thought to be mentally defective. The mistaken judgment occurs because such children are unable to utilize their mental capacities and they show retarded thought processes and sluggish emotional reactions. However, impaired mental functioning due to psychoses is an entirely different condition from mental retardation, although the diagnostic differentiation may be difficult to make. On the other hand, it is possible for a mentally retarded child to develop a psychotic type of reaction, in general, or a form of childhood schizophrenia, in particular. In such case the child is *both* mentally retarded and psychotic, whereas, in the former type of case, the child is psychotic and *appears* to be mentally retarded.

Benda feels that childhood autism is a *symptom* that indicates the

[25] Bettelheim, B., *Love is Not Enough.* New York: Free Press of Glencoe, Inc., 1950.

inability of the child to establish satisfactory contact with his environment.[26] There may be several underlying causes of the autism. These, according to Benda, include: (1) injuries of the central nervous system, especially those due to asphyxiation; (2) severe psychogenic factors, such as severe rejection or severe grief reactions due to loss of a beloved person; or (3) childhood schizophrenia.

The behavioral reactions of the retarded child with severe ego damage differ from those of the more normal child to some extent. Such retarded children tend to be described as engaging in either "too little" or "too great" an amount of activity. They are described as being either depressed and melancholic, or given to temper outbursts; given to stupor or to rage; apathetic or excitable. The most prevalent picture of a mentally retarded child with severe personality involvement, however, appears to be one in which there are severe withdrawal symptoms (*catatonia*) and numerous odd or "queer" mannerisms.

The phrase *"primitive catatonic psychosis of idiocy"* has been applied to the psychotic state shown by many mentally retarded individuals. Psychosis in retardates tends to differ from that in children with higher intelligence in that it is manifested more in *motor* behavior in the former, whereas it is manifested more in *symbolic* behavior in the latter. It should be noted that symbolic behavior requires higher levels of intellectual functioning.

MacGillivray has added to our knowledge of psychoses in mental deficiency.[27] Based upon a review of the literature on the subject and his own studies of psychotic children who were mentally defective, he concluded that such types of psychotics were likely to display catatonic-like behavior—that is, behavior characterized by withdrawal and reduction in activity. He noted that, whereas psychotic children average or above in intelligence showed a greater variety of specific, differentiated forms of psychoses, psychotic children in the mentally defective range were more apt to display diffuse, ill-defined and nondifferentiated forms of psychoses. Like other workers, he found that there were special difficulties in treating psychoses in mentally retarded cases, one of these being the great difficulty in gaining any access to the nature of their thought processes.

But Wolfensberger does not agree with the contention that it is more

---

[26] Benda, C. E., *Developmental Disorders of Mentation and Cerebral Palsies.* New York: Grune & Stratton, Inc., 1952, p. 503.

[27] MacGillivray, R. C., "The larval psychoses of idiocy," *Amer. J. ment. Defic.,* 1956, *60*, 570-574.

difficult to communicate with the mentally retarded schizophrenic child than with one of more nearly normal capacities.[28] He believes that the retarded child is unable to create his own high-level symbolic world, and has limited informational resources. Consequently, withdrawal from the outer world is more difficult for him than it is for the non-retarded schizophrenic child. Wolfensberger believes that the retarded schizophrenic child is unable to remove himself from the symbolism of his cultural group, and so he may be approached more readily and treated by the therapist.

All schizophrenic children communicate through non-verbal behavior (one of the many "currencies of psychotherapy"), but this is particularly true of the child who is, in addition, retarded. Such a child communicates essentially through non-verbal symbols, such as patting or touching part of the body, grimacing, gesturing and the like. One additional factor which facilitates communication, according to Wolfensberger, is based on the contention that the retarded child is less capable of creating an extensive fantasy world. As a result, he remains more exposed to reality, and his psychotic state is characterized by brief episodic periods of disturbance, which facilitates the processes of communication and psychotherapy.

PROBLEMS IN PUBERTY AND ADOLESCENCE

Puberty is certainly a critical period for the mentally retarded child, as it is for all children. The retarded child has had numerous problems throughout his childhood, but puberty brings additional stresses that create difficulty in adjustment. We shall first discuss the more general problems of the retarded adolescent child, then next turn our attention to two specific types of problems that are of great importance, the problems of sexual and aggressive maladaptive behaviors.

General adjustmental problems

The period of puberty ushers in sudden changes in both physical and psychological areas. There are rapid physiological changes, among which increased hormonal activity is especially important. Secondary sex characteristics develop and require, of themselves, new psychological adjustments on the part of the child. In the boy, for example, the growth of pubic hair, and also of facial hair, makes his image of himself (his

---

[28] Wolfensberger, W., "Schizophrenia in mental retardates: Three Hypotheses," *Amer. J. ment. Defic.*, 1960, *64*, 704–706.

self-percept) different. In the girl, the beginning of menstruation and the development of breasts assume similar importance.

From the psychological standpoint there are important problems during puberty. The increased sexual drives and the great importance attached by society to the development of secondary sexual characteristics make unusually difficult the readjustment of the mentally retarded child, whose capacity for understanding and dealing with these phenomena is limited. It is difficult for the child to know how to handle his increased sexual excitement. Many of his former conflicts are reactivated by this sudden upsurge of sexuality. He may now be regarded as more of a man by society, yet be totally unable to accept the responsibilities of his new role. The weak ego of the retarded child is not strong enough to cope with this, and he is, therefore, frequently overcome by strong emotional states.

The gap between the retarded child and other children of his own age widens during puberty and is more and more evident both to others and to *himself*. He is less able to interact socially with children of his own age group, he is not a part of their closely-knit interest groups, and he is, in general, not accepted by them. *They* go on to high school, with its plethora of activities, while *he* remains behind. The children of more average intelligence are concerned, during puberty, with their future life plans and vocational goals, while the retarded child is still struggling to master the rudiments of social adjustment. In academic areas the differences between others and himself are now very pronounced and quite obvious to all. Younger siblings have begun to "catch up" or pass him in school, and this creates additional emotional burdens for him. He sees himself more and more as a defective person, and his self-percept of being worthless and unfavorably unique is reinforced.

Ringness has investigated some of the differences among the self-concept of children of low, average, and high intelligence.[29] He compared 40 children whose *Wechsler Intelligence Scale (WISC)* scores were between 50 to 80 with 40 children whose I.Q.'s were between 90 and 110, and with another 40 children whose I.Q.'s were over 120. He obtained measures of the self-concept in the following areas: success in learning arithmetic, English, spelling and writing; reading ability; acceptance by parents and adults; success in sports and game activities; leadership of peers; and intellectual abilities. He found that the mentally retarded youngsters tended to *over-estimate* their successes more than did the

[29] Ringness, T., "Self concept of children of low, average, and high intelligence," *Amer. J. ment. Defic.*, 1961, *65*, 453–461.

average or bright children. The brighter children tended to rate themselves as more capable than they were, while the retarded ones tended to rate themselves *lower* than they actually were.

The retarded children generally had a much less realistic picture of themselves than did either the average or the bright children, and their self-ratings were significantly less reliable. The findings of this important research study indicate that mentally retarded children, as compared with other children, have a less well formulated self-concept, are less reliable in their test results, and differ more in diverging from reality in the image they hold of themselves.

In puberty the retardate tends to be subjected to overt rejection on all sides—by social institutions, by the family, by neighbors, and by other children. There is scarcely a single area in which rejection is not pronounced. Friendships, especially with children of the opposite sex, are difficult to establish, and the lack of heterosexual relationships makes the task of dealing with his increased sexual drives more difficult for him to handle. He usually does not have a "girl friend," and therefore meets further frustration in dealing with his sexual drives. There are fewer parties, dances, "swing" sessions, shows, or "dates" to provide the normal outlets for his needs. Unless he is indeed fortunate, he is relegated to the category of undesirable, to the portion of humanity that is shunned and is better off (from the standpoint of the rest of society) when not seen or recognized. Adolescents are ruthless when they deal with deviants of even normal intelligence in their own group—they are (partly due to projection of and reaction formation to their own fears) even more so in their treatment of the mentally retarded child. They simply do not want him "cluttering up" their activities. At best, he is ignored.

Truppe, in an excellent article, has discussed the social psychology of exceptional children in general.[30] He makes the point that when the goals of success, prestige, and status are held as desirable for all members of society, then considerable deviant behavior may result if the means of obtaining such goals are not available to the individual. He further states that our contemporary American culture seems to hold promise of success for all people, but that it is true that many groups of individuals in our society do not enjoy equal opportunity to obtain adequate recognition and reward. According to Truppe, it is very rare that a person with little formal education or inadequate economic resources achieves social success, despite the widely held belief in our society that success is open to all. The deviate behavior which then results

---

[30] Truppe, M. J., "The social psychology of exceptional children: Part II, Items of factors in society," *Except. Child.*, 1959, *26*, 171-175.

comes about not because the members of the groups are (exceptionally) biologically different, but because, as Truppe puts it, they are responding normally to unique conditions. We feel that this point of view is especially important.

At puberty, then, the retarded child becomes a still more serious problem to his parents. They now have to grapple with a new group of questions, including the very pressing one of pre-vocational training. The question, "What is Johnny going to do?" assumes tremendous practical significance. Then, too, they react emotionally to the constantly increasing "gap" between their child and the children of the neighbors. In turn, their own emotional reactions affect their relationship with their child (see Chapter Ten).

For these reasons the mentally retarded child may show unusually severe behavioral reactions during puberty, even more so than those shown by the child of more average intelligence. This is demonstrated by a study by Foale on the incidence of psychoneuroses in mentally retarded children.[31] He pointed out that while only 6% of normal adolescents develop psychoneurotic reactions, 12% of mentally retarded adolescents show such personality involvements.

The emotionally disturbed and retarded adolescent may show any of the maladaptive behavioral responses discussed in the preceding section on childhood. In addition to the constant educational problems of such a child, two additional specific types of problems are of special importance to him during puberty. These are the problems of sexual and aggressive maladaptions. They will be discussed in the following sections.

Sexual maladjustments

As we have pointed out, the retarded adolescent has extreme difficulty in dealing with the increase in sexual drives that occurs during puberty. His resultant maladaptive behavioral reactions may take a number of different forms, but the consequences of the faulty resolution of the conflicts resulting from the increased sexual energies may, in general, be placed into three categories. There may be: (1) a significant diminution of sexual interests and activities, (2) an excessive increase of sexual interests and activities, or (3) the development of perverse forms of sexual behavior. We shall discuss each of these in turn.

DIMINUTION OF SEXUAL INTERESTS AND ACTIVITIES. The increase in intensity of sexual drives that occurs during puberty results in the pro-

[31] Foale, *op. cit.*

duction of a tremendous anxiety within all children. The mentally retarded child has similar reactions, since he does not differ in his basic
sexual characteristics from the child of more average intelligence. As we
have seen, however, due to his severe fixations at earlier developmental
levels, he has a limited number of defenses with which to cope with all
types of stress situations, and so has severe difficulties in dealing with
his increased sexual drives. When sexual excitements are aroused within
him he may feel guilty, remorseful, and in some way "dirty." When such
guilt feelings occur, all sexual impulses then tend to be repressed, and as
a consequence he withdraws more and more from all external activities
and interests. More infantile defenses tend to be utilized; those of denial, repression, isolation, reaction formation, and projection are dominant.

When the previous history of the retarded child has been one of
severe inhibition or repression of his interests and behavior by the
parent, then it is to be expected that he will tend to curtail (*inhibit*) the
expression of his increased sexual drives. For example, an inhibiting
parent might be overly concerned with the child's masturbatory behavior, and so deal very harshly and punitively with him. As a result
the child would tend to overly conform to most parental and societal
demands in his later life (due to his own severe superego). He would
also tend to see his own inner drives as "unacceptable," and so inhibit
their expression.

INCREASED SEXUAL INTERESTS AND ACTIVITIES.   As we have seen, the
mentally retarded child has strong fears and anxieties concerning his
own adequacy as a person. Such anxieties frequently lead to an *increase*
in the child's sexual activities. This increase may be regarded as an
attempt through compensation to remove his fears, and to prove his
adequacy to himself. For this reason sexual activity, particularly in
the case of the retarded child, tends to become an end in itself, and
sexual excitement itself, rather than the derivation of pleasure in being
able to relate to another person in a heterosexual situation, becomes the
end goal. In such an event the need for sexual gratification tends to
distort all the other interpersonal values and needs of the child. Increased sexual activities assume importance to him because they serve
to help to avoid feelings of loneliness, offer him consolation following
disappointments, and, in general, serve as a way of escape from his
conflicts and frustrations.

An increase in sexual activities may be manifested in different ways
by the child. There may be an increase in masturbation. There may be

increasing manipulatory and exploratory activities with children either of the same or opposite sex. There may be a seeking for frequent direct sexual intercourse. The retarded child frequently does not understand the nature or consequences of the sexual act—his store of sexual information is scanty and usually faulty. As a result he too often contracts a venereal disease; in the case of the girl, she may also become pregnant. There are thus important needs for the mentally retarded child to be given information about sexual activities at a level that he can comprehend, but this information in itself will not serve to reduce the intensity of his sexual activities (see Chapter Eleven).

PERVERSE SEXUAL BEHAVIOR. If the infantile aspects of the sexual drives of the child persist, as they are more probable to do in the retarded child, then he is apt to engage in some form of *perverse* sexual behavior. A perversion is a form of sexual behavior in which pleasure is derived from some *partial* aspect of the sexual act—it is an *infantile* form of sexuality. Probably all human beings use such forms of infantile sexuality in the heterosexual behaviors that precede sexual intercourse (*foreplay*). They are then not perversions—the major difference is that, in the perversion, these partial acts are *goals in themselves;* whereas, in normal behavior, they are part of the *movement toward* the final goal of sexual intercourse. Due to the fixations and conflicts characteristic of the mentally retarded adolescent, he is more prone to show such forms of behavior than is the more average child. It should be stressed that he does not engage in a perverse activity because of conscious or deliberate choice; rather he is compelled to obtain his sexual gratification through the perversion.

There are many forms of perversions. *Homosexuality* is a frequent form. It involves the choice of a sexual partner of the same sex as the *preferred* object in achieving sexual satisfaction. Sometimes the sexual interest is displaced from the genital organs to some other part of the body or to some object. This is a form of perversion known as *fetishism.* The *fetishist* derives his major sexual pleasure from looking at, thinking about, or touching the object to which the sexual interest is displaced. Common fetishes are: shoes, stockings, underwear of the opposite sex, jewelry, hair, feet, ears, etc. *Voyeurism* is a sexual perversion in which the desire to *look* has replaced the desire for normal sexual gratification. *Exhibitionism* is another form of sexual perversion. In this type of behavior the compulsive need to expose one's genital organs to other persons has become the method used to achieve some degree of sexual release. The perversion in which the mouth replaces the genitals as the primary zone for sexual satisfactions is known as *fellatio*.

None of these forms of sexual perversions are unique to the mentally retarded adolescent. All may be, and frequently are, manifested by the adolescent of average (or above) intelligence.[32] Sexual perversions may be regarded as *infantile forms of sexual behavior*. They involve the use of sexual modes that *were* appropriate during earlier, formative years, before adult sexuality developed. In a perversion, what was formerly a part, often an unimportant, incidental part of infantile sexual behavior, has replaced the normal, genital sexual outlet appropriate for the more mature individual. Perversions are usually more common in the mentally retarded child because he has more often been subjected to severe emotional trauma with which he could not cope, and so has become fixated at infantile levels. Later, during conflict, he tends, therefore, to regress to these earlier levels.

There is considerable misunderstanding in our society of the nature of sexual adjustment and maladjustment. Deviant forms of sexual behavior tend to be automatically labeled as "bad," but they often are merely arrested or retarded forms of sexual behavior. Perversions in retarded children are frequently of this type. Mentally retarded children, even when they reveal perversions, are *not* necessarily "fiends." Rather, their sexual behavior simply reflects their more infantile level of development and their emotional retardation in general. Often they *will respond* to psychotherapy, and develop more appropriate social forms for gratifying their sexual needs.

Many of the sexual maladjustments of the mentally retarded child stem from his inadequate information and his lack of appropriate sex education. The more normal child learns much about sexual matters from his peers at a relatively early age, but this informal learning is not so common in the case of the retardate. Furthermore, in many instances, even though a formal program of sex instruction is provided, the retarded child, due to his condition, is often unable to understand the symbolism and language in which sexual information is usually couched. As a result, he is either ignorant of many sexual matters, or has a store of faulty and sketchy information. Hence, it is becoming more evident that the mentally retarded child (boy or girl) should be taught fundamental sex facts at the level appropriate to his age and degree of retardation.

[32] Kinsey, A. C., *et al.*, *Sexual Behavior in the Human Male*. Philadelphia: W. B. Saunders, Co., 1948.

Aggressive behavior

Rebellion against authority figures is quite characteristic of the adolescent. It is not to be thought of as psychopathological in itself, but may be regarded as an attempt on the part of the adolescent to develop initiative and independence. When it takes extreme forms or persists over a long period of time it is more likely, however, to be psychopathological. When it results in the breaking of laws, apprehension by civil authorities and conviction, it is termed "delinquency." It has been thought that mentally retarded children are predisposed to delinquent and criminal behavior. Research evidence does not confirm this mistaken belief. An example of such research is that of Levy, who studied the relationship of mental retardation to criminal behavior.[33] He found the rate of mental deficiency in the population of a state penitentiary to be approximately the same as that in the general population of the United States. He concluded that mental deficiency *per se* did not play such an important role in the causation of criminal behavior as had formerly been assumed.

The retarded child, like other children, will sometimes engage in delinquent behavior. Often he is not aware of the consequences of his behavior—often he is oblivious to the fact that he is breaking some particular law. (Rather than being called "immoral," his behavior should be called "amoral.") Then, too, his impulses are not as readily controlled and tend to emerge in an impulsive manner. Further, when he does become involved in some delinquent act he does not have the capacity to "cover up" or to "get away," and is more readily apprehended. It is, therefore, surprising that the popular stereotype that mentally retarded children are inevitably delinquent is not more closely approached in fact. It would seem that many more such children would be likely to engage in poorly controlled "amoral" behavior (which looks "delinquent" to the observer), and that they would be apprehended more readily. We can only surmise that there are compensating factors which tend to keep the frequency of such behavior within "average levels," such as closer supervision by parents and other adults, and the tendency of retarded children to be conformists because of their previous experience in being supervised.

Since frustration is one of the primary causes of aggression, it is not surprising that the retarded child frequently may manifest aggressive behavior, since he is presumably subjected to so many more frustrating

[33] Levy, S., "The role of mental deficiency in the causation of criminal behavior," *Amer. J. ment. Defic.*, 1954, *58*, 455–464.

situations than is the child of more normal intelligence. Forbes has elaborated upon this point in detail.[34] She points out that the normal child begins to work with symbols, "the tools of our modern day civilization," at a much earlier age than does the retardate. As a consequence, the retarded child cannot experience pleasure in competition with other children, since it is not possible for him to win. He then reacts with behavior which is designed to "keep his rivals away," and this, in most instances, is centered around aggressive reactions. Sibling rivalries and aggression toward other children are then commonly manifested.

The problems stemming from frustration are intensified as he approaches adolescence. As Forbes indicates, ideals ordinarily are developed by the normal child at about age eight. But this is not so in the case of the retarded child, who probably never completes this part of his development in an adequate manner. Also, in our culture, the child learns to achieve recognition by producing things and by being industrious. If he is incapable of doing so, then he feels inadequate and inferior to other children. Particularly in the case of the mildly retarded child, the perception of the difference between himself and his peers is not acute until approximately the high school level, when the discrepancy in abilities is clearly obvious, and he learns that the tasks easily accomplished by other adolescents are beyond his ability. He may then regress to earlier stages of rivalry and manifest aggressive behavior.

When the retarded child is in an academic situation in which the work is beyond his level to achieve, he is constantly exposed to frustrating situations which foster aggression. In many instances, the transfer of the child to a special class may dramatically reduce the incidence of overt aggressive and hostile acts, since the stress situation to which he is exposed is alleviated. But such a transfer in itself may not result in the desired alteration of behavior. There are levels of performance even within the special class, and the child may perceive his level of achievement as still being inferior to that of the other children, resulting in feelings of frustration. Further, even though the child is removed from the pressure of the normal classroom and adjusts adequately to the program of the special class, the frustrations may be maintained by pressures from many different sources outside the classroom.

One source of pressure may stem from the parent who mistakenly views the special class as a place where the child's academic achievement is to be accelerated. Such a class is often seen by the parent as a "tutorial"

---

[34] Forbes, L., "Some psychiatric problems related to mental retardation," *Amer. J. ment. Defic.*, 1958, *62*, 637–641.

class, in which the child is to be given special help in reading, arithmetic and other academic subjects. The parent then berates the child for not making the progress he expects. An example of this type of situation follows:

Johnny is a twelve-year-old boy of borderline intelligence. As would be expected, his academic progress was poor, and he consistently failed all academic subjects. The child was finally placed in a special class removed at some distance from his home, and the mother was required to drive the child to and from the school each day. This gave her ample opportunity to see the teacher, and her invariable complaint was: "I can't understand what is wrong with that boy. I do everything for him, I even bring him here so that he can get special help, and he isn't doing any more in his work than he was last year. The reason I bring him here is because there are only 15 children in the room, and he can get special help. There's no reason why he shouldn't be able to go faster than he is."

Another source of pressure may arise from discrepancies within the levels of achievement of the children in the special class. A child who is not achieving at the level of his chronological age peers, may, even though he is in a special class, still perceive himself as being inadequate. This was the case with Bill:

Bill, a fourteen-year-old boy of borderline intelligence, was transferred to a special class following repeated school failures. His academic achievement was far below the level at which he could be expected to achieve, and as a result the work which was given to him was below that of all the other children in the room. Bill began to bully the younger children, and began to show many primitive rage states. He would destroy their belongings, break their pencils, tear up their papers, and the like. At times his rages were almost uncontrollable, and he would physically attack the other children with his fists or even with articles of furniture. Fortunately, the teacher soon acquired insight into Bill's problem, and began to look for some particular assets which could be stressed. She felt that Bill had (comparatively) good visual-motor coordination, and that he was more comfortable working alone than with a group. Accordingly, the teacher gave Bill the job of preparing scrapbooks to be used in the science and social studies units, and he worked on these for a period of time without any stress being placed upon formal academic work. The entire class then utilized the scrapbooks that Bill had prepared. The overt aggressive and hostile behavior did start to diminish, but it was many months before Bill was able to relate adequately to the group.

Frequently, the frustration stems from the retarded child's inability to cope with the reactions of more normal children in his neighborhood. Even though, in the school situation, he relates quite well to his classmates, he may be unable to relate adequately to more normal children outside the classroom in which he is more protected. The special class is only one part of his life, and the children with whom he relates during the school day are usually not those with whom he comes in contact in the evening, on weekends, or during school vacations. This fact is often overlooked.

It is best to attempt to deal with aggressive behavior by first exploring the possible frustrating situations to which the mentally retarded child is exposed, and to attempt to alleviate them by altering or manipulating such situations. But in many instances, despite such attempts, the aggressive pattern of behavior may persist. In such an event, attempts should be made to alleviate the undesirable behavioral reaction by some form of psychotherapeutic intervention. (See Chapter Twelve.)

Adolescence is a period of shifting values, one in which the child is required to move from the dependent status of childhood to the more independent status of adulthood. It is difficult enough for the normal child to achieve such a new role, but it is much more difficult for the mentally retarded child. If the period of puberty is described as a period of "storm and stress" for the child of average intelligence, as it often is, then it could well be termed a "typhoon" of cataclysmic proportions for the retarded child, particularly for the one who lacks adequate guidance. The degree to which such a child manages ultimately to resolve the conflicts that are reinforced and initiated during the period of puberty is not a function of his retardation *per se*, but, rather, is more related to his basic personality characteristics and the help he receives.

ch. 9

ASSESSMENT AND

EVALUATION

I N THIS CHAPTER WE SHALL DISCUSS OBJECTIVES AND METHODS OF evaluating mental retardation. We shall see that such an evaluation is a complex process, often involving the integrated efforts of a number of highly trained specialists. Our focus will be on mildly and moderately retarded children, and not the severely retarded who require institutionalization.

THE FUNCTION AND MEANING OF INDIVIDUAL ASSESSMENT

It is appropriate, at this point, to ask the question: What are the objectives of the assessment of the characteristies of the mentally retarded child? In the first place, the assessment or evaluation of such a child should give us information about the *extent* of the deficit. (In the case of Johnny Jones detailed in Chapter One, the evaluation indicated that he was a child of subnormal intelligence, but not so inferior as to require institutional placement. Further data were also secured in regard to his deficits in academic work.) In the second place, the assessment should furnish information relative to the qualitative aspects of the deficit and its emotional consequences. (Johnny had very poor memory, and could not concentrate. He was functioning below his age expectancy in academic work. He had many emotional problems, such as hostilities toward his siblings, ambivalent feelings toward his mother, and the like.) In the third place, the assessment should determine the *reasons* for the mental retardation and the emotional maladjustment—the basic "why." (In Johnny's case there were no definite indications of the primary cause of his intellectual deficit. However, physical illnesses, school problems, and home relationships were found to be of importance in the production of Johnny's maladaptive behavior.)

Assessment thus involves much more than the administration of psychological tests and the determination of the level of mental functioning. It involves an exploration of many aspects of a child's life, in order to determine the reasons for the difficulty, the nature of the problem, and prospects for dealing with or improving the condition. It involves a detailed study of the *whole* child. The assessment should indicate, insofar as possible, the etiologic and precipitating factors underlying the child's mental retardation, and should describe the specific level at which he functions. It should be concerned not only with an assessment of the child's deficiencies, but with his assets as well. Further, assessment should include a *prognosis* (prediction as to the future development of the child), and should lead to helping the child achieve a more adequate adjustment.

The process of assessment of the retardate is intricate, and involves several major areas of investigation. These include: (1) securing adequate personal, historical information in various areas, (2) assessment of the physical condition, (3) evaluation of personality characteristics, and (4) complete psychological evaluation. We shall discuss each of these major areas in turn.

Personal history

A complete assessment and evaluative study of a mentally retarded child necessitates the compilation and evaluation of many types of background data. There should be a summary of the child's physical development, including such items as, for example: the nature of his birth process; the developmental phenomena, such as walking, speech, and dentition; illnesses and surgical operations; and reports of laboratory findings. These data should preferably be compiled by a physician or medical specialist. A detailed social case history should also be obtained. This includes a description of the nature of the child's social environment, both inside and outside the home. It should deal with the nature of the personality characteristics of the parents, and the problems they manifest in dealing with the child, stressing both parental liabilities and assets. It should stress the characteristics and interrelationships of the child's family structure. Of particular importance in the social case history is an evaluation of the attitudes and emotional reactions shown by the members of the family toward the child—and, specifically, how they react to the child's mental retardation. Further, there should be an "adjustmental history" which should give a detailed picture of the child's adjustment to various situations throughout his life. The social and adjustmental case histories are usually compiled by a social worker.

Physical condition

Although we need to secure adequate historical data concerning the child's past life, data in regard to his current status are also necessary.

The total assessment should include a detailed medical examination of the child. This entails the referral of the child, in some instances, to various medical specialists. For example, referral to a physician specializing in the treatment of problems involving *glandular* difficulties (an *endocrinologist*) might be necessary. A complete neurological examination by a *neurologist* might be required in order to explore the possibility of any central nervous system involvements. There may be a need for further detailed examinations, such as X-rays of the brain or other organs (by a *radiologist*), studies of the "brain waves" (which may reveal the presence of some organic brain pathology) by means of the *electroencephalograph* (commonly called the *E.E.G.*), or additional laboratory examinations. Physical assessment should also be made of the child's motor skills, both in his play and other activities, in order to ascertain how well coordinated the child is in the use of large and small muscles.

Adjustmental characteristics

The total assessment should include a summary of the way in which the child is *currently* adjusting, emphasizing both the child's assets and liabilities. This phase of the evaluation asks such questions as: How is the child relating to members of the family? How well is he doing in school? How does he get along with his playmates? What kinds of activities does he engage in? What are his characteristic defenses? It should cover the entire range of the child's behavior, including his relationships with adults, his peers, and the community. These data are usually secured by either the social worker or the clinical psychologist, and are obtained from interviews with the parents and other persons having contact with the child, as well as from the child himself, when this is possible.

Psychological evaluation

It is important that the assessment of the retarded child include a detailed evaluation of his psychological characteristics. This portion of the total assessment process is based upon psychological tests and interviews. To be adequate, the psychological evaluation should cover many areas, including: (1) intellectual capacities, (2) personality characteristics, (3) academic abilities and disabilities, and (4) special skills and interests. We shall present a brief introductory discussion of these problems, and then devote the remainder of the chapter to a more detailed analysis of the specific methods utilized in exploring each of these areas. The psychological evaluation is done by a clinical psychologist.

INTELLECTUAL CAPACITIES. The evaluation of the retarded child's intellectual deficit should include an estimate of the general degree of deficit, and of the types of assets and liabilities. For example, some retardates are more seriously handicapped in their capacity to deal with verbal material than they are with concrete objects and situations; others are equally handicapped in both areas. The evaluation of specific and other psychological functions is important. Such abilities as verbal skills, non-verbal skills, memory (auditory and visual), general comprehension, capacity to integrate and synthesize experience, capacity to deal with reality, and the like should be assessed. A child is not necessarily equally retarded in all intellectual functions, and an evaluation of his unique pattern of abilities is helpful in guiding him more effectively.

The psychological evaluation of a mentally retarded child is often a complex process. It is complicated by the fact that, in many instances, the child is unable to express himself adequately and to relate to others. He often manifests both receptive and expressive difficulties in communication. An adequate psychological assessment must involve *not only* an evaluation of the current intellectual performance of the individual, but, at least equally important, it must also involve an estimate of the innate intellectual *potentialities* of the individual. Such evaluations in cases of suspected mental retardation are made more difficult not only because of frequent communication difficulties, upon which intelligence tests depend so heavily, but also because of perceptual, motoric, and cultural limitations.

Doll points out that there are essentially two approaches to evaluation of intellectual functions. In the first, one might make an inventory of the factors which might interfere with receptive and expressive behavior, and then, in light of these, infer from the performance of the retarded child the underlying potentialities. In the second, the process might be reversed, so that we would then start with the performance and evaluate the factors which might lower the level of the performance. Doll points out that, in practice, the clinician uses both approaches.[1] This demands an extensive battery of tests to cover a variety of situations and behavioral capacities.

EVALUATION OF PERSONALITY CHARACTERISTICS. A careful evaluation of the personality characteristics of the retarded child is highly important. In order to provide the best possible program for the child we need to know how mature the personality is, the level of ego development, the nature and strength of conflicts, the characteristic psychological defenses that are utilized, and the degree to which psychopathological reactions are present. This part of the assessment is significant in suggesting leads for treatment and in estimating prognostic limits. Such a personality evaluation is particularly difficult in the case of the retardate, especially because of his limited communicative and expressive skills, but it is essential to adequate planning of the treatment program. It is usually done by a clinical psychologist, a psychiatrist, or both.

The vast array of psychological tests, scales, and assorted techniques utilized to assess personality variables has been developed primarily for the evaluation of the normal individual, and they have been applied, in most instances, only secondarily to the evaluation of persons with severe intellectual handicaps. Gallagher has discussed this important consideration. He points out that, while there are many instruments for the assessment of personality factors, there are very few which are easy to apply and to interpret in the case of the mentally retarded child.

Gallagher has reviewed the shortcomings of various types of techniques of personality assessment as applied to retarded children.[2] *Self-reports,* or methods which involve questionnaires—as exemplified by the *California Test of Personality,* and by the *Rogers Test of Personal Adjustment*—are, in his opinion, and ours, not satisfactory. Such methods require at least a third-grade reading level, require that the child be perceptive of his own inner feelings, and require that the child report his own feelings truthfully. Gallagher indicates that the mentally retarded child is inadequate in at least two of these respects.

Most *projective* methods are also difficult to apply to the retardate.

---

[1] Doll, F. A., *Mental Evaluation of Children with Expressive Handicaps.* Devon, Pa.: Devereaux Schools.

[2] Gallagher, J., "Measurement of personality development in preadolescent mentally retarded children," *Amer. J. ment. Defic.,* 1959, *64,* 296–304.

Such children's responses are frequently determined by environmental events that immediately precede the testing session, more than they are by basic internal needs. Thus, the reactions of the retarded child are curtailed and determined by his *time-bound* and *situation-bound* behavioral tendencies.

Further evidence supporting the hypothesis that the mentally retarded child tends to react to projective test material more in terms of immediate environmental stimuli, rather than in terms of deep inner dynamics, is found in a study by Matthews and Levy.[3] They gave the *Children's Manifest Anxiety Scale* (*CMAS*) to 30 institutionalized children who were mentally retarded, in a test-retest experiment. They also administered a specially designed response-set scale prior to the second administration of the *CMAS*. They found that the *CMAS* scores were influenced by response-sets as well as by situational and capacity variables, and they concluded that the *CMAS* was not too appropriate an instrument for evaluating institutionalized retarded individuals.

Observational methods have some value, but those currently in use still leave much to be desired. The same objections that were raised to projective tests would also be applicable to observational techniques. In addition, short observational periods would not be of great value. Gallagher proposes that observers be trained to match the child to behavioral descriptions related to significant stages of personality development. These would be based upon the types of relationships the child would form with others in his environment. They would include: (1) Isolation tendencies; (2) Dependency reactions; (3) Omnipotence feelings; (4) Imitation of adults; (5) Identification with adults; (6) Imitation of peers; (7) Identification with peers; and (8) Self-determination behaviors. Gallagher's proposal, even though the mechanics and rationale have not been developed, does have some merit, in that it would tend to provide a dynamic description of the personality characteristics of the mentally retarded child.

ACADEMIC ABILITIES AND DISABILITIES. A part of the total assessment program includes an evaluation of the academic skills of the child. Such questions as the following are of importance: How well does he read? Can he write? What are his arithmetical capacities? Particularly important is the question of whether the child's academic achievements are at a level commensurate with his intellectual capacities. (We saw

---

[3] Matthews, C., and Levy, L., "Response sets and manifest anxiety scores in a retarded population," *Child Develpm.*, 1961, *32*, 577–584.

in Chapter Eight, for example, that children often fail to read at the level they are capable of attaining.) Further, the evaluation of academic abilities and disabilities should stress skills in which the child has a relatively high degree of proficiency. (One child in a group of retarded children won an elementary school spelling contest!) The assessment should also include a prediction of the highest academic level the child is likely to attain. (Such predictions should never be regarded as "final," but only as "best possible" estimates.) This assessment is usually the responsibility of the clinical psychologist.

EVALUATION OF SPECIAL SKILLS AND INTERESTS. As we have pointed out, the retarded child is a unique individual. He often has relatively high degrees of skill in specific areas (such as some mechanical skills, cooking, performing various industrial tasks, and less frequently in some academic areas), as well as various deficiencies in others. It is important that these be explored and evaluated as the child gets older so as to provide for more effective guidance. His vocational aptitudes as well as vocational interests need to be assessed, and information relative to motor skills in general should be gathered. Usually the psychologist performs this part of the assessment.

Integration of material

A wealth of material from many different sources and specialists is required before completely adequate planning can proceed for a specific child. After this material has been accumulated it must be integrated to provide the most reliable representation of the *total* child. Such an integration is best accomplished through the interaction of and discussion by the specialists involved in his total assessment process. (See the discussion of the team approach in Chapter Eleven.) It requires the united efforts of the physician and other medical specialists, the clinical psychologist and other psychological specialists, the social worker, the teacher, the parents, and all other individuals who can contribute to the formation of a better understanding of the child.

An example of how such materials are integrated is furnished by the case of Bobby, which follows. This material is presented in summary form, and although the dynamics are interesting in themselves they will not be discussed at length. The case material presented is intended to serve primarily as an illustration of the need for integration of all available information in the evaluation of a child thought to be mentally retarded.

Bobby was referred to the clinical psychologist for evaluation, since it was thought that he was a mentally retarded child. At the time of referral he was 16 years of age, and history material had been obtained by the social worker and physician. The social worker stressed the fact that Bobby's home environment was particularly undesirable. He lived with his mother in a small structure that was described as being quite "substandard" housing. Bobby had been excluded from school at six years of age, after attending less than a week, because he had been thought to be a "feebleminded" child. There was no record of any psychological evaluation of Bobby at that time, and no specific reasons were given for arriving at the conclusion that he was mentally retarded. He had not attended school at all since his exclusion. His appearance was very unfavorable—he was very dirty and unkempt when first seen. The results of the detailed medical examination conducted at the time of referral indicated no specific physical defects other than a general condition of malnourishment. Bobby played very little with other children, and spent almost all of his time at "home." He had no close companions, and knew only a few children living in his immediate neighborhood. Bobby did not belong to any group of children. For instance, he had never attended Sunday School or any church or Scout activities, and had never engaged in any organized group activity. There were no siblings. The father had deserted the mother when Bobby was approximately one year of age. His mother was felt to be an ineffectual person, who did not have the capacity for providing adequately for Bobby.

The *Wechsler-Bellevue Intelligence Scale* was administered to Bobby by the clinical psychologist. He noted that Bobby's results on the various subtests of this scale showed that his stock of everyday information was extremely poor, and that his comprehension of daily events was impaired. Memory functions, as tested, were poor. Bobby did, however, have the capacity to relate events to each other. All of his verbal capacities were at a much lower level than his non-verbal (*performance*) capacities. His performance on such non-verbal tasks was, however, considerably below those of an average child of his own chronological age. It was observed that he had some insight into his disabilities, and when he made an error he was aware of "something being wrong" and he did try to correct it. On the basis of these results alone, it might be concluded that Bobby was functioning at a mentally retarded level. However, it was recognized that a test such as the *Wechsler-Bellevue* might be inappropriate for a child who had never attended school, and so further evaluation of his intellectual capacities was conducted through appropriate analysis of the projective tests that were administered. (See later section for discussion of the characteristics of such tests.)

Bobby did extremely poorly on all the standardized tests of academic achievement that were administered. His achievement was consistently below that of a first-grade child. He could not read a single word, and he could neither write nor print his name. Even though he could count from 1 to 10, he could not write any number or perform even the most elementary arithmetical operations.

The projective tests of personality (such as the *Rorschach, Bender-Gestalt,* and *Draw-a-Person*) that were administered indicated that Bobby was a very tense and anxious child. He perceived the world as a hostile and severely threatening place. Bobby felt rejected and worthless—no good to himself or to anyone else. Further, he passively "accepted" himself as worthless. What little aggressive reactions he did show were turned inward upon himself rather than expressed outward against the world.

The total picture was one of severe deprivations in all areas—emotional, physical, and social. Yet, despite the extremely harsh childhood experiences that had left deep impressions on Bobby, it was evident that the ego structure was relatively intact. He still had good potentialities for forming positive relationships with people once his initial fears of being hurt were allayed. However, his conflicts were severe and numerous. Bobby attempted to deal with them through withdrawal and repression.

In the light of the evidence it was concluded that Bobby was not a mentally retarded child, but, rather, was *pseudofeebleminded.* At the time of examination he was functioning at a mentally retarded level, but this was due to the extreme deprivations that the histories indicated he had experienced in so many areas, and not to any innate intellectual deficit.

Keeping in mind the general principles we have discussed in the foregoing pages, we shall now discuss the primary functions and characterestics of intelligence tests in general, then turn to consideration of methods of evaluation of intellectual and related functions. Next, we shall discuss methods of exploring personality characteristics and assessment of social factors. Finally, we shall discuss techniques of evaluating academic achievement and vocational aptitudes. At all times we shall stress the need for integration of all aspects of the retarded child.

THE PRIMARY CHARACTERISTICS AND FUNCTIONS OF PSYCHOLOGICAL TESTS

The psychological test has come to be regarded, perhaps unfortunately, as an "indispensable" and "self-sufficient" tool in the diagnosis and evaluation of suspected mental retardation. We have seen, from the preceding material, that the adequate assessment of a retarded child, however, involves much more than the information obtained through the administration of a psychological test or even a battery of such tests. No psychological test, by itself, should be used as the sole basis of diagnosis of retardation (or any other condition, for that matter). In particular, there has been overemphasis upon the utilization of intelligence tests, and they have been employed, in too many instances, as the sole diagnostic instruments for the evaluation of retardation. We shall return to this point in our discussion of intelligence tests.

Despite the overemphasis on the psychological test, it is of considerable value in many ways: (1) as an aid in the establishment of a more valid diagnosis of mental retardation; (2) in providing for a more adequate evaluation of the degree of retardation, both from quantitative and qualitative standpoints; and (3) for aid in the assessment of the retardate's skills, assets, and deficiencies in many areas, such as academic, social, intellectual, emotional, vocational, and the like.

In our present consideration of the characteristics and functions of psychological tests, we shall first consider what they purport to do in general. We shall then discuss the ways in which they are constructed.

The general functions of psychological tests

The fundamental purpose of any psychological test is to measure some human trait— to attempt to put into figures or to categorize in some other way a particular psychological characteristic of the individual. From one point of view such a device may be regarded as being somewhat analogous to a yardstick, or to some other measure by means of which we make various physical measurements. However, although they both "measure" something, there is an essential difference between the nature of a psychological test and that of a yardstick. By means of the yardstick we measure a property of an actually present physical object, an object that can be handled, felt, or seen. On the other hand, a psychological test attempts, in most instances, to measure attributes of the person by means of *indirect methods*. We often measure physical phenomena that possess similar intangible qualities, too. Examples of such measurements include measures of the strength of a magnetic field, or the strength of an electric current. In these instances what is measured cannot be directly perceived, but, rather, is inferred through the responses made by specially designed instruments. Their presence, as well as the degree of their strength, can *only be inferred from the observed reactions of the measuring instrument*. This kind of measurement is particularly true of psychological tests—the strength of the trait that is measured is inferred from the reaction to the test ("instrument"). In general, the more intangible the particular "thing" we attempt to measure, the more difficult it is to construct an instrument through which we can accurately make such a measurement. For example, it is relatively more easy for us to measure the length of a table top than it is to measure the amount of radioactivity present in the atmosphere. It is even more difficult for us to measure accurately the intensity of any particular psychological characteristic of the individual.

All types of measurement, physical as well as psychological, require that we apply some type of standard measuring instrument to the thing that we are attempting to measure. This allows us to make our desired measurement in a more meaningful way. In the National Bureau of Standards in Washington, D.C., there are very carefully preserved standards of length and weight for a foot, a yard, an ounce, a pound, a pint, a quart, and the like. These are the prototypes on which our everyday measuring instruments are based. Our everyday yardsticks and rulers are made to approximate the size of the basic standards as closely as possible. Because of the existence of the standards, we have no doubt at all as to the exact length of an inch, a foot, or a yard. Of course, these particular standards were first determined in a rather arbitrary way, but once determined they have been rigidly maintained. In the same way that standards had to be developed for the measurement of physical characteristics, so it was necessary that standards be developed for the measurement of various psychological characteristics, such as intelligence. The standard for the measurement of such characteristics is the test itself. In the same manner that we apply a yardstick to an object to measure its length, we may apply a psychological test to an individual to measure the strength of a particular psychological trait.

We cannot utilize a standard developed for the measurement of one characteristic to measure another. For example, we cannot properly measure the distance from point A to point B with a voltmeter. The standard must be applicable to the particular situation for which it is intended. This is also true of any psychological measurements that we wish to make. *The psychological test must be specific to the trait that we wish to measure.* For example, we cannot utilize a test (or standard) developed for the purpose of measuring reading ability to determine intellectual level. Each psychological standard (or test) must, therefore, be carefully developed to measure *validly* what it is supposed to measure, and it must be *selected* by the examiner to be properly applicable to the situation in which he applies it.

We should bear in mind, thus, that psychological tests are "standards" that are applied to individuals or groups in an attempt to measure some specific trait or some group (*cluster*) of traits. From one point of view, a psychological test may, therefore, be regarded as a standardized situation to which an individual is subjected. On the basis of his performance he may be compared with his peers, and the strength of a trait estimated.

Construction of psychological tests

We shall discuss several aspects of psychological test construction in the following paragraphs. Attention will be paid to: (1) test reliability, (2) test validity, and (3) general standardization procedures.

RELIABILITY. We stated earlier that our standards for physical measurement were precisely constructed and very carefully maintained. We try to be as sure as possible that they will not vary from one time to another. This is necessary so that repeated measurement of the same thing by the same standard under the same conditions will give us the same results. We wish to be sure that our measuring instrument measures *consistently*. If the obtained measure varies from one time to another, while the thing measured does not, then the measure is relatively worthless. If we measure a table top today and find it to be 5 feet 2 inches long, and measure it the next day and find it to be 5 feet 6 inches long, then one or more of the following three things may have happened: (1) the table top may have changed in length; (2) the standard that we are using may have changed; or (3) we may have incorrectly used the standard. If we can rule out incorrect use of the standard and the possibility of any significant change in the size of the table top, then the discrepancy in the measurements must be due to variability within the measuring instrument. We may conclude that the instrument does not measure *consistently* what it purports to measure. The degree of consistency of measurement by a test is referred to as *reliability*—the higher the reliability of a psychological test, or any other standard, the more consistently it measures a particular trait.

The reliability of a test is not an all-or-nothing matter; that is, a psychological test is not either totally reliable or unreliable. It is a matter of degree. A test must be sufficiently reliable, however, before we can utilize it to describe or predict human behavior. If an intelligence test, for example, yields markedly discrepant scores from one day to the next, then we must be skeptical regarding its reliability (provided, of course, that it is administered properly and that there is no corresponding change in the person tested).

The reliability of a test may be determined in many ways. One method is to administer two alternate (and equivalent) forms of the test to the same individual and see how closely the measured results agree. Another method is to retest the same person with the same test within a short interval of time. A third way is to divide the test into equivalent halves, and check one half against the other by giving both to the same person. (In this method we treat the single test as if it were two tests, using a procedure that is similar to the first method.)

In order to obtain a measure of the degree of reliability of a test we may give the same test to the same group of individuals on two occasions within a short time interval or we may give the same group two alternate forms of the test (or split-halves of the test) at the same time. Then we correlate the results, obtained by one of these methods, in order to determine the degree of reliability (*i.e.,* the *correlation coefficient*).*

If the same test is given twice, we keep the interval of time short to be sure that the individuals do not change in the meantime. The more nearly the two sets of measures agree the more reliable the test is, and the higher the correlation coefficient.

VALIDITY. We have stressed the fact that a test should measure consistently what it purports to measure. It is equally important that a test measure *validly* what it purports to measure. A measure of height should actually measure height, and not weight or any other dimension. A test of intelligence should measure intelligence and not, for example, reflect the amount of educational experience to which a person has been exposed. This implies that a psychological test should be constructed for a particular purpose. In the same way that a measure of length (a yardstick) cannot be used to measure weight, so a test purportedly measuring a certain personality trait cannot be used to measure some other trait. If a test measures adequately what it purports to measure, then it is said to be a valid test.

Like the reliability of a test, its validity is not an all-or-nothing affair. A test is usually not perfectly valid, but it must be a sufficiently valid psychological measure for the purpose that we wish to use it.

The validity of a test may be established by determining how well the test performance correlates with criteria that we have sufficient reason to believe are functions of the trait to be measured.[4] For example, tests of intelligence are usually checked against or *correlated* with the following kinds of criteria: (1) known groups of individuals (such as superior or mentally retarded); (2) scholastic grades and cumulative scholastic records; and (3) judgments and ratings by teachers. Adequate standardiza-

---

* *Correlation* refers to the relationship between two variables. If one variable changes in exactly the same degree as the other, the two variables are perfectly correlated. There is a constant relationship between the diameter of a circle and its circumference, for example. Traits may be *positively* correlated—that is, as one variable increases so does the other—or *negatively* correlated—with one variable decreasing as the other increases. A perfect positive correlation is expressed by the *correlation coefficient* of +1.00, and a perfect negative correlation by the coefficient of −1.00. A total lack of correlation is expressed as 0.00. Human traits are seldom perfectly correlated, but lie somewhere between +1.00 and −1.00. The greater the relationship is between two traits, the higher is the correlation coefficient (either positively or negatively).

[4] For a detailed discussion of reliability and validity see:
    (a) Anastasi, A., *Psychological Testing.* New York: The Macmillan Co., 1954.
    (b) American Psychological Association, *Technical Recommendations for Psychological Tests and Diagnostic Techniques.* Washington: American Psychological Association, 1954.

tion of a psychological test involves such procedures as the standardization of the techniques of administration of the test, refinement of the test items, selection of adequate samples of the population for standardization purposes, determination of the test validity, determination of the test reliability, the establishment of norms, and other such procedures.

STANDARDIZATION PROCEDURES. It is obvious from the foregoing discussion that any psychological test can only be as useful as the adequacy of its standardization permits.

Cronbach and Meehl[5] point out that three major types of validity studies of psychological tests have usually been employed. *Predictive validity* refers to studies in which the experimenter administers a test, obtains measures on certain criteria that he feels to be appropriate, and determines the correlation between the psychological test score and the criterion score. *Concurrent validity* studies are those in which the test score and criteria scores are obtained at the same time. *Content validity* refers to those studies in which the test items are shown to be adequate samples of the attributes of the person that the researcher is measuring. As Cronbach and Meehl point out, however, it is very difficult at times to establish adequate criteria with which to correlate the test. This is true when we deal with such a general trait as intelligence, and even more so when we deal with personality characteristics. To deal with such a situation they propose a fourth type of validation approach, called *construct validity*. It involves an acceptance by the researcher of an operational definition of what he wishes to measure, since the criteria themselves are inadequate. As we have pointed out, we have great difficulty in setting up adequate criteria of intelligence. Thurstone[6] noted that it has been the custom to define the validity of an intelligence test in terms of its correlation with some outside criterion, but he feels that this approach alone is too coarse, and should be considered obsolete. He feels that the validity of a test that measures intellectual functions should be determined by criteria of internal consistency—that is, how well the test items relate to each other.

As an example of standardization procedure we shall review the

(c) Cronbach, L. J., *Essentials of Psychological Testing.* New York: Harper & Row, Publishers, 1949.
(d) Garrett, H. E., *Statistics in Psychology and Education.* New York: David McKay Co., Inc., 1953.

[5] Cronbach, L. J., and Meehl, P. E., "Construct validity," *Psychol. Bull.*, 1955, *52*, 281–302.

[6] Thurstone, L. L., "The criterion problem in personality research," *Psychometr. Lab. Reps.*, No. 78. Chicago: University of Chicago Press, 1952.

method by which the *New Revised Stanford-Binet Tests* of intelligence were developed. Our presentation of the standardization of these tests is considerably simplified.[7] However, the following condensation will give the reader some awareness of the complexities of the problem.

First, a great many intelligence test items were examined, and a list of such items was drawn up. These items were then initially screened on the basis of their practical applicability and their known correlation with various other measures of intelligence. The most promising of these items were then selected on an *a priori* basis for preliminary trial. They were administered to approximately 1,000 subjects, but not all items were given to each subject. On the basis of the statistical findings, each of the items was then assigned to a particular chronological level (or level of intellectual difficulty). The best of these items were then selected according to the following criteria: (1) the apparent validity of the items; (2) the ease and objectivity of the scoring of the item; and (3) such practical considerations as the time necessary to administer the item, its interest to the subject, and the need for including a variety of types of items in the final test. (About 30% more items were included in the provisional scale thus established than were included in the final scale.) The next step was to provide intensive training to examiners in the methods of administration of the provisional scale. They were given two months of closely supervised training so that each examiner would administer the test in exactly the proper manner.

Great care was given to the selection of the children (the standardization population) upon whom the test was then finally standardized. All subjects of the first standardization were American-born, white children. In order to ensure proper geographical distribution, children from seventeen different communities of the country were selected. Rural as well as urban children were proportionately included. A tabulation of the socio-economic levels of the children's parents was made, the population was matched with that taken from a census report. Care was also taken to utilize a representative sample of both preschool and older children, since such children were not randomly available. A total of 3,184 subjects was utilized in the first standardization of the test.

Following this preliminary part of the standardization, the least satisfactory test items were eliminated, and the test blanks rechecked for accuracy of scoring by the various examiners. The test items that were retained were then statistically re-examined, and given their final age

[7] For a more detailed discussion of this method the reader is referred to: Terman, L. M., and Merrill, M. A., *Measuring Intelligence*. Boston: Houghton Mifflin Company, 1937.

placement in terms of difficulty. Reliability and validity studies were conducted. (These are still being continued with the present scales.) Thus, the standardization of the *New Revised Stanford-Binet* involved: (1) selection of suitable test items; (2) perfection of methods of administration; (3) adequate sampling of the population for standardization purposes; (4) determination of the test norms; and (5) continuing studies relating to the reliability and validity of the test. This simplified account gives evidence of the variety of procedures and the great amount of labor involved in the standardization of the psychological test.

ASSESSMENT OF INTELLECTUAL FACTORS

There are several types of tests for determining the intellectual capacities of children. We shall discuss some of the more widely used of these tests in the following pages. Our presentation will include such types of tests as intelligence tests and developmental scales.

Intelligence tests

We shall first briefly discuss the early history of intelligence testing, and then discuss some specific tests. It was as recently as 1890 that the term "mental test" was first used by Cattell in American psychological literature.[8] At that time Cattell was interested in determining the intellectual capacities of college students. The tests he devised and employed involved, predominantly, sensory and perceptual functions, such as vision, reaction times, and memory. This was in keeping with the emphasis placed on such functions by psychologists at that time. It was thought that tests of such functions would provide measures of the individual's intellectual capacities. This approach was criticized by Binet and Henri, in France, who felt that measures of sensory and perceptual functions were not adequate indices of intellectual capacities.[9] Their belief was shared by other psychologists.

In 1904 the Minister of Public Instruction in Paris became concerned about children who were not responding adequately to instruction in the public schools, and he appointed a commission to study the matter. This Commission included Binet and Henri. As part of their attack on the problem they devised an intelligence test in an attempt to classify the children in terms of their capacities to learn and to profit from classroom instruction. Although they included some sensory and perceptual items

[8] Cattell, J. McK., "Mental tests and measurements," *Mind*, 1890, *15*, 373–380.
[9] Binet, A., and Henri, V., "La psychologie individuelle," *Année Psychol.*, 1895, *2*, 411–463.

in their test, they stressed language items. This first scale was modified by Binet and Henri in 1908, and was further modified by them in 1911. The test was first used in America by Henry Goddard at the training school for mentally retarded children at Vineland, New Jersey. The most widely used early American revision of the Binet test was published in 1916 by Terman and Merrill. Thus, the modern intelligence testing movement is only about 50 years old.

A number of basic assumptions underlie all intelligence testing, and we should become familiar with them in order to understand the values and limitations of all intelligence tests. Whenever a child is given an intelligence test it is assumed that he has had the background and experiences suitable to the test that is employed. (For example, a test that is dependent upon language functions cannot be given to a child who has not had an adequate background in such language functions.) Further, it must be assumed that the test is given and scored by an examiner who has been adequately trained in the administration and interpretation of the test. Another basic assumption is that the child functions on the test in a manner that is indicative of his true capacities. This implies that the child is adequately motivated to take the test, is cooperative in the test situation, is not unduly anxious, and is not physically incapable of responding maximally to the test items.

The changes which have occurred in the concepts of intelligence and intellectual functioning have also made it necessary to revise our thinking concerning intelligence tests. (See Chapter Three.) As we have indicated, it is essential that cognitive abilities be assessed in the best possible manner. There is considerable doubt, however, whether our present instruments (intelligence tests) really do the job that we would like them to do.

Gallagher and Moss have summarized some of the implications of the more modern concepts of intelligence as they pertain to the evaluation of mentally retarded children.[10] They state that there are four major generalities in regard to measures of intelligence that are commonly accepted at this time. These are summarized as follows:

1. It is agreed that intelligence test scores are not too stable in children. They may fluctuate widely during the first ten years of the child's life. It is the experience of the authors, supported by research studies, that the greater the maladjustment of the child, the more likely there will be significant variability in intelligence test scores.

[10] Gallagher, J., and Moss, J., "New concepts of intelligence and their effect on exceptional children," *Except. Child.*, 1963, *30*, 1–4.

2. The same intelligence tests measure different cognitive functions at different ages.
3. Each test measures only a small part of the complex phenomenon we call intelligence. There are (as we shall see later in this chapter) a large number of intelligence tests, each purporting to measure various abilities and cognitive functions. But these tests only tap a portion of the total cognitive abilities of the child. It may well be that some of the more important and fundamental factors are as yet unknown, and so are not evaluated by our present instruments.
4. Gallagher states that intelligence tests have three major functions that are often confused with each other. These are: *first*, to predict school performance; *second*, to determine the patterning of abilities in a given child; and *third*, to provide information leading to clarification of the child's problems.

Since the time of the Binet tests, many different types of intelligence tests have been developed for use with children. They may be classified as follows: (1) individual tests, (2) group (paper and pencil) tests, (3) verbal tests, and (4) performance tests. Each of these will be discussed in turn, in the following sections.

A given intelligence test may be an individual verbal test, an individual performance test, a group verbal test or a group non-verbal (or performance) test.

There are many types of intelligence tests, and the particular test used should be carefully selected in terms of the particular characteristics of the child. Any interpretation of a test is dependent upon its particular characteristics as well as those of the child who is being tested. When told of the results of an intelligence test, we must always ask: "What type of test was administered?" and "Was this type of test suitable for this child?"

INDIVIDUAL INTELLIGENCE TESTS.   As the name implies, an individual intelligence test is one that has been developed for administration to only one person at a time. This type of test usually provides us with the best possible estimate of the child's intellectual level. Since the examiner has to interact with only one person at a time, the situation permits him to form a suitable relationship with the child during the period of test administration. The examiner is, therefore, able to provide suitable motivation for the test and is able to make more valid observations of the child's reactions and behavior, and is, therefore, better able to interpret the test results.

GROUP AND PAPER AND PENCIL TESTS.   Group intelligence tests are constructed so as to be given to a number of children simultaneously. A class of children, or an entire small school, for example, may be examined at the same time. This type of test has the advantage of being a considerable time-saver, since test results may be secured for a group of children in the same length of time it would ordinarily take to secure results on one child by means of an individual examination. However, such tests do not permit the examiner to make extensive behavioral observations of each child. Opportunities for developing and evaluating interpersonal relationships are not as adequate as in the case of individual examinations. The results of a group test are, in general, not as valid as those obtained with the use of an individual intelligence test. The greatest value of group tests is their use as a general screening instrument to determine the possible need for more detailed assessment of certain children.

Paper and pencil tests consist of a series of questions or tasks that are printed on paper. This printed material is given to the child, and he is required to perform the task or answer the question by writing on the test blank. Instructions, however, may be given orally by an examiner. Most group tests of intelligence are paper and pencil tests. The content of such tests may involve either verbal or performance skills.

VERBAL TESTS. *Verbal* tests require the use of language on the part of the child. Such tests may be of the individual or group variety. The child is asked questions depending on language comprehension, and responds verbally. Examples of verbal test questions are: "If you bought nine cents worth of candy, and gave the clerk a dime, how much change would you get back?" or "When is Lincoln's birthday?" There are many types of verbal items. For example, they may deal with reasoning capacities ("What makes a sailboat move?"), with memory ("Repeat after me: I saw a pretty little dog on the street"), with verbal proficiency ("What does 'scorch' mean?"), and the like. The use of such tests presupposes that the child has had the average exposure (for a child of his age) to language experience, and has no auditory or speech difficulties that would significantly affect the test results. If these assumptions are not correct, a verbal test is not applicable and will not yield a valid measure of intellectual capacities.

PERFORMANCE TESTS. Performance tests are non-verbal in nature and do not require any significant use of language on the part of the child. In many tests of this type, instructions can be given in pantomime. The familiar formboard, in which the individual is required to place differently shaped blocks in their proper holes, is an example of a performance test. Tests of this kind are useful in a variety of situations. The child's background may have been so impoverished that he did not have adequate experience with language; or he might have come from a foreign country; or perhaps he might suffer from auditory or speech defects that would tend to impair his responses on verbal tests. In such cases a performance test may give a more valid estimate of the child's intellectual capacities than a verbal test. Obviously, performance tests should not be used if the child has physical or sensory defects (such as a crippled hand or extremely poor vision) that would significantly impair his test performance. As in the case of the verbal tests, performance tests may be either individual or group tests, but, as might be expected from the nature of such tests, most are devised for individual administration.

The results of many studies show that performance tests do not correlate highly with verbal tests of intelligence. Thus, it may be said that verbal and performance tests do not measure the same kinds of intellectual functions. Each of these types of intelligence tests contributes uniquely to the assessment of the intellectual capacities of the retarded child.

The Grace Arthur Formboard (Courtesy Test Division, C. H. Stoelting Company, Chicago)

Mental age concept

Items on an intelligence test may be arranged (*ordered*) acccording to their difficulty. For example, we could group together several test items that could be successfully completed by average 10-year-old children, but not by average 8-year-old children. In theory, we might expect that an average 10-year-old child should be able to pass all items at the 10-year and lower levels, and would fail all items above the 10-year level. However, this is not the case. An average 10-year-old child is usually able to pass most 10-year-old items, fails a few items at lower levels, and passes a few items at higher levels. Nevertheless, his results on the test add up to a total mental age of 10 years. For example, on the 1937 *Revised Stanford-Binet* test he might perform in the following manner:

Year level	Number of items passed
8	all
9	5
10	5
11	2
12	none

He obtains a total mental age of 10 years (obtained by adding to the "basal age" of 8 years, 2 months credit for each of the 12 items passed on years 9 through 11, a total of 24 months), even though he failed items at the 9- and 10-year levels and passed items at the 11-year level. If a child who had a chronological age of 9 years obtained a mental age of 10 years, he would be advanced one year in intellectual development; if he had a chronological age of 11 years, then he would be retarded one year in intellectual development.

We should be very careful to understand the *meaning* of a given mental age (or M.A.). If a child of 8 years has an M.A. of 10 years, it does not mean that he is exactly *like* an average 10-year-old child. Because he may not have had some experiences appropriate for the test, because of emotional factors, and because of certain maturational factors in which children differ, an 8-year-old child with an M.A. of 10 is different from both a 10-year-old child and a 12-year-old child, each with an M.A. of 10 years. An M.A. of 10 years simply means that, on a particular test, a child achieved successes that are achieved by average 10-year-old children. Similarly, if a child of 8 years achieves an M.A. of 6 years, it does not mean that he is exactly *like* an average 6-year-old child. It means that the child achieved, on that test, successes that are ordinarily achieved by the average 6-year-old child. We, therefore, cannot evaluate mental age by itself—it must be considered in relation to the chronological age of the child.

One convenient way of expressing this relationship is through the use of the *intelligence quotient* (or *I.Q.*). This quotient expresses the ratio of the mental age to the chronological age (or *C.A.*) of the child. It is calculated by means of the following formula:

$$\text{I.Q.} = \frac{\text{M.A.}}{\text{C.A.}} \times 100$$

(The quotient is multiplied by 100 to eliminate the decimal point.) Thus, if a 10-year-old child has an M.A. of 10 years, he has an I.Q. of 100. If a 12-year-old child has an M.A. of 16, he has an I.Q. of 133. If a 10-year-old child has an M.A. of 7, he has an I.Q. of 70.

Thus, children with the same mental age may differ widely from each other, and do not necessarily function in the same way. A child with a C.A. of 8 years and an M.A. of 10 years differs from a child with a C.A. of 12 years and an M.A. of 10 years—the former is *brighter*. The I.Q. may thus be considered an index that expresses the brightness of a particular child.

OBJECTIONS TO THE MENTAL AGE CONCEPT.   As we have implied in the previous discussion, the mental age concept has certain limitations. The most general limitation, as we have already noted, is that the mental age is an *average score* that is obtained on test items from various age levels. Therefore, the M.A. does not completely and accurately characterize the mental ability of all persons whose average score is the same. (This is true of all averages.)

David Wechsler has offered another objection to the use of the M.A. as a basis for obtaining the I.Q.[11] He points out, and in our opinion quite rightly, that the use of M.A. limits the possible range of scores that may be made on a particular intelligence test. One reason for this, as many studies have shown, is that, on the average, M.A. scores do not continue to increase with increasing chronological age. A person 60 years of age obviously does not have an M.A. of 60 years, even if he is average in intelligence. If the test is too easy, then the top M.A. obtained on that test will tend to be too low. *Mental age is only a score.* If the test on which it is based is an easy one, then subjects will tend to achieve the maximum score at a lower age (on the average) than if the test is a more difficult one. On the easier test, therefore, a high M.A. *may* not be indicative of the person's true intellectual capacities. Such a score may be misleading. Wechsler offers the example of an individual who achieves an M.A. of 20 years on a test. This score can be interpreted as (1) the average mental age of a person 20 years of age, or (2) a score higher than that of the average person but expressed in terms of mental age. As we have stated, there is a point beyond which M.A. scores cease to increase with increasing chronological age. Wechsler feels that if the M.A. is higher than that obtained by the age group where such an increase

---

[11] For a complete discussion of this point of view see: Wechsler, D., *The Measurement of Adult Intelligence*. Baltimore: The Williams & Wilkins Co., 1944, pp. 19–35.

stops, then it cannot adequately be utilized to define levels of mental ability.

Wechsler also objects to the utilization of the C.A. as a divisor in computing the I.Q. He states that the C.A. is also a score—it is the number of months an individual has lived. It may be worthwhile to quote his argument:[12]

An intelligence quotient is the ratio between a particular score which an individual gets (on a given intelligence test) and the score which an average individual of his life age may be assumed to attain on the same test, when both scores are expressed in the same notation (*e.g.*, in terms of months and year). The usual formula:

$$\text{I.Q.} = \frac{\text{M.A.}}{\text{C.A.}}$$

should be really stated as follows:

$$\text{I.Q.} = \frac{\text{Attained or actual score}}{\text{Expected mean score for age}}$$

According to Wechsler, then, the intelligence quotient defines *relative* intelligence. It has been assumed by many authorities to be largely constant, but, as he stresses, many studies indicate that it does not remain constant when extreme groups (such as bright or retarded children) are studied, although it does tend to remain *relatively* constant for individuals ranking at about an average level.* He also points out that, in practice, we cannot use the person's actual C.A. as the denominator in arriving at the I.Q.—but, rather, we use the highest C.A. beyond which M.A. has been demonstrated *not* to increase (for the particular test). When we use a fixed denominator for ages beyond that point, then we assume that mental ability is constant with increasing age after the critical level is reached. When this procedure is followed we are actually comparing individuals not with those of their own age group, but, rather, with a highly selected group, probably of superior persons. We are thus computing what is probably an *efficiency quotient* rather than an intelligence quotient. To summarize, Wechsler objects to the usual practice of utilizing the M.A. in arriving at the I.Q. on the following grounds: (1) the I.Q. is not equally constant in all ranges of intelligence, but is relatively constant only around the average range; (2) the I.Q. is not constant for all ages, because a linear relationship between M.A. and C.A. is

---

[12] *Ibid.*, p. 24.

* See discussion of constancy of intelligence quotient at a later point in this chapter.

not maintained; and (3) I.Q.'s computed for adult subjects are really efficiency quotients.

In the standardization of his own intelligence scale, Wechsler eliminated the use of the M.A. but retained that of the I.Q. However, on his test the I.Q. merely defines a person's relative position in the particular group with which he is being compared (his own age group). The I.Q. is computed by comparing directly the number of points achieved on the test with a distribution of the scores achieved by the standardization group of the same age. Wechsler feels that this is a much more adequate procedure than the use of the M.A. in arriving at the I.Q. because: (1) it does not require assumptions about relationships between mental and chronological ratings of growth; (2) it does not require that we use any fixed average adult M.A., as each age defines its own denominator; (3) the I.Q.'s obtained by his method have some meaning at all age levels; and (4) the obtained I.Q. retains the only important meaning of an intelligence quotient—as an index of relative brightness.

Some individual intelligence tests for children

There have been a very large number of intelligence tests constructed during the past several years—far too many to review in detail at this point. However, we shall review several of the most important and most commonly used tests. We shall confine our discussion to individual intelligence tests. The ones that we shall discuss are: (1) the Terman-Merrill revisions of the *Stanford-Binet Test* (essentially verbal in nature); (2) the *Wechsler Intelligence Scale For Children* (combining both verbal and non-verbal scales); (3) the *Grace Arthur Point Scale of Performance Test;* (4) the *Progressive Matrices Test;* and (5) the *David-Eells Games.* We shall then turn our attention to representative tests constructed for specific application to infants and very young children.

THE 1937 REVISED STANFORD-BINET. The original Stanford revision of the *Binet-Simon Intelligence Test* (developed by Terman) was first published in America in 1916. It continued to be the most widely used individual test of intelligence until the new revisions of the scale by Terman and Merrill, first published in 1937, gradually took its place. As pointed out by Terman and Merrill, it was felt by most psychologists using the original 1916 scale that; (1) it did not provide adequate measures of intelligence at either end of the scale (at either the very young or adult levels); (2) it was inadequately standardized; (3) no alternate form was available for retesting purposes; and (4) the considerable length of time that had passed since the 1916 scale was constructed caused many of the items to become "dated." For these reasons, among others, Lewis M. Terman and Maud A. Merrill undertook the tremendous task of constructing what amounted to two entirely new tests of intelligence. These two forms of the test were different with respect to specific content, but were equivalent with respect to "difficulty, range reliability, and validity." The first of these they called *Form L* and the second *Form M*. They believed that these new scales covered a wider chronological age range, were more adequately standardized, provided a richer sampling of abilities, and had more rigidly defined procedures than did the older 1916 scale.[13] Both revisions utilized the basic assumptions of Binet's mental age scale of measuring intelligence. Each form contains a total of 129 test items. (The earlier form of the test contained 90 items.) Each form of the revised scale extends from the two-year level to the Superior Adult III level, and is thus applicable to individuals ranging in age from early childhood to the adult level. The items are arranged or grouped by age levels. The test items, of course, increase in difficulty from one year level to the next. Credit, in terms of a number of months of mental age, is given for each task correctly completed by the subject. Table 8 summarizes the year level, number of tasks at each level, credit for each successfully completed task at each level, and a sample item from each level.

In administering the test, the subject is given items from several levels so that a *basal age* is established (the highest level at which he passes all the items), and a *maximal age* (the lowest level at which he fails all the items). All the test items of the intervening year levels are also administered. Credit (in terms of months of mental age) is given for each of the items passed (see page 256). These partial credits are then added to the basal age, the total then being the mental age of the subject. An example of this method of scoring follows:

Year Level	Items Passed	Mental Age Credit for Each Item	Total Credit
VII	6 (all)	2 months	7 years (basal age)
VIII	4	2 months	8 months
IX	3	2 months	6 months
X	1	2 months	2 months
XI	0	2 months	0 months
			Total M.A. = 8 years 4 months

---

[13] See Terman and Merrill, *op. cit.*

TABLE 8. REPRESENTATIVE ITEMS OF THE 1937 TERMAN-MERRILL REVISION OF THE STANFORD-BINET (FORM L)

Year Level	Number of Items	Credit for Each Item (Months)	Representative Item
II	6	1	A card with pictures of common objects is shown. The child is asked to identify the objects.
II-6	6	1	The child is asked to repeat a series of 2 digits.
III	6	1	The child is asked to copy a circle.
III-6	6	1	The child is asked to tell about a picture.
IV	6	1	The child is asked to complete a drawing of a man.
IV-6	6	1	The child is asked to identify the "prettier" of two pictures.
V	6	1	The child is asked to count a series of objects.
VI	6	2	The child is shown pictures of common objects with parts missing. He is asked to name the missing parts.
VII	6	2	The child is shown pictures depicting absurd situations. He is asked to recognize the absurdity.
VIII	6	2	The child is asked to define a series of words.
IX	6	2	A series of absurd situations is related, and the child asked to identify the absurdity.
X	6	2	The child is asked to repeat a series of 6 digits.
XI	6	2	The child is asked to define abstract words.
XII	6	2	The child is asked to repeat a series of digits backwards.
XIII	6	2	The child is asked to repeat a series of words.
XIV	6	2	The child is given an absurd picture and asked to spot the absurdity.
Average adult	8	2	The subject is asked to give the difference between pairs of abstract words.
Superior adult I	6	4	The subject is asked to give the similarity between pairs of words.
Superior adult II	6	5	The subject is asked to reconcile pairs of words that have opposite meanings.
Superior adult III	6	6	The subject is asked to repeat a series of digits from memory.

256

It is assumed that the child would pass all items below year VII and fail all items above year XI. His mental age, therefore, would be 7 years plus 16 months, or 8 years, 4 months (100 months). If he were 7 years and 6 months of age at the time of the examination his I.Q. (computed by dividing his M.A. of 100 months by the C.A. of 90 months and multiplying this ratio by 100) would, therefore, be 111. In computing the I.Q. of an adult a correction is made in the C.A. utilized. The highest C.A. used in computing the I.Q. of an adult is 15 years and 6 months, regardless of actual C.A. The highest possible I.Q. that can be achieved by an adult is 152.

As may be noted from the type of items listed in Table 8, the *Revised Stanford-Binet* scale is essentially verbal in nature. A few performance items are included, particularly at the lower end of the scale, but the test is predominantly verbal. It requires approximately one hour to administer. It should be observed that the tasks are essentially different at the various year levels.

The latest revision of the Binet test by Terman (the third such revision) was published in 1960.[14] It retains the essential characteristics of the preceding *Stanford-Binet* tests, but incorporates in one form the subtests from Forms L and M of the 1937 scales thought to be most valid. The "new" test is called the *L-M Form*. A group of 4,498 children between the ages of 2 years, 6 months and 18 years was used to prepare the new scale. The criteria for selection of the test items were: (1) increase in per cent passing with age (or mental age); and (2) validity, which was determined by biserial correlation of the items with the total test score. Some subtests were found to have changed in difficulty since the time of the original standardization, and these, in the new revision, were either relocated at a more appropriate age level, or dropped entirely.

Previously accumulated standardization data relative to the distribution of I.Q.'s by age on the 1937 scales demonstrated that the obtained I.Q.'s showed atypical variability at certain age levels. In the 1960 revision Terman dealt with this problem by introducing adjustments so that the average mental age derived by use of the L-M form of the scale more nearly corresponds to the average chronological age at each age level. Conversion tables were provided to correct for such atypical variability in I.Q. by age, so that the I.Q. is, in effect, a standard score which is more directly comparable for all chronological age groups.

Cronbach has summarized some of the shortcomings of the 1937

---

[14] Terman, L. M., and Merrill, M. A., *Stanford-Binet Intelligence Scale.* Boston: Houghton Mifflin Company, 1960.

Stanford-Binet scale.[15] These are: (1) the scores on the *Stanford-Binet* do not reflect native capacity, but are affected by previous educational experiences; (2) the subtests are essentially verbal in nature; (3) there is evidence to indicate that cultural differences affect the test scores; (4) scores at different levels represent different mental abilities; (5) the varying standard deviations affect the various I.Q. distributions; (6) the scores are affected by emotional involvements; and (7) specific mental abilities cannot be defined by use of the test..

Although these criticisms were made in regard to the 1937 revision of the Binet scales, they would apply just as well to the 1960 revision, since the materials have not been modified. Despite these limitations which we believe to be significant, many surveys agree in indicating that the *Stanford-Binet* test is one of the most widely used tests of intelligence. The clinician deals with its weaknesses by also employing other tests which are designed to measure more adequately in the areas in which the Binet is considered to be inadequate.

The L-M form of the *Stanford-Binet* is being utilized extensively for the evaluation of retarded children, and some validation studies have been published. A typical study is that of Rohrs and Haworth, who compared the 1960 Binet test with two older intelligence tests: the *Wechsler Intelligence Scale for Children (WISC)* and the *Goodenough Draw-A-Man* test.[16] The primary purpose of the study was to determine the degree of agreement between the 1960 Stanford-Binet and each of the other two tests. But, in addition, Rohrs and Haworth attempted to determine the degree to which the Binet test scatter pattern served to differentiate familial from organic brain damaged mental defectives. A total of 46 subjects were studied; of these, 20 were diagnosed as "familial," and 26 as "organic" mental defectives. The mean I.Q. for the familial group was 61.05, with a standard deviation of 5.61, while the mean I.Q. for the organic group was 61.15, with a standard deviation of 5.44. The mean age of the familial group was 12.5 years, and that of the organic group was 12.4 years.

For the group as a whole, the mean I.Q. was 61.12, with a standard deviation of 5.45; the mean age was 12.5 years, with a standard deviation of 1.98; and the mean length of institutionalization was 3.28 years.

Rohrs and Haworth found, for the total group, that the mean *Stanford-Binet* I.Q. was 56.91, the mean *WISC* I.Q. (Full Scale) was 52.76, and the mean *Goodenough Draw-A-Man* I.Q. was 56.46. The dif-

---

[15] Cronbacn, *op. cit.*

[16] Rohrs, R., and Haworth, M., "The 1960 Stanford-Binet, WISC and Goodenough tests with mentally retarded children," *Amer. J. ment. Defic.*, 1962, *67*, 853–859.

ference between the *Stanford-Binet* and *WISC* I.Q.'s was found to be statistically significant, while that between the *Stanford-Binet* and *Good-enough* quotients was not significant. It was also concluded that, on the L-M form of the *Stanford-Binet* test, the scatter patterns did not differentiate validly between the familial and organic mental retarded children.

THE WECHSLER-BELLEVUE INTELLIGENCE SCALE FOR CHILDREN. As pointed out in the previous section, the *Terman-Merrill* tests are based on the mental age concept, and the test items are grouped at their appropriate levels. Since each year level includes different test items, the items given to a particular child will thus vary in accordance with his chronological age and intellectual capacities. Thus, different test items are given to an average 10-year-old child than to an average 8-year-old child, although there may be some overlap at the upper extreme of items for the 8-year-old and lower extreme of the items for the 10-year-old. The *Wechsler* scale is, however, constructed in an entirely different manner. (See the section dealing with Wechsler's objections to the mental age concept.) Each child is given the same test items regardless of his mental or chronological age; there are no groupings of items according to year level. The child is given credit for each item he passes. The score consists of the total weighted credits earned on all subtests (the raw subtest scores are converted into weighted scores and these are then totaled). This total weighted score is converted directly into an I.Q. by means of tables for each chronological age group. The younger the child, the higher is the I.Q. that is allotted to a particular total weighted score. A child 10 years of age achieving a total weighted score of 80 would thus score a higher I.Q. than a child 12 years of age achieving the same score.

The *Wechsler* scale is divided into two major sections: (1) a verbal scale, yielding a verbal I.Q., and (2) a performance scale, giving a performance I.Q. Scores on both sections are combined, yielding a full-scale I.Q.

The verbal section of the scale consists of five categories (subtests) of items, plus an alternate category. These are:

1. *General information:* The child is asked questions relating to his fund of general information.
2. *General comprehension:* These items measure the child's capacity to use common information in dealing with everyday situations.
3. *Arithmetic:* These items consist of arithmetic problems to be solved mentally.
4. *Similarities:* The child is required to state how paired objects are similar in nature. This subtest measures verbal concept formation.

5. *Vocabulary:* The child is asked to define, in his own language, a series of words.

The performance section is also composed of five subtests, plus an alternate category. These are:

1. *Picture completion:* The child is presented with a series of pictures, each of which has a part missing. He is asked to state what is missing from each of the pictures.
2. *Picture arrangement:* This category is composed of a series of groups of separate pictures depicting various incidents. Each group is presented in a mixed-up order to the child, who is then asked to put the pictures in the proper (temporal) order.
3. *Block design:* The child is given a number of blocks, all of which are colored in the same way. The faces of each block have different colors. He is given a number of cards, on each of which there is a design printed, and is told to reconstruct each design using the colored blocks.
4. *Object assembly:* This subtest consists of a number of objects, each of which has been cut into a number of pieces (like a very much simplified jigsaw puzzle). The pieces for each object are presented in turn to the child, who is told to "put it together again."
5. *Coding:* The child is given a code, and is requested to translate a series of symbols according to the code.

Studies of correlations between the *Wechsler* scale and other intelligence tests indicate that the verbal portion of the scale correlates most highly with other verbal tests, such as the *Revised Stanford-Binet*, whereas the performance section correlates most highly with such other performance tests as the *Grace Arthur Point Scale of Performance Test*.

The *Wechsler Intelligence Scale* is designed to be used for children between the ages of 5 and 15 years.

Thorn, Schulman, and Kasper have reported on the reliability and stability of the *WISC* when used with retarded boys.[17] They studied a group of 39 mentally retarded boys, whose chronological ages ranged from 11 years to 14 years, 11 months. The range in verbal I.Q. for the group was 49 to 79, the range in performance I.Q. was 33 to 87, and the range in full-scale I.Q. was 36 to 69. Thorn and his co-workers retested their subjects with the *WISC* after a three- to four-month interval. They reported the following test-retest correlation coefficients: full-scale I.Q., .95; verbal I.Q., .92; performance I.Q., .89. They also reported that the test-retest correlation coefficients for the subtests of this scale were highly

---

[17] Thorn, M., Schulman, J., and Kasper, J., "Reliability and stability of the WISC for a group of mentally retarded boys," *Amer. J. ment. Defic.*, 1962, *67*, 455–457.

reliable. It may be concluded that, *under the conditions of this study,* the *WISC* was a reliable intelligence test for mentally retarded children over a short period of time.

Many investigators have been concerned with the development of a short form of the *Wechsler Intelligence Scale* for children, in order to reduce the time involved in the assessment process. For instance, Finley and Thompson have developed one such form, which they report as correlating highly with the full *WISC*.[18] Kilman and Fisher have applied this abbreviated scale to the evaluation of both brain-damaged and familial retardates.[19] They first examined 145 mentally retarded children between the ages of 8 and 16, and then divided them into three groups. In the first, the undifferentiated group, there were 70 children, with a mean chronological age of 12 years, 9 months; in the second, the brain-damaged group, there were 44 children, with a mean chronological age of 12 years, 6 months; and the third, the familial group, consisted of 31 children, with a mean age of 12 years, 4 months.

A regression equation was developed to predict the full-scale I.Q. from that obtained by use of the short form of the test. It was found that the mean I.Q. obtained by use of such a regression equation was significantly higher than the short-form I.Q. for all three groups. However, when the full-scale I.Q. was calculated by pro-rating the obtained short-form scores, there were no significant differences found between the full- and short-form I.Q.'s. The authors reported the following correlations between short- and full-scale I.Q.'s: for the total sample, .87; for the undifferentiated group, .91; for the brain-damaged group, .80; and for the familial group, .80.

It may be that short forms of intelligence tests have some value. But an intelligence test should not be regarded as an instrument designed only to yield a score. One does not give any intelligence test merely to obtain an I.Q. As we have previously pointed out, it also provides an opportunity to interact with the child, and to observe his behavioral reactions over a period of time. Any reduction in test material thus reduces the interaction potentials between the examiner and the child. Further, the *WISC* provides a variety of different tasks through which various functions can be assessed. Any short form of the test reduces the amount of the total information available to the clinician for evaluation. Since

---

[18] Finley, C., and Thompson, J., "An abbreviated Wechsler Intelligence Scale for Children, for the educable mentally retarded," *Amer. J. ment. Defic.*, 1958, *63*, 473–480.
[19] Kilman, B., and Fisher, G., "An evaluation of the Finley-Thompson abbreviated form of the WISC for undifferentiated brain damaged and familial retardates," *Amer. J. ment. Defic.*, 1960, *64*, 742–746.

the evaluative process should be one which is as complete as possible, and is an exceedingly difficult task at best, the use of a short form of an intelligence test is difficult to condone in the evaluation of a retarded child. It defeats the purpose of an adequate evaluation and has little place in the total assessment process if the results are to have value for the individual.

THE PEABODY PICTURE VOCABULARY TEST (PPVT). This test was developed by Dunn in order to assess the intellectual capacities of handicapped persons.[20] Essentially, it is a modified picture vocabulary test, in which the subject is required to point to the best picture in each set of four possible responses, or to say the number of the best picture in response to the stimulus word. The test is not timed, and only requires ten to fifteen minutes to administer to the usual subject. It was designed to test the physically or verbally handicapped subject, and is of particular value in assessing the intellectual potentials of persons who have difficulties in a prolonged testing situation.

Many studies have been centered upon the relationships between the *PPVT* and other measures of the characteristics of the retarded child, and it has been demonstrated that the *PPVT* correlates highly with measures of academic performance. For instance, Wolfsenberger correlated *PPVT* scores with academic achievement scores.[21] He utilized 61 subjects with a mean age of 18.12 years, and a mean *PPVT* mental age of 6.80 years. The obtained correlations between the *PPVT* scores and scholastic achievement scores were: .52 with reading; .33 with spelling; and .35 with arithmetic. He concluded that the *PPVT* correlated significantly with measures of academic achievement.

Mein correlated the *PPVT* test with the *Stanford-Binet* intelligence test.[22] A total of 80 institutionalized subjects with a mean mental age of 58.7 months were studied. Mein reported a correlation coefficient of .71 between the two tests, and it may be concluded that they were moderately correlated with each other. However, this degree of correlation indicates that considerable discrepancies do occur in the results obtained for some individuals with these two tests.

Budoff and Purseglove investigated the reliability of the *PPVT* with

[20] Dunn, P., *The Peabody Picture Vocabulary Test Manual.* Minneapolis: American Guidance Service, 1959.
[21] Wolfsenberger, W., "The correlation between Peabody Picture Vocabulary Test and achievement scores among retardates," *Amer. J. ment. Defic.,* 1962, *67,* 450–451.
[22] Mein, R., "Use of the PPVT with severely subnormal patients," *Amer. J. ment. Defic.,* 1962, *67,* 269–273.

mentally retarded individuals.[23] They administered the tests to a group of 46 retarded children on two separate occasions, one month apart. The same examiner administered both tests to each subject. A reliability coefficient of .80 was reported for the total sample, and it may be concluded that, for the group as a whole, the *PPVT*, as far as test-retest reliability is concerned, is only a moderately reliable test. However, when the total sample was divided into high- and low-I.Q. subjects, the reliability coefficient for the low-I.Q. group was found to be moderately high, but that for the high-I.Q. group was found to be only .45, which is quite low. Budoff and Purseglove concluded that questions may be raised as to the usefulness of the *PPVT* in assessing the intellectual capacities of high-grade institutionalized delinquents.

THE AMMONS FULL RANGE PICTURE VOCABULARY TEST. The *Ammons* test was developed in 1948, and is somewhat similar in principle to the *PPVT*. It was developed primarily to assess the intellectual capacities of children and others with severe handicaps, such as cerebral palsy, and it has proved to be of value in evaluating mentally retarded children. For example, Ho and White studied the use of the *Ammons* test with retardates.[24] They gave the *Ammons* and Form L of the 1937 *Stanford-Binet* test to 100 retarded children between the ages of 4 and 18. All of the subjects had a *Stanford-Binet* I.Q. of less than 80. The mean *Binet* I.Q. was 51, with a standard deviation of 14, and the mean *Ammons* quotient was 66, with a standard deviation of 18. The correlation coefficient between the two tests was .87, indicating a high degree of correlation.

Ho and White concluded that the *Ammons* test may be used to supplement other tests for mentally retarded children. They further concluded that, even though the I.Q.'s correlated highly, the mean *Ammons* I.Q. was significantly higher than the mean *Stanford-Binet* quotient. Of course, considerable research is still needed before this test can be properly evaluated.

THE GRACE ARTHUR POINT SCALE OF PERFORMANCE TEST. *The Grace Arthur Point Scale of Performance Test* was first published in 1930.[25]

[23] Budoff, M., and Purseglove, E., "Peabody picture vocabulary test performance of institutionalized mentally retarded adolescents," *Amer. J. ment. Defic.*, 1963, *67*, 756–760.

[24] Ho, P., and White, D., "Use of the Full Range Picture Vocabulary Test with mentally retarded," *Amer. J. ment. Defic.*, 1963, *67*, 766–774.

[25] Arthur, G. A., *A Point Scale of Performance Tests*, Vol. I, *Clinical Manual* (2nd Ed.). New York: Commonwealth Fund, 1943.

Another performance test of value in the assessment of the retarded child is the *Cornell-Coxe Performance Ability Scale*. This test is composed of a number of per-

It is a performance test, and no items require the utilization of verbal abilities on the part of the subject. The test itself is composed of nine different categories of test items. These had previously been standardized as single tests of intelligence, or were parts of other scales. These subtests are described in the following paragraphs.

APPARATUS FOR THE GRACE ARTHUR TEST—FORM I (Courtesy Test Division, C. H. Stoelting Company, Chicago)

1. *The Two-Figure Formboard.* This is a formboard composed of two geometric figures that have been cut into several parts. The child is required to assemble the pieces in the appropriate spaces in the board. This test serves as an "icebreaker" or introductory test, and is not included in the final score.
2. *The Seguin Formboard.* This is a board with appropriately shaped recesses in which the subject is requested to place ten geometric forms (such as a square, star, oval, and circle).
3. *The Casuist Formboard.* A more difficult formboard.
4. *Mare and Foal.* This is a colored picture of a mare and foal. Several pieces are cut out of the picture, and the child is required to insert each piece in its appropriate place.

---

formance items that were previously used in the *Army Performance Scale.* See: Cornell, E. L., and Coxe, W. W., *A Performance Ability Scale: Examination Manual.* New York: Harcourt, Brace & World, Inc., 1934.

5. *Feature-Profile*. This is a profile of a human head that has been cut into eight pieces. The child is requested to assemble the profile. It is preceded by the Manikin Test. This is a model of a person, with the arms, legs, and head and trunk separated. The child is required to put them together to form a completed figure.

6. *The Healy Picture Completion*. This is a picture of a rural scene. Ten pieces, all squares, have been cut from the picture. The child is presented with a box containing a large number of pieces, each of which is the same size as the cutouts. He is required to select the appropriate pieces and insert them in the cutouts of the scene.

7. *Knox Cube*. This is a test of memory. Four cubes are placed in front of the child. The examiner than taps these, with another block, in varying sequences (*i.e.*, 1–2–3–4, 1–3–2–4, etc.). The child is required to tap the blocks in each of the sequences from memory.

8. *Porteus Mazes*. The child is presented with a series of printed mazes which are graduated in difficulty. He is required to trace the shortest path from the entrance to the exit in each maze.

9. *Kohs Block Design*. The child is given a number of one-inch cubes, all of which are colored in the same way. The faces of each block have different colors. He then is presented with a series of 17 colored designs, each of which is printed on a card, the series of designs being graduated in difficulty. He is required to assemble the blocks so as to reproduce the design on the card.

There are two alternate forms of the *Grace Arthur Test. Form II* contains a slightly different set of subtests.[26] *Form I* was standardized on children between the ages of 5 and 15. *Form II* has a slightly larger range in norms, and depends less than *Form I* on verbal directions. Points are given to the child for successes or partial successes on each of the subtests. These points are totaled and are translated into a mental age. An I.Q. is then computed.

THE PORTEUS MAZE TEST. The *Porteus Maze* test consists of a series of increasingly difficult printed mazes which are given to the child to solve in an individual test situation. The mazes were developed by Porteus, who in 1913 worked with mentally defective children in Sidney, Australia, and who first published the results of his work in 1915.[27] The maze test has been used extensively since that time in evaluating the intellectual functions of mentally retarded children.

Porteus maintains that traditional psychological concepts of intelli-

[26] Arthur, G. A., *A Point Scale of Performance Tests, Revised Form II. Manual for Administering and Scoring the Tests*. New York: Psychological Corp., 1947.

[27] Porteus, S., "Mental tests for the feebleminded: A new series," *J. Psycho-Asthenics*, 1915, *19*, 200–213.

gence omit consideration of the child's *planning ability* as an essential component of the nature of intelligence.[28] This, he states, includes *"prevision and prehearsal"* as necessary factors in the attainment of a goal. Porteus maintains that planning and foresight have been considered as non-intellectual factors, instead of being considered as fundamental components of all intelligent behavior. These two functions are supposed to be tapped by his *Maze* test, and this provides, according to Porteus, a better estimate of the social adjustment of the mentally retarded individual than does a test of intelligence like the *Stanford-Binet*.

There have been numerous studies conducted in an attempt to validate the *Porteus Maze* test. These are reviewed in the most recent work by Porteus.[29] An example of a recent study relating to the predictive value of the *Maze* test is the research completed by Dentler and Mackler, who studied the relationship of *Maze* scores to certain "functioning abilities" of retarded children.[30] Dentler and Mackler stated that it has been maintained that both the *Wechsler* intelligence scale for children and the *Stanford-Binet* intelligence test measure functions that are essentially restricted to verbal criteria. Further, both tests tend to ignore the assessment of cultural, maturational, and situational factors. On the other hand, the *Porteus Maze* test is more abstract and non-verbal in nature, so Dentler and Mackler proposed to investigate the relationships between *Porteus* scores and measures of specific behavioral functions.

The *Porteus Maze* test, and tests of language, social maturity, and accuracy of immediate surroundings, were administered to 29 institutionalized mentally retarded children. The mean chronological age of the subjects was 9.61, with a range of from 6.6 to 12.8 years, and the mean mental age was 5.5 years. Dentler and Mackler reported that the correlation between the *Porteus Maze* test and the accuracy of the surroundings test was 0.66, for the language test was 0.71, and for the social maturity test was 0.64. They concluded that the *Porteus Maze* test was of value in predicting specific functional abilities of the retarded child. The authors have found the *Porteus Maze* to be an excellent supplementary instrument for assessing the capacities of the retarded child, since it taps functions other than those measured by either the *Wechsler* or the *Binet* type of intelligence tests.

[28] Porteus, S., *The Maze Test and Clinical Psychology.* Palo Alto: Pacific Books, 1959.

[29] *Ibid.*

[30] Dentler, R., and Mackler, B., "The Porteus Maze Test as a prediction of the functioning abilities of retarded children," *J. consult. Psychol.*, 1962, *26*, 50–55.

THE PROGRESSIVE MATRICES TEST. *The Progressive Matrices Test* was developed in England by Raven.[31] This test consists of a total of 60 abstract designs, from each of which a portion has been deleted. They are graduated in order of difficulty. The child is required to select the missing piece for each design from either six or eight alternatives. Originally the test was standardized on individuals between the ages of 6 and 65 years of age, but a new revision in 1947 was standardized on children between the ages of 5 and 11. This is a performance type of test, and does not require the use of verbal abilities on the part of the subject.

THE DAVIS-EELLS GAMES. *The Davis-Eells Games Test* consists of a series of pictures that center around experiences thought to be common to children in our culture.[32] The examiner reads statements about each of the pictures, and the child is required to check on the test blank the most appropriate statement for each of the pictures. There are four subtests: (1) verbal problems, (2) money problems, (3) best-way problems, and (4) analogies. The originators of this test feel that it does not yield a conventional I.Q., but they prefer to regard the obtained score as an index of the child's problem-solving ability (*IPSF—Index of Problem Solving Factors*). This test is of interest, since it is felt to be free from specific influences of various subcultures and the social class biases of our society. It is designed for children in the first six grades of school.

Tests for infants

The psychological tests discussed in the previous section were not specifically designed for use with very young children or infants. With the exception of the *Terman-Merrill,* they are more properly applicable to children of about school age and up. The psychological examination of the infant poses unique problems that are not as pertinent in the examination of the older child. The infant cannot talk. Usually another person needs to be present during the examination, since the infant, because of physical immaturity, has either to lie down or be held by another person. Because of his social and emotional immaturity, the presence of a

---

[31] For detailed discussions of this test see:
    (a) Raven, J. C., "Standardization of Progressive Matrices, 1938," *J. Med. Psychol.,* 1941, *19, 137*–150.
    (b) ——, *Progressive Matrices, Sets I and II.* Dumbries, England: The Crichton-Royal, 1947.
    (c) ——, *Guide to Using Progressive Matrices* (Rev. Ed.). London: Lewis, 1952.
[32] Davis, A., and Eells, K., *Davis-Eells Games: Davis-Eells Test of General Intelligence or Problem-Solving Ability, Manual.* New York: Harcourt, Brace & World, Inc., 1953.

familiar person—usually the mother—is needed. His visual-motor functions are immature, and, of course, both fine and gross muscle controls have not yet been adequately established. Further, the infant cannot comprehend verbal instructions. For these reasons the tests and scales developed for the infant are based essentially on sensory reactions and rudimentary motor skills.

THE GESELL DEVELOPMENTAL SCHEDULES.   Probably the best known and most widely used instrument for the psychological evaluation of infants is the *Gesell Developmental Schedules.* Gesell and his co-workers at Yale University developed a number of such schedules.[33] They were standardized on infants as young as four weeks of age. They are unique, in that Gesell conducted longitudinal studies; that is, he followed up (through retesting) the *same* group of individuals over a period of time. They provide a means of evaluating the levels of behavior of the infant in four major areas. These are:

1. *Motor behavior.* Here both gross and fine motor reactions are evaluated. (How does the infant sit? Does he walk or creep? Does he reach for objects? Can he manipulate objects?)
2. *Adaptive behavior.* This portion of the schedule is concerned with visual-motor reactions and solution of problems. (How does the infant react to the ringing of a bell, or a dangling object?)
3. *Language behavior.* This area refers to all means of communication, which include reaction to attempts at communication by others. (What changes occur in facial expressions, posture, gesture, and the like?)
4. *Personal-social behavior.* This involves the infant's reactions to the particular social environment in which he is reared. (How does he play and feed? What are his toilet training responses? Does he smile? How does he respond to other individuals?)

In administering these schedules, the essential role of the examiner is to present test objects and to evaluate the responses made by the infant. In interpreting the nature of the infant's development, use is made of data obtained through interview with the parents (usually the mother).

In the case of these schedules, unlike the previously discussed tests, no single score or I.Q. is computed for the entire test. Rather, each of the four developmental areas is evaluated by the examiner, sometimes on the basis of subjective judgments, and a *developmental age* (in months) is assigned to the infant's performance in each. This is done by comparing (on a subjective basis) the infant's reactions with the norms for infants

[33] Gesell, A., *et al., Gesell Developmental Schedules.* New York: Psychological Corp., 1949; see also: Gesell, A., and Amatruda, C. S., *Developmental Diagnosis* (2nd Ed.). New York: Hoeber Med. Div., Harper & Row, Publishers, 1949.

and children at ages 4, 18, 28, and 40 weeks, and at ages 12, 18, 24, and 36 months. In this way the extent of the child's retardation may be estimated.

THE CATTELL INFANT INTELLIGENCE SCALE. Cattell has developed a downward extension of *Form L* of the *Terman-Merrill Scales*.[34] Included in this extension is material from *Form L* of those scales, selected material from the *Gesell Developmental Scales,* and new test items devised by Cattell. The revised scale extends from a low chronological age of two months to a high age of 30 months. As in the case of the developmental schedules, the test items deal chiefly with perceptual and motor reactions. The scale yields an I.Q. that is supposed to be comparable to that obtained on the *Stanford-Binet.*

Many other intelligence tests have been devised for use with infants. Characteristics of several of these are summarized in Table 9.

TABLE 9.   REPRESENTATIVE INTELLIGENCE TESTS FOR YOUNGER CHILDREN

Test	Age Range	Method of Reporting Results
California First Year Mental Scale	1 to 18 months	M.A., I.Q., and Standard Score
Cattell Infant Intelligence Scale	2 to 30 months	M.A. and I.Q.
Gesell Developmental Schedules	4 weeks to 36 months	Developmental age for each area evaluated
Gesell Pre-School Schedule	15 months to 6 years	Developmental ages
Kuhlmann-Binet (1939 revision)	4 months upward	I.Q.
Merrill-Palmer Scale	24 to 36 months	M.A., Percentile, Standard Score
Minnesota Pre-School Scale	3 to 5 years	C-Scores
Northwestern Infant Intelligence	4 to 36 weeks	I.Q.
Oseretsky Tests of Motor Proficiency	4 to 16 years	Motor Age
Valentine Intelligence Scale	2 to 8 years	M.A. and I.Q.
Vineland Social Maturity Scale	Birth to 25 years	Social Age and Social Quotient

ASSESSMENT OF PERSONALITY FACTORS

As we have noted, a very important part of the task of assessing the mentally retarded child is the evaluation of his personality charac-

[34] Cattell, P., *The Measurement of Intelligence of Infants and Young Children.* New York: Psychological Corp., 1947.

teristics. We shall first discuss the general characteristics of psychological tests designed for this purpose, then turn to a consideration of
specific personality tests.

Characteristics of personality tests

Personality tests are designed to explore the emotional characteristics
of the child. Like intelligence tests, they may be either group or individual in nature. In general, the group forms of personality tests are
not suitable for administration to retarded children. One reason for
this is that the group type of test is not as valid as the individual type.
The statements made previously in regard to group intelligence tests
would apply equally well to the group forms of personality tests. In addition, most group tests assume that the child can read adequately; therefore, the test items are usually beyond the comprehension of the retarded
child. Some persons have attempted to administer such tests to non-read-
ing children by reading the test aloud to them, and then writing down
the responses that the child makes, but such an approach is unsatisfactory, and it is unlikely that the results obtained in this manner are valid
representations of the retardate's personality characteristics. We prefer
to use tests designed for individual administration that do not depend on
the reading and writing abilities of the child.

Personality tests may also be characterized as being *structured,
partially structured,* or *unstructured* in form.[35] The psychological tests
previously discussed were, in general, highly standardized approaches
to the measurement of the intellectual capacities of the child. The test
tasks were specifically validated against various criteria of intellectual
functioning, and yield numerical scores that are considered to be indices
of intellectual abilities. In general, intelligence tests, such as the 1937
Stanford-Binet and the *Wechsler,* may be characterized as *structured*
tests, in which the test material has clearly apparent meaning and the
task to be performed is delineated as clearly as possible for the subject
—he is told as precisely as possible what he is to do. An *unstructured*
test is one in which the test material is ambiguous in meaning and does
not require a specific response by the child. It is one in which the possible
responses are almost unlimited. Unlike the response to the structured task,
a response on this type of test is not considered as either "right or wrong,"
but is rather evaluated by the examiner to obtain insight about the personality structure and functioning of the child. The task given to the child
in an unstructured personality test, in contrast to that usually typical

[35] See: Hutt, M. L., "The use of projective methods of personality measurement
in Army medical installations," *J. clin. Psychol.,* 1945, *1,* 134–140.

of the intelligence test, may be considered as being comparatively vague and nonspecific in nature. Many personality tests are *unstructured* or *partially structured;* such tests are known as *projective tests.*

Projective tests are among the most valuable of all types of personality tests, we believe. We shall limit our present discussion to these.

Characteristics of projective tests

We have noted that on intelligence tests the child is given a highly specific task that requires a specific response scorable as right or wrong. On projective tests his task is less specific; in fact, he is asked to place his own interpretation on the test material. There are no "right" responses. The child thus "projects" his own unique perception of the material and organizes his responses in a unique manner. His responses are functions of his total personality.

Sargent points out that the stimulus situation in a projective test has different meanings to each subject, depending upon his particular personality characteristics. It is chosen because of this ambiguity, and not because the experimenter has arbitrarily decided that it should have a particular meaning.[36] As Sargent further points out, projective methods seek to uncover the underlying determinants of mental life. Let us consider a very simple illustration (not part of a test) of the way in which an individual may impose his own private meaning on a stimulus. Let us look at the relatively simple pattern in Figure 14 and then ask ourselves the question: "What does this look like to me?"

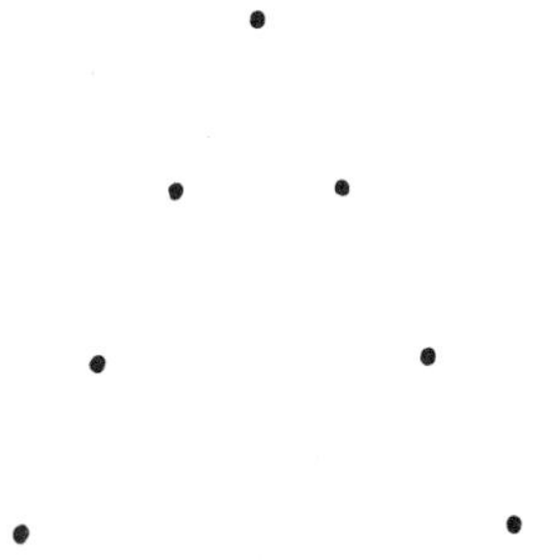

FIGURE 14. An Unstructured Stimulus

Many possible responses might be made, of course. The figure might look like: seven dots, a triangle, a wedge, a piece of pie, a flock of flying geese, an Indian teepee, or any number of other things. No one of these

[36] Sargent, H., "Projective methods: Their origins, theories, and their applications in personality research," *Psychol. Bull.*, 1945, *42*, 257–293.

responses is a "correct" response; on the other hand, no one is a "wrong" response. Rather, the response is determined, among other factors, by the total personality characteristics of the individual making it.

Rapaport points out that projective procedures are characterized by the fact that they are procedures in which the "subject actively and spontaneously structures unstructured material, and, in so doing, reveals his structural principles—which are the principles of his psychological structure."[37] As he points out, the use of a projective technique assumes that the examiner is seeking something of which the subject is unaware, otherwise he could be asked about it directly. Projective techniques, therefore, are "indirect questions," and the responses to them are "indirect answers." Rapaport stresses the fact that in projective tests *all* aspects of thought processes come into play (as well, of course, as emotional factors). Hence, such tests are extremely valuable in the psychological evaluation of a child. They help us in arriving at a *dynamic* interpretation of the intellectual functioning of the retarded child which is unlike the more static measures of intelligence tests.[38]

Bell has discussed the broad theoretical foundations that underlie the utilization of projective procedures.[39] These, in summary form, are as follows:

1. The personality of an individual is not a static but, rather, a dynamic process. It changes and fluctuates and is modified by passage through time. The projective test reflects these dynamic qualities.
2. The personality, even though it fluctuates, is nevertheless still relatively structured. As Bell stresses, the structure of the individual is developed by the particular range of physiological, psychological, and physical-social-cultural influences that are brought to bear upon him. These forces produce a dynamic and evolving, but nevertheless structured, unit.
3. The personality structure of the individual is revealed in his behavior,

[37] Rapaport, D., *Diagnostic Psychological Testing*, Vol. 2. Chicago: Year Book Medical Publishers, Inc., 1946, p. 3.

[38] For further, detailed discussion of projective techniques, see:
    (a) Anastasi, *op. cit.*
    (b) Anderson, H. H., and Anderson, G. L. (eds.), *An Introduction to Projective Techniques*. Englewood Cliffs, N.J.: Prentice-Hall, Inc., 1951.
    (c) Bell, J. E., *Projective Techniques*. New York: David McKay Co., Inc., 1948.
    (d) Brower, D., and Abt, L. E. (eds.), *Progress in Clinical Psychology*, Vol. 1. New York: Grune & Stratton, Inc., 1952.
    (e) White, R. R., "Interpretation of imaginative productions," in *Personality and the Behavior Disorders*, Vol. 1 (J. McV. Hunt, ed.). New York: The Ronald Press Company, 1944, pp. 214–251.

[39] Bell, *op. cit.*

since behavior is functional. Our behavior itself reflects the relationship between the demands of the self and those of the situation in which we find ourselves. It may thus be considered, from one point of view, as an adaptation of the personality to the complex interaction of internal and external forces.

4. Personality is not a shallow surface phenomenon, but, rather, is one of depth. The surface reactions shown by the person are manifestations of the deeper forces within him, many of which are hidden from the person himself and from others. (They exist at an unconscious level.) The projective techniques explore these deeper layers of the personality.

Some projective tests

We shall now discuss some representative projective techniques that are useful in the evaluation of mentally retarded children. We shall not, at this point, deal with the specific contributions of these techniques to the development of theories of the psychopathology of intellectual deficit, but, rather, we shall describe the techniques and discuss their applicability.

THE RORSCHACH TEST. Of all the projective techniques, the *Rorschach* is probably the best known and most widely used test. It consists of a series of ten cards, on each of which is printed an ink blot design. In fact, the test is often popularly referred to as the "ink blot test." Some of the designs are colored, and some are in black and white. Psychologists had been utilizing ink blots for a number of years prior to the advent of the *Rorschach Test* in order to investigate such traits as imagination.[40] In 1911 Hermann Rorschach, a Swiss psychiatrist, began to experiment with the use of various relatively unstructured designs in order to develop a psychodiagnostic method of assessing mental illness. He first published his techniques and results in 1921.[41] Many revised editions have been published since that time in many languages,[42] and the *Rorschach* technique is now used internationally.

The *mechanical* administration of the Rorschach is relatively simple. Each of the *Rorschach* cards is given in turn to the subject. He is instructed to look at the card and to tell the examiner everything that he

[40] See: Binet, A., and Henri, V., *op. cit.;* Tulchin, S. H., "The pre-Rorschach use of ink blots," *Rorschach Res. Exch.*, 1940, *4*, 1-7.

[41] Rorschach, H., *Psychodiagnostik: Methodik und Ergebnisse eines Wahrnehmungsdiagnostischen Experiments. Deutenlassen von Zufallsformen,* 1st Ed. Bern: Bircher, 1921.

[42] Rorschach, H., *Psychodiagnostics, a Diagnostic Test Based on Apperception.* New York: Grune & Stratton, Inc., 1942.

sees. This part of the procedure is known as the *free association*. All of his responses are recorded exactly as they are given. Usually the total time required for the whole card, and the time elapsing between the presentation of the card and the initial response, are recorded. Following the presentation of the last card, the examiner then returns to the beginning of the series and again presents each card in turn to the subject. He now questions the subject about each response in order to determine what areas of the blot were used in the response, and to determine what characteristics of the blot determined the response. This procedure, known as the *inquiry*, is difficult because the examiner must not suggest any way in which the subject should respond.

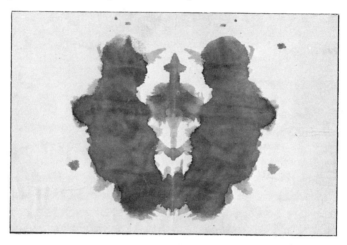

A Rorschach-Like Blot

The responses (free association and inquiry combined) are then scored by the examiner. This is a complex process, which involves four major categories of scoring. These, in a much simplified manner, are:

1. *Location.* What area of the design is utilized? Does the subject use the whole blot, a large, usually seen area, or a small, rare, minor section of the design? Does he utilize the white spaces of the design?
2. *Determinants.* What characteristics of the design determined the response? Some of the major determinants are form, color, shading, texture, vista, and movement. In the event that multiple determinants are involved, which are primary?
3. *Content.* What is the content of the response? Is it animal, human, anatomical, geographical, or the like? There are many content categories.
4. *Popularity or originality.* Is the response one that is usually seen by most people, or is it a highly original one that is rarely given?

Each response is scored for each of these categories. Various symbols are assigned to the various aspects of the response to facilitate scoring —a kind of "shorthand" notation. In the location category the symbols are: the whole blot, W; the white space, S; a large, usually seen area, D; a minor area, Dd. The major determinant symbols are: color, C; shading, Y; vista, V; human movement, M; form, F; and texture, T. The form response is further scored as good form (F plus) or poor form (F minus), depending on whether or not it is appropriate to the area of the blot utilized. The content categories are abbreviated (such as A for animal, Ad for part of an animal, H for human, and Hd for human detail). Some examples of *Rorschach* responses and their appropriate scorings are:

Card No.	Response	Location	Determinant	Content	Original or Popular
III	Blood—it is red like blood	D	C	Blood	
VI	A bear rug—it is shaped like one and it is shaded light and dark just like one too	W	FY plus	Ad	P
VII	A woman dancing—she is shaped just like a woman	D	M plus	H	
IX	A man's head—it is just shaped like a man's head —nose here, mouth here, shape of head here	Dd	F plus	Hd	

After each of the responses has been scored, the scores are totalled and analyzed. The tabulation of scores is referred to as the *psychogram.* Many ratios of total score categories are computed. Then the psychogram as well as qualitative aspects of the test performance are interpreted. The interpretation of a *Rorschach* record (the *protocol*) is a very complex and difficult process, and the *value of the final report depends greatly upon the skill of the psychologist utilizing the technique.*

The *Rorschach* technique was originally standardized upon adults, but has been extended downward to be applicable to young children.[43] The same cards are used as stimuli, but the norms and standards, of course, are different from those for adults. An extensive bibliography of research and areas of utilization of the *Rorschach* may be found in the volume on projective techniques by Bell.[44]

[43] Ford, M., "The application of the Rorschach Test to young children," *Univ. Minn. Inst. Child Welf. Monogr.,* No. 23, 1946.
[44] Bell, *op. cit.*

The *Rorschach* enables us to assess basic personality characteristics of the retarded child, and this aids us in understanding his emotional assets and liabilities.

THE THEMATIC APPERCEPTION TEST.   The *Thematic Apperception Test* (also known as the *T.A.T.*) is a projective technique developed by Morgan and Murray in 1935.[45] It consists of a set of 30 pictures. Some of these are designed to be used for both men and women, some for men alone, some for women alone, some for boys and girls, some for boys alone, and some for girls alone.

Each of the pictures selected by the examiner from the total set is shown to the subject, who is instructed to tell a story about the picture. He is asked to tell what is happening, what led up to the scene pictured, and how he thinks the story will end. In other words, he is asked to give a past, present, and future for each of the pictures. He is also instructed to tell what the people in the story feel and think. In dealing with retarded children, of course, it is not always possible to get such completeness.

Each of the stories is recorded in as complete detail as possible and is then analyzed by the examiner. Murray originally analyzed the stories according to five major characteristics. His categories are:

1. *The hero.* This represents the subject himself, and reflects his personality characteristics.
2. *The needs of the hero.* These are representative of the needs of the subject.
3. *The presses.* These are forces that either hurt or are of value to the hero. They are the external forces that are brought to bear upon him.
4. *The thema.* This may be roughly regarded as the plot of the story.
5. *The outcome.* This refers to how the story is ended. For example, is it pleasant or unpleasant?

The *Thematic Apperception Test* is a method for the exploration of the fantasy of the child. Basic to the clinical utilization of the technique is the hypothesis that the individual makes use of material from his own unique personal experiences in making up the stories. Both conscious and unconscious determinants are present, and thus his personality dynamics may be inferred from the stories that are constructed.

Like the *Rorschach*, the *T.A.T.* requires that the examiner be highly trained and experienced in the use of the technique.

[45] Morgan, C. D., and Murray, H. A., "A method for investigating phantasies: The Thematic Apperception Test," *Arch. Neurol. Psychiat.*, 1935, *34*, 289–306.

Bergman and Fisher found the *T.A.T.* to be useful in diagnosing and understanding the dynamics of the mentally retarded child, as well as in facilitating psychotherapy.[46]

Thompson and Bachrach have introduced color in the *T.A.T.*[47] Some studies have shown that retarded children respond more readily to such color. Lubin studied the performance of a group of retarded children on the colored *T.A.T.*[48] He found that their productivity increased; they produced a larger number of themas on the colored than they did on the non-colored test. It was hypothesized that the use of color tended to make the picture more "reality bound," and facilitated the identification of the child with the picture. (There is still considerable controversy regarding the value of color in this test, in terms of the effect on the validity of the derived measures.)

The original *T.A.T.* was felt to be applicable to individuals seven years of age or older. However, there have been special forms of the test developed for various age groups. Symonds has constructed a test for adolescents, in which the pictures represent situations that are thought to be pertinent to teenagers.[49] Bellak and Bellak have constructed what they term the *Children's Apperception Test*.[50] This test employs situations concerning animals rather than people. The rationale for this is that children between the ages of three and ten years probably would tell more clinically useful stories in reacting to pictures involving animals as the central figures than to those using human beings.

Many clinicians do not accept this hypothesis. In a recent review of the literature relative to the *Children's Apperception Test*, Budoff concluded that previous research had, in general, failed to support Bellak's hypothesis.[51] He then proceeded to explore experimentally the hypothesis that children with a "young" mental age would identify more readily with animal rather than human figures, since such children were essentially very concrete thinkers. Budoff utilized 23 first-grade students

---

[46] Bergman, M., and Fisher, L., "The value of the Thematic Apperception Test in mental deficiency," *Psychiat. Quart. Suppl.*, 1953, *27*, 22–42.

[47] Thompson, C. E., and Bachrach, A. J., "The use of color in the Thematic Apperception Test," *J. proj. Tech.*, 1951, *15*, 173–184.

[48] Lubin, N. M., "The effect of color in the Thematic Apperception Test productions of mentally retarded subjects," *Amer. J. ment. Defic.*, 1955, *60*, 366–370.

[49] Symonds, P. M., *Symonds Picture Story Test: Manual*. New York: Bureau of Publications, Teachers College, Columbia University, 1948.

[50] Bellak, L., and Bellak, S. S., *Children's Apperception Test*. Chicago: Stoelting, 1950.

[51] Budoff, M., "The relative utility of animals and human figures in a picture story test for young children," *J. proj. Tech.*, 1960, *24*, 347–352.

with *Otis Alpha* I.Q.'s ranging from 70 to 91, and with chronological ages from 5 years, 1 month, to 7 years of age.[52]

He then divided the total group of subjects into two subgroups. The first, the borderline group, was composed of 12 subjects, who ranged from 70 to 78 in I.Q., and who had a mean mental age of 4 years, 5 months. The second subgroup was composed of 11 subjects, with a range in I.Q. of from 87 to 91, and with a mean mental age of 5 years, 8 months. Budoff then administered the *CAT* test, omitting one card which depicted bears in a cave (card 5 of the *CAT*). Following this, he administered a revised *CAT*, in which the animal figures were replaced with human figures. Both forms of the *CAT* were administered within a two- to three-week interval.

Budoff utilized two measures in order to compare the test responses. The first was a word count of all the words in the body of the story made up by the child, and the second was a *"transcendence"* level score, which was a measure of the number of comments made about the picture other than those of pure description. The inter-judge reliability for the word count score was 1.00, and that for the transcendence level score was .83. The scores were thus highly reliable. Budoff then compared the performances of both groups of subjects on both measures for each of the *CAT* tests. It was found that Bellak's hypothesis was not substantiated, and that the retarded children did not respond more to the animal than to the human figures. Rather, *exactly the opposite situation prevailed*. The children gave *longer and more imaginative* stories to the human cards than they did to the animal cards. This finding was contrary to what had been expected, but was in accord with the clinical experience of the present authors.

THE MICHIGAN PICTURE TEST.   Like the *Thematic Apperception Test*, this test is based on responses to pictures. It is unlike the *T.A.T.* in several respects, however. First, it is specifically designed for children in the age range of about eight to fourteen years. In turn, this means that the pictures were so selected as to be appealing and relevant for this age group, and the methods of analysis are applicable for this population. Second, the pictures were further selected, on the basis of extensive clinical and experimental testing, to tap common conflict areas. For example, one picture depicts a family scene at breakfast, and another shows a group of boys walking along a country road. A third feature of this test

[52] Budoff, M., "Animal versus human figures in a picture story test for young mentally backward children," *Amer. J. ment. Defic.*, 1963, *68*, 245–250.

Two Pictures Used in the Michigan Picture Test (Courtesy Science Research Associates, Chicago)

was the development of a number of objective and easily scored measures that would yield general and specific measures of personality reactions. Still another feature was the provision for flexible testing procedures: there are four "core pictures" that serve as a common, basic set of testing materials applicable to all subjects; there are also other pictures, some for boys only, some for girls only, and some for both sexes, all or some of which can be used to explore specific conflict problems that may be of interest in a particular case.

The total set of materials includes 16 pictures and a comprehensive manual discussing the theory, standardization, administration, and interpretation of the results.[53] The test can be given individually or in groups (although *group* testing is not applicable to retarded children). It yields a "tension index," based on relatively simple scoring that a clerk can be trained to do. The score provides a general measure of the degree of maladjustment. There are also norms for specific types of personality measures. Moreover, the responses can be scored and evaluated clinically in the same ways that the *T.A.T.* responses are analyzed. All in all, the test should prove very useful in a variety of situations calling for the assessment of mentally retarded children.

THE BLACKY TEST. Another projective test that is useful in exploring the personality characteristics of children is the *Blacky Test*, devised by Blum.[54] This test is composed of a series of 11 cartoons, depicting a dog named Blacky in various situations. Blum created the test primarily in order to investigate Freudian hypotheses relative to the psychosexual development of the individual, but it has since been utilized to explore the major psychological defenses of the person. We may illustrate the nature of the test by describing one of the cards: Blacky's tail has been placed upon a block of wood, and a large knife hovers over the tail. (This card would presumably elicit the castration anxieties of the child, and reveal the characteristic ways in which he deals with them.)

The child is given the cards one at a time. He is required, first, to make up a story about the picture (somewhat similar to the *T.A.T.* procedure), and then is required to answer specific questions about each card.

[53] Andrew, G., Hartwell, S. W., Hutt, M. L., and Walton, R. E., *The Michigan Picture Test*. Chicago: Science Research Associates, 1955.

[54] Blum, G. S., *The Blacky Pictures: A Technique for the Exploration of Personality Dynamics: Manual*. New York: Psychological Corp., 1950.

This test has proved valuable in the personality evaluation of the retarded child, who enters readily into the test situation.

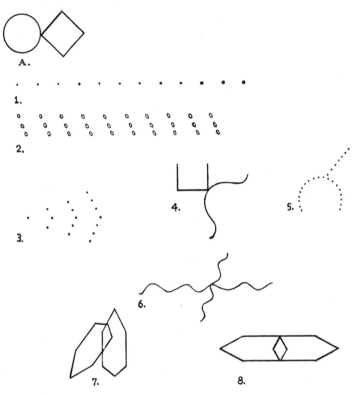

FIGURE 15. The Figures for the Visual Motor Gestalt Test (Courtesy Dr. Lauretta Bender and the American Orthopsychiatric Association, Inc. Reproduced from the manual, *Instructions for the Use of Visual Motor Gestalt Test,* 1946.)

THE BENDER GESTALT TEST AND THE HUTT ADAPTATION OF THE BENDER GESTALT TEST. This test consists of nine relatively simple geometrical designs, ranging in maturational difficulty from about three years (for the simplest parts of some of the figures) to about eleven or twelve years. When the test was first published, Bender offered the figures shown in the accompanying illustration.[55] These were adapted from the work of Wertheimer.[56] Hutt made changes in these figures

[55] Bender, L., *A Visual Motor Gestalt Test and Its Clinical Use.* New York: Amer. Orthopsychiat. Ass. Monogr., No. 3, 1938.

[56] Wertheimer, M., "Studies in the theory of Gestalt Psychology," *Psychol. Forsch.,* 1923, *4,* 301-350.

because his experience showed that some of the characteristics of the figures limited their clinical usefulness.[57]

The *basic administration* of this test is simplicity itself, since all that is required is to ask the subject to copy the figures as they are presented to him. The child, drawing freehand, uses paper and pencil in copying the figures. The visual and motor abilities necessary to perceive and copy these figures are dependent on the general rate of biological maturation. Hence the drawings may be evaluated for general maturity level. As will be seen in our later discussion of this test, evaluations of mental maturity may be derived from scores on this test which are closely correlated with other measures of general mental development.

This test is particularly useful for assessing various aspects of the retarded child's development for several reasons, as Hutt indicates. In the first place, it is largely independent of cultural deprivation, as well as of linguistic skills, and is, therefore, particularly applicable to this group. In the second place, it is highly useful in assessing the presence of organic or neurological dysfunctions. Third, it can be used to evaluate the presence of emotional disturbances. For these reasons, the test is now widely used in the differential diagnosis of suspected cases of mental retardation.

Hutt was able to demonstrate that the test could be used *projectively* to evaluate the presence of dynamic features of the individual's conflicts, defenses, and ego strengths.[58] It would therefore be useful in guidance and therapeutic programs. When used in this way, after the basic administration, the test is readministered, and the subject is asked, this time, to modify the drawings so as to make them more pleasing to him. This is called the *elaboration phase.* He is then asked to associate to the original stimuli as well as to his elaborations, and the content of these associations is evaluated to define areas of conflict; this is called the *association phase.*

Tolor and Schulberg have reviewed the evidence on this test, in both the original Bender form and the Hutt adaptations[59] and have shown some of the many useful applications of it. Even more recently, Koppitz has reported specific research studies and methods of assessing degree of mental development, emotional disturbance, and severity of neurological

[57] Hutt, M. L., and Briskin, G. J., *The Hutt Adaptation of the Bender Gestalt Test.* New York: Grune & Stratton, Inc., 1960.

[58] Hutt and Briskin, *idem.*

[59] Tolor, A., and Schulberg, H. C., *An Evaluation of the Bender-Gestalt Test.* Springfield, Ill.: Charles C. Thomas, Publisher, 1962.

disability.[60] Taken together with Hutt's and Briskin's volume, there is now available, therefore, a variety of methods of appraising the subject's performance, highly useful in clinical and educational programs.

Some of the recent research with Hutt's adaptation of this test has shown that there are several special advantages in this method. For instance, in a research program for evaluating and habilitating deaf-retarded patients conducted by the Mental Hygiene Department of the State of Michigan, the findings on this test were useful in selecting patients who were capable of profiting from special, experimental treatment.[61] It was found that many of these patients showed promise of better-than-retarded levels of development, despite their presumed severely retarded status as defined by more conventional standardized tests of intelligence.

Two measures for evaluating the nature of the subject's disability have also been found to be particularly useful. One of these is a 19-factor score of psychopathology, largely independent of linguistic and cultural factors.[62] Another, a measure of perceptual adience-abience, has held considerable promise in evaluating the general degree of avoidance or approach potentialities of the patient, and seems be to related to the prognosis for amelioration of behavior and adjustment with appropriate training and therapy.[63] This latter measure has received validation against retarded, psychiatric, and normal cases.

PLAY TECHNIQUES. The need to play is almost "instinctive" within the child, and many theories have been developed in an attempt to explain why he engages in such activities and how they may be utilized in personality diagnosis. Play techniques have been utilized in a therapeutic as well as in a psychodiagnostic manner. At this point, however, we are concerned only with their psychodiagnostic applications. Freud utilized the play activities of a five-year-old child in order to analyze his personality characteristics.[64] Many others since that time have utilized the technique for diagnostic purposes.

In the psychodiagnostic use of play, the child is provided with a

---

[60] Koppitz, E. M., *The Bender Gestalt Test for Young Children.* New York: Grune & Stratton, Inc., 1964.

[61] Research in Progress on the Michigan Deaf Retarded Project, Dept. of Mental Health, Lansing, Mich.

[62] Hutt and Briskin, *idem.*

[63] Hutt, M. L., and Feuerfile, D., "The clinical meanings and predictions of a measure of perceptual adience-abience for a deaf-retarded group," Paper presented at the Amer. Psychol. Convention. Philadelphia: September, 1963.

[64] Freud, S., *Collected Papers,* Vol. III. London: Hogarth, 1925, pp. 194–195.

medium through which he can express his basic personality dynamics. This medium may or may not involve the need for extensive verbalization with the psychologist. The personality characteristics of the child are inferred from his play behavior. For example, the child may be given a series of dolls with which to play. These dolls represent the father, mother, siblings, and other persons. If, for example, the child destroys the sibling dolls, then one might infer the presence of strong sibling rivalries and hostilities. Attitudes and emotions of the child toward the parents are also inferred from his reactions to the doll substitutes.

Bell summarizes the uses of play techniques as:[65] (1) providing the child with a natural avenue of approach to the clinician; (2) serving as a diagnostic tool for the therapist; (3) offering a cathartic experience to the child (that is, permitting him to express socially unacceptable feelings and strong emotions); (4) reducing anxiety; (5) providing a social relationship; (6) giving the child a new orientation to the world; and (7) restoring to the child elements of growth of which he has been deprived. Bell stresses the fact that, with young children, play is the most important of all the projective techniques.

There have been some attempts at standardization of specific play situations. One of these is the *Make a Picture Story Test* by Shneidman.[66] This consists of 22 pictorial backgrounds, and a total of 67 cardboard cutouts of various people, popular cartoon characters, and animals. The child selects the characters to be placed against a particular background and makes up a story about the scene that he constructs.

ASSESSMENT OF ACADEMIC ACHIEVEMENT AND VOCATIONAL APTITUDE

There are other areas of the assessment of the retarded child in addition to those previously discussed. These include assessment of scholastic achievement and vocational and interest aptitudes. We shall discuss each of these briefly in the following paragraphs.

Assessment of academic achievement

In both educational planning and in appropriate guidance it is important to know the nature of the retardate's academic abilities, in general, and the extent to which his academic achievement is commensurate with his intellectual capacities. (See discussion of reading

---

[65] Bell, *op. cit.*, p. 440.

[66] Shneidman, E. S., *Make a Picture Story*. New York: Psychological Corp., 1952.

retardation and reading disability in Chapter Eight.) We should know, for example, how well he can read or use simple number skills and what specific disabilities he has in these and other skills, if any. Levels of achievement in the traditional scholastic subjects are evaluated by means of tests known as *achievement tests*. These are usually paper and pencil tests, and may be administered either as group or individual tests. In addition to the general achievement tests, there are others that evaluate specific disabilities in a given academic subject, known as *diagnostic achievement tests*. Another type of test is designed to assess the readiness of the child to be taught to read. Tests of this type are known as *reading readiness tests*.

Achievement tests are designed to measure the child's skills in one or several academic subjects. There are achievement tests in reading, arithmetic, spelling, writing, geography, and other subjects. They are not intended to serve as predictive tests (that is, to predict the future achievement of the child), but, rather, to indicate the level and types of skills with which the child is functioning at the time of the test.

The results of achievement tests are usually expressed as *grade norms;* that is, the child's achievement on the test is expressed in terms of the grade level to which it is equivalent. For example, Jeanne, a twelve-year-old child, may have a third-grade reading level, fifth-grade spelling level, and a fourth-grade arithmetic level. Some tests have norms for a variety of skills within the same subject. For example, a reading achievement test may have norms for reading vocabulary, general comprehension, and rate of reading.

Diagnostic tests do not measure primarily the achievement level of the child. Rather, they are designed to help the teacher discover his particular disabilities in a given subject. For example, an achievement test in reading indicated that Ellen was reading at a level below that expected from her mental age. The diagnostic reading test, administered by the teacher, revealed that Ellen had little ability in the use of phonics. A program designed to deal with this disability was then planned for her.

As pointed out, achievement tests have been developed for all academic subjects. We shall discuss, first, the various types of achievement tests with some representative samples, and then examine some of the tests that are devoted to the assessment of specific aspects of reading.

ACHIEVEMENT TESTS. Achievement tests may be designed to assess the child's abilities in a single subject, or to assess his achievement in a group of subjects. The latter type is known as an achievement test *battery*. The *Stanford Achievement Test* was one of the earliest batteries of achievement tests.[67] It was first published in 1923, and was revised in 1929, 1940, and 1953. The present battery consists of five equivalent forms of the test, so that frequent retesting of the same child is possible. It covers academic achievement in grades two to nine. There are many different norms available for the interpretation of the test results. The child's achievement may be interpreted in terms of age and grade norms, or in terms of percentiles for each grade for each of the various subjects.

Another achievement battery is the *Metropolitan Achievement Test*.[68] It covers the range from the first grade to the first half of the ninth grade. Still another battery, the *California Achievement Tests*, covers grades one through thirteen.[69] This latter test differs from the *Stanford* and *Metropolitan Achievement* batteries in that it is concerned only with the basic academic skill subjects. It can purportedly be used as a diagnostic instrument to detect specific disabilities within a given subject.

DIAGNOSTIC READING TESTS. These tests provide diagnostic evaluations of the child's reading abilities. They purport to reveal areas in which he has specific disabilities. Examples of such tests are: the *Gates Basic Reading Test*,[70] the *Gates Reading Diagnosis Test*, the *Gray Standardized Oral Paragraphs*, [71] and the *Durrell Analysis of Reading Difficulty*.[72] The *Gates Reading Test* investigates four specific attributes of reading: (1) reading for general significance, (2) reading to predict the outcome of events, (3) reading to understand precise directions, and (4) reading to note details. It extends from grade three through grade eight. The *Gray* test is concerned with the child's oral reading abilities from grade one through grade eight. The *Durrell* diagnostic test is designed to be used in grades one through six. It is concerned with diagnostic evalua-

[67] Kelley, T. L., Madden, R., Gardner, E. F., Terman, L. M., and Ruch, G. M., *Stanford Achievement Test: Manuals for Primary, Eelementary, Intermediate, and Advanced Batteries*. New York: Harcourt, Brace & World, Inc., 1953.

[68] Hildreth, G., Bixler, H. H., *et al.*, *Metropolitan Achievement Tests: Manual for Interpreting*. New York: Harcourt, Brace & World, Inc., 1948.

[69] Tiegs, E. W., and Clark, W. W., *California Achievement Tests: Manuals of Directions for Primary, Elementary, Intermediate, and Advanced Batteries*. Los Angeles: California Test Bureau, 1951.

[70] Gates, A. I., *Gates Basic Reading Tests: Manual of Directions*. New York: Bureau of Publications, Teachers College, Columbia University, 1943.

[71] Gray, W. S., *Standardized Oral Reading Paragraphs: Manual*. Bloomington, Ill.: Public School Publishing Company, 1915.

[72] Durrell, D. D., *Analysis of Reading Difficulty: Manual of Directions*. New York: Harcourt, Brace & World, Inc., 1937.

tion of oral reading, silent reading, recall of material read, both orally and silently, speed of recognition of words, writing, and spelling.

READING READINESS TESTS. As pointed out, we often wish to know whether a given child has reached the level at which he is *ready* to learn to read. Reading readiness implies that the child has appropriate social and communication skills, an adequate vocabulary, sufficient use of oral language, and no severely handicapping perceptual or motor problems. This readiness may be evaluated in part through the use of tests known as *reading readiness tests*. These tests measure such abilities as simple number concepts, word meaning, information, knowing the use of objects, and copying abilities. Examples of such reading readiness tests are: the *Gates Reading Readiness Test*,[73] the *Metropolitan Reading Readiness Test*,[74] the *Monroe Reading Aptitude Test*,[75] and the *Betts Ready to Read Battery*.[76] Such tests may be given by the teacher or by a clinical psychologist.

Assessment of vocational aptitudes and interests

It is important that the aptitudes of the retarded child be assessed to provide adequate planning in his total program. Tests devised for such purposes are referred to as *aptitude tests*. They differ from the achievement tests in that they attempt to *predict* the future performance of the child in vocational areas, whereas the achievement tests measure scholastic abilities at the time of testing. Aptitude tests have been developed in many areas, such as musical, artistic, clerical, motor, and mechanical areas. For the sake of illustration, we shall discuss the latter two areas only, since they have more general significance for the vocational guidance of the retarded child.

ASSESSMENT OF MOTOR APTITUDES. Tests of motor functions center around two major functions—*speed* of motor responses and *coordination* of muscular reactions. Examples of tests designed to explore motor abilities are: the *O'Connor Finger Dexterity* and *Tweezer Dexterity*

[73] Gates, A. I., *Gates Reading Readiness Tests: Manual of Directions*. New York: Bureau of Publications, Teachers College, Columbia University, 1942.

[74] Hildreth, G., and Griffiths, N. L., *Metropolitan Readiness Tests: Directions for Administering and Scoring*. New York: Harcourt, Brace & World, Inc., 1949.

[75] Monroe, M., *Reading Aptitude Tests: Manual*. Boston: Houghton Mifflin Company, 1935.

[76] Betts, E. A., *Betts Ready to Read Tests: Manual*. Meadville, Pa.: Keystone View Co., 1934.

Tests,[77] the *Crawford Small Parts Dexterity Test,*[78] the *Purdue Peg-board,*[79] and the *Bennett Hand-Tool Dexterity Test.*[80] Many other tests in this area have been devised, but these will serve as samples.

In the *O'Connor Test* the child is required to insert small pins into holes. In one phase of the test the insertion is done directly by hand, and in another phase with the use of a small pair of tweezers. The *Crawford Test* utilizes somewhat the same procedure. The subject first uses a pair of tweezers to insert small pins into a series of holes, then he is required to place a small collar on the end of each of the pins. Further, he is required to screw small screws into holes with the aid of a screw driver. Both the *O'Connor* and *Crawford Tests* involve small muscle coordination and skills. The *Purdue Pegboard* evaluates both gross and fine manual dexterity. It requires the insertion of pins in small holes with each hand separately, then together, and the as-sembly of a series of pins, collars, and washers. The *Bennett Test* attempts to measure ability in the use of common hand tools, such as a wrench, and is concerned also with coordination and skill in the manipulation of objects. The child is required to take apart and then re-assemble a series of nuts, bolts, and washers.

It should be noted that all these tests involve specific motor skills. Studies have shown that even though such tests appear to be reliable, they have low validity in general. They serve to give us only a rough idea of the abilities of the retarded child, and cannot be used to predict accurately vocational success for a given child.

TESTS OF MECHANICAL APTITUDE. The so-called "mechanical apti-tudes" include such capacities as: motor skills, perceptual capacities, comprehension of spatial relationships, reasoning about mechanical re-lationships and processes, and speed of motor responses. Many mechani-cal aptitude tests involve the manipulations of actual objects, whereas others are written tests.

[77] O'Connor, J., "Administration and norms for the Finger Dexterity Test, Work Sample No. 16, and Tweezer Dexterity Test, Work Sample No. 17," *Tech. Rep. Hum. Engr. Lab., No.* 16, 1938.
[78] Crawford, J. E., and Crawford, D. M., *Small Parts Dexterity Test: Manual.* New York: Psychological Corp., 1949.
[79] Tiffin, J., *Examiner Manual for the Purdue Pegboard.* Chicago: Science Re-search Associates, 1948; Tiffin, J., and Asher, E. J., "The Purdue Pegboard: Norms and studies of reliability and validity," *J. appl. Psychol.,* 1948, *32,* 234–247.
[80] Bennett, G. K., *Hand-Tool Dexterity Test: Manual.* New York: Psychological Corp., 1947.

Examples of mechanical aptitude tests are: the *Minnesota Spatial Relations Test*,[81] the *Kent-Shakow Industrial Formboards*,[82] the *MacQuarrie Test for Mechanical Ability*,[83] the *Stenquist Mechanical Aptitude Test*[84] and the *Bennett Mechanical Aptitude Test*.[85]

The *Minnesota Spatial Relations Test* is based on form and space perception. It is made up of four formboards, each having 58 differently shaped inserts. The subject is required to insert the pieces into the board as rapidly as possible. The *Kent-Shakow* formboard consists of a formboard with five recesses. There are a series of eight blocks to be inserted into each of these, each series of blocks being of greater difficulty. It apparently is a test of motor speed, motor dexterity, and of capacities of dealing with spatial relationships. The *MacQuarrie Test* consists of seven subtests: tracing, tapping, dotting, copying, location, blocks, and pursuit. It is essentially concerned with spatial relationships and motor skills. The *Stenquist Test* may be regarded as a mechanical reasoning test. The subject is required to assemble a number of common objects, such as a mousetrap, electric bell, and door lock. The test was originally developed during the first World War, but has been restandardized and is now known as the *Minnesota Mechanical Assembly Test*.[86] The *Bennett Test* evaluates the subject's understanding of mechanical processes, and is a paper and pencil test.

All these tests are designed for use with the older retarded child, and may be of some help in his vocational guidance and counseling.

VOCATIONAL INTEREST. Many studies have shown that vocational success is, in part, a function of the interest that the individual has in his occupation. This is certainly true for the retarded individual. If his interests are not congruent with his work situation, then he will have greater difficulty in achieving success in his vocation. Since an individual may have aptitude in a given area but have relatively low

[81] Paterson, D. G., *et al., Minnesota Spatial Relations Tests: Manual*. Minneapolis: Educational Testing Bureau, 1930.

[82] Kent, G. H., and Shakow, D., "Grade series of formboards," *Personnel J.,* 1928, *7*, 115–120.

[83] MacQuarrie, T. W., *MacQuarrie Tests for Mechanical Ability: Manual*. Los Angeles: California Test Bureau, 1943.

[84] Stenquist, J. L., "Measurement of mechanical ability," Teachers College, *Columbia Univ. Contrib. to Educ.*, No. 130, 1923.

[85] Bennett, G. K., *Test of Mechanical Comprehension, Form AA: Manual*. New York: Psychological Corp., 1948.

[86] Paterson, D. G., *et al., Minnesota Mechanical Assembly Test: Manual*. Chicago: Stoelting, 1930.

interest in that area, information relative to his aptitudes must be supplemented by information relative to his vocational interests.

Many tests have been devised to explore vocational interests. Examples of such tests are: the *Cleeton Vocational Inventory,* for grades 9 to 16 and adults;[87] the *Kuder Preference Record,* for grades 9 to 16 and adults;[88] the *Thurstone Interest Schedule,* for ages 9 to 16 and adults;[89] and the *Strong Vocational Interest Blank for Men and Women,* ages 17 and over.[90] Detailed references to these and other interest tests may be found in Buros' yearbook of mental measurements.[91]

Such interest tests as those cited are valuable in developing a vocational program for the average child, but it is our opinion that they are not particularly applicable to the retardate. This is, in part, due to the fact that the reading level of the retarded child is not high enough for the reading content of the tests. Further, the tests deal with situations that he has usually not experienced. For these reasons the results obtained by the use of vocational interest tests are not sufficiently valid for him. Until more appropriate interest tests for the retarded child have been developed, information relative to his vocational interests must be secured by other means.

We have found the methods of observation and interview to be of value. The child should be provided with a variety of occupational experiences. His reactions and feelings can be explored through discussion and through observation of his behavior. These findings can then be integrated with his vocational aptitudes and other characteristics. As we have noted previously, there is a wide range of occupations in which he can succeed. The vocational adjustment of the retardate is discussed in detail in Chapter Eleven. The exploration of his interests is an important part of the assessment and guidance program. As we shall see, it is a continuing process that starts at an early age. It continues beyond adolescence, and needs to be highly integrated with the child's total program of education and guidance.

[87] Cleeton, G. U., *Cleeton Vocational Inventory Specimen Set and Manual,* Bloomington, Ill.: McKnight and McKnight, n.d.

[88] Kuder, G. F., *Kuder Preference Record—Vocational: Manual.* Chicago: Science Research Associates, 1953.

[89] Thurstone, L. L., *Thurstone Interest Schedule: Manual.* New York: Psychological Corp., 1947.

[90] Strong, E. K., *Vocational Interest Blank for Men: Manual.* Stanford, Calif.: Stanford University Press, 1951; and *Interest Blank for Women: Manual.* Stanford, Calif.: Stanford University Press, 1951.

[91] Buros, O. K. (ed.), *The Fourth Mental Measurements Yearbook.* Highland Park, N.J.: Gryphon Press, 1953.

ASSESSMENT AS A CONTINUING PROCESS

The material presented in this chapter reveals the wide range of assessment procedures and techniques that can be applied to the retarded child. It also emphasizes the need for the services of a wide variety of specialists. However, not all of the assessment procedures discussed are applicable at the same time. For example, we do not need to evaluate the mechanical aptitude of a six-year-old retarded child. Assessment should be viewed as a continuing process, in which certain attributes of the child are evaluated as the needs arise. Further, the retarded child is not a static organism, but is constantly evolving, particularly if given adequate growth-stimulating programs (see Chapter Eleven). He is, therefore, in need of continued re-appraisal in light of his constantly changing pattern of abilities and emerging capacities.

In view of the complexity of the phenomena of mental retardation, we can easily see how important it is that there be a continuous re-evaluation when this condition is suspected. All too often, a child is given an intelligence test, and if the I.Q. is found to be low, he is placed in a special class for retarded children. The likelihood is then great that he will remain in such a class for the remainder of his school attendance. Such a practice, it appears to us, is more than folly; it is tragically based on the idea that a single test, at a given time, can predict the static (or unchanging) development of the child. Instead, the practice should be one in which regular and frequent re-evaluation is carried out. In this *longitudinal* re-assessment, the observations by the teacher of the actual adjustment and achievement of the child are crucial. In addition, retesting with standardized tests of mental capacities, re-study with personality tests, and re-interview by the psychologist or psychiatrist are needed. It is only with this kind of continuing re-assessment that the most effective educational and mental health programs can be charted.

ch. 10

PARENTAL REACTIONS

WE HAVE DISCUSSED THE EMOTIONAL PROBLEMS AND RESULTANT maladaptive behavior of the mentally retarded child. In addition to the problems of the child himself, the presence of such a child in any family group tends to result in disturbed emotional reactions by the parents. These emotional problems vary in severity, and, in general, their degree and type vary with the characteristics of the parents. There are, however, many common emotional reactions that occur in almost all of them. We shall first discuss these usual patterns of parental reactions, and then turn our attention to methods by which such emotional problems may be alleviated.

PATTERNS OF PARENTAL REACTIONS TO MENTAL RETARDATION

The presence of a mentally retarded child in a family unit has far-reaching effects. At the periphery of the circle of which he is the center are the effects of his retardation upon society at large, which ultimately has to bear responsibility for his management and treatment. At the core are the tremendous impact made by his condition upon his parents and siblings, and these effects indeed may be catastrophic. Nor should it be overlooked that the reactive effects of the family and society upon such an individual are reciprocal.

It may be stated categorically that all parents of mentally retarded children are likely to show some undesirable personality reactions to the fact that their child is retarded. Such reactions vary both in degree from one parent to another and in their particular nature, depending upon a multiplicity of intricate and closely interwoven factors. They also vary from one time to another in the life span of a given parent, as we shall see. For instance, the emotional reactions of the parent, when he first becomes aware of the degree of the intellectual deficit of his child, may be somewhat different from those he manifests ten years later. Or, the pressure of the stress situations to which he may be subjected by the retardation of the child may increase and become more devastating over time.

As in the case of any human being, the retarded child does not live in a vacuum. He needs, as do all persons, close emotional relationships with others—and these relationships must be satisfying and stress-reducing if he is to achieve his maximum potentialities. Further, as with all children, the relationships between the retarded child and his parents are of great importance. If the parents manifest negative personality reactions to the child's deficient abilities, then it becomes more difficult for wholesome relationships to be established. The greater the negative emotional reactions of the parents, the less likely it is that the child will achieve the level of emotional maturity he is capable of attaining. Negative reactions of the parents, thus, can adversely affect the full maturational development of the retardate.

There are other significant concomitant effects which are also important. In many instances, as we shall see, the emotional reactions of the parent lead to his own personal dissatisfactions and personality maladjustments. He may develop severe anxieties, and other undesirable behavioral reactions may occur. For instance, marital difficulties may arise, ranging in depth from minor irritations to possibly a complete disruption of the family unit. Thus, the parental reactions to mental retardation are important, not only for the welfare of the child, but for the welfare of the parents themselves and the entire family group.

Considerable attention in the literature has been devoted to study of many aspects of the retarded child, but very little has been given to study of the emotional reactions of the parents. This is unfortunate, since it is a truism that the welfare of the child depends, in large measure, upon the well-being of the parents; in general, "as the parent goes, so goes the child."

We shall consider, at this point, the various characteristic emotional reactions of the parents of retarded children. First, case material that, in our opinion, is representative, will be presented. Next, some typical, broad patterns of parental reactions will be sketched, and, finally, the dynamics of characteristic specific personality reactions of the parents will be discussed.

Cases illustrating differing parental reactions

Some characteristic and important reactions of parents of mentally retarded children are summarized in the following three cases.

THE CASE OF ANN. This case illustrates some positive and constructive attitudes of parents who were accepting of the problems of their child:

Ann is a mildly retarded child, approximately 10 years of age. She is currently attending a private day school for academically disabled children. Prior to special class placement, Ann's first-grade teacher observed that she was not making adequate progress, and, upon recommendation of the school principal, she was referred to a psychologist for evaluation. The psychological examination indicated that Ann had a verbal I.Q. of 76, a performance quotient of 81, and a full-scale quotient of 78 on the *Wechsler Intelligence Scale for Children.* On Form L of the *Stanford-Binet* she achieved an I.Q. of 79. The psychologist noted, on the basis of interviews, case history material, and projective tests, that Ann did not show any severe emotional disturbance, and he felt that the test results were valid indicators of her retarded intellectual capacities.

The results of the evaluation were discussed in detail with the parents, the school principal, and the teacher. Following these conferences, attention was devoted to planning Ann's academic program. Since no facilities for a specialized academic program were available in the public school which she attended, it was recommended that Ann attend a private day school where the curriculum could be tailored to meet her unique needs.

Both of Ann's parents expressed the desire for continuing counseling and guidance by the psychologist. The mother, in particular, felt that she needed help. She stated: "I find myself wanting to do too much for Ann. I know that she can do many things if I let her, but I have to be careful that I don't step in too often and not let her make her own mistakes so that she can learn. Then, too, I find myself feeling very sorry not only for Ann but for myself too, and I think I want to wrap her in cotton wool. I know that I baby her, and give her too much attention. This isn't right, either for Ann, for myself, or for her brother and sister.

"Of course, I love Ann, and her happiness is very important to me. But I think I should love her in the same way that I do the other children. I need help on this."

Ann's mother accepted the degree of retardation Ann manifested. She perceived that Ann has many limitations, but also perceived that Ann has many assets. "I feel that it is my job to see that Ann's potentialities are developed just as far as possible, but, at the same time, I don't want to put pressures on her to do things that she simply can't do."

At home, Ann is encouraged to mingle freely with all guests, and to partake in all family activities. These are not tailored necessarily in all instances to Ann's capacities, and she always partakes in all family vacations, outings, and trips. As far as possible she does what other members of the family do, and is encouraged to be an individual in her own right. Ann's father is able to see many of the ways in which he reacts emotionally to Ann's retardation. He said: "I've had some difficult times about this. I've overlooked a lot of things in Ann's behavior that I really shouldn't have. I let her get away with things that I should have corrected. For example, at one time she didn't do anything around the house. This was largely because I felt sorry for her and didn't feel that she could do things. But now she straightens up her room and helps her mother with the dishes and some housework. She got her own way in a lot of things, but now she knows what is expected of her and I try to make certain things stick." The father has set limits for Ann, so that she knows what is reasonably demanded of her, and she is expected to conform to certain rules and regulations.

Ann's mother and father attend social events and parties in the neighborhood, and hire a babysitter to sit with Ann and the two younger children. At first they had a great deal of trepidation about this. "We were really afraid to go out, and we found ourselves pulling away from our friends. We were getting to be social hermits, and our lives were getting very narrow. But we realize that we have our own lives too, and it wasn't the best thing for Ann or for us to just sit around at home."

Both parents are concerned about Ann's future, but they realize that they cannot solve all the problems which may arise in the years ahead. As Ann's father said: "I think about what Ann is going to do when she grows up. At first, I felt that everything was hopeless, but I see now that she can do many useful things and that there is a good possibility that she will get married. I used to lie awake nights and worry about what the future holds, but this is foolish. It seems that my wife and I should be concerned with what we can do at the present time, and take things as they come, with some planning, of course. But our job right now is to give Ann the best program and handling that we can, so that she will be better able to take care of herself years from now. I wanted Ann to go to college, I guess, and I still have some feelings about that. And I realize that high school is out of her reach. However, there are a lot of things that she can do, but it was hard for me to give up my first ideas about what Ann could do. It seems that we should love Ann for what she actually is, and not fool ourselves with the picture we have inside ourselves of what we want Ann to be like."

In the case of Ann, the mother had a clear insight into the nature of Ann's retardation. She sought competent guidance in order to help her solve the complex problems with which she was faced, but, even more than this, was accepting of the counseling she received. The mother was aware that Ann did have severe disabilities, but, on the other hand, was able to see that Ann also had many assets. The degree of insight the mother demonstrated in regard to her own behavior and feelings was surprising. She perceived that she wanted to protect Ann, and that she tried hard to keep her from suffering either psychological or physical hurt. However, she realized that her own tendencies toward overprotection would not benefit Ann, but might, in fact, prove to be detrimental to her intellectual and emotional maturation.

Ann's parents fully accepted her as a person in her own right, and were able to acknowledge her as a full member of the family group. They did not feel shame in regard to her intellectual disabilities, but encouraged Ann to participate (to the appropriate degree) in all family and many social activities.

Ann was not allowed complete license to act as she wished. Rather, the parents set limits upon her behavior, as they did for the other children in the family, and Ann was not permitted any special privileges or given favors out of a sense of pity, a feeling of shame, or a feeling of guilt. Standards of behavior (realistically determined) were set for Ann, and she was expected to be a contributing member of the family (she was assigned tasks in the household, and had definite regular chores for which she was held responsible).

It is noteworthy that the parents were not overly anxious concerning their social relationships, and did not perceive Ann's disability as being detrimental to themselves. They participated freely in community social affairs, and were secure enough to trust Ann with a neighbor's daughter who acted as babysitter. The parents perceived that they were individuals also, and that they had needs and obligations toward each other as husband and wife. Ann did not, therefore, dominate and control the total family behavior.

Rather than being concerned about Ann's distant future, the parents realistically attempted to resolve her more immediate problems. They perceived that education is for the present, and not always designed primarily to meet future life problems. They were, of course, concerned about Ann's eventual life as an adult, but not overly so, and, consequently, primarily were concerned with her present-day problems, growths and adjustments. They perceived that adequate concern with these would make Ann more secure in the future. Ann is indeed fortunate. The parents, in her case, were mature individuals, who were well able to cope with the problems she presented, and did not develop any serious emotional problems of their own.

THE CASE OF BOBBY. The parents in this case were not perceptive of the difficulties of their retarded son, and had limited insight into his problems:

Bobby is an 11-year-old boy, who has experienced difficulty in school ever since he entered the first grade. The school records show that, on Form L of the

1937 *Stanford-Binet* test, he achieved an I.Q. of 79. This test result has been confirmed on numerous occasions throughout his five years in the public school.

Bobby failed the first grade, and at that time the parents were advised by the school principal that he was a very slow learning child who would be likely to experience difficulty throughout his academic life. Special class placement was recommended.

Mr. Smith, Bobby's father, became very indignant and aggressive when told that Bobby could not keep up with his class. He stated that there was nothing, in his opinion, "wrong with the child," and that he was not retarded in any area. "There is absolutely nothing wrong with Bobby. The trouble is that there are too many children in the classroom, and he just doesn't get the proper kind of teaching. It's no wonder he can't read."

The following year, in opposition to the recommendation of the principal, Mr. Smith secured the services of a tutor, in order to "teach Bobby how to read." After a three-month period of little progress, the tutor discontinued her services. Another tutor was employed, and again little headway was made. At the end of his second year in the first grade, Bobby was then "socially promoted" to the second grade, but still was unable to do adequate academic work.

Both parents frequently visited the school, and talked with the teachers and principal. They were complaining and found fault with the school in many areas, and also stressed vehemently that Bobby's problem was due to his lack of interest in school work, and that he "really didn't try." Great pressure was placed upon Bobby at home; the mother constantly had the child read to her and the father drilled him in simple airthmetic operations.

This type of dissension continued throughout the third year of school, when Bobby was again "socially promoted" to the third grade. This school year was characterized by a large number of visits to various clinics and physicians. First, Bobby was taken to a reading clinic, and a thorough evaluation conducted. The parents were advised that Bobby could not be expected to read much beyond the level he had attained, and the degree of mental retardation present was interpreted to the parents. In light of the retardation, Bobby was not accepted for remedial reading by the clinic, and the parents were advised that he could not profit from remedial reading but was more in need of a total specialized academic program.

In succession Bobby saw various medical specialists for eye, ear, gland, tonsil, neurological, and metabolism examinations. The results of all these examinations were essentially negative, but the parents still could not accept Bobby's limitations. They still sought a specific cause for his inability to achieve in school, a fault which could then, in some way, be treated miraculously.

Meanwhile, the school reports concerning Bobby's poor adjustment continued to mount. Bobby was constantly in difficulties with the teacher, in that he was becoming aggressive and hostile in the classroom. He fought constantly with the other children, and frequently kept the class in a turmoil. Currently, the principal is seriously considering the question as to whether Bobby should be permitted to attend school next year.

The parents continually discuss Bobby's scholastic disabilities with the neighbors. They complain about the school program and its functions to all who will listen, and express hostile feelings toward the teachers and the school administrators. Also, the parents point out the tremendous efforts that they have made in attempting to "find out what is wrong with Bobby," and complain that no one as yet has been able to give them any satisfaction or to do anything about his condition. The neighbors do not relish such discussions, and are reluctant to invite Bobby's parents to neighborhood social events. There has been a gradual process of diminishing social interaction, which has been accelerated by the increasing reluctance of the parents to accept such invitations when they are forthcoming.

Bobby's parents present a much different picture from those of Ann, in that they were unable to accept his limitations. Rather, they perceived them as being shameful and derogatory, and so tried to disguise their true nature from Bobby and other people. They attempted vainly to find some "external" cause for Bobby's shortcomings. They blamed the school, and, even more than this, also blamed Bobby for being a "lazy and uncooperative" child. The parental pressures upon the child to achieve were tremendous, and only served to aggravate an already serious situation.

The desperate attempts of the parents to discover a specific remediable cause of the mental retardation are evidence of the needs of the parent to disguise the nature of a situation which they were totally unable to accept. Their reactions imply that they perceived Bobby's disability as threatening to themselves, and that they had a deep sense of shame. In effect, Bobby was thoroughly rejected by the parents, although they, of course, did not accept this implication of their behavior.

The parents consistently rejected the counsel that they sought initially. They refused to accept either the recommendations of the school principal or the reading tutors who attempted to work with Bobby. They were seeking some sort of magical cure, and expressed the neurotic hope that time would solve the problem. "In the end everything will come out all right." Thus, these parents were clearly emotionally unable to cope with the problem of Bobby's mental retardation. The conflict within their own personalities is also reflected in the disturbance in their social relationships. The anxieties engendered by their reaction to Bobby spread to many of their social interactions, and, as a result, they tended to isolate themselves from other people.

It is not surprising that Bobby began to develop unacceptable patterns of behavior in school. The basic pattern of rejection by the parents, as well as the increased pressures to which he was subjected, caused him to find an outlet in his hostile feelings and aggressive reactions not only toward his classmates but also toward his teachers. Bobby suffered, but so did the parents. They were under considerable stress and showed many symptoms of severe anxiety. Their relationships with other people suffered, and even their feelings toward themselves began to show change. Life began to be more and more miserable for everyone concerned.

THE CASE OF JEANNE.   This case material illustrates the development of some serious adjustment problems in both the father and mother of a retarded child:

Jeanne is a seven-year-old girl. She was referred to the school psychologist for evaluation when it became clear to her first-grade teacher that she could not begin to do the work of her grade. Toward the end of the school year, Jeanne could not write her name or read at even a pre-first-grade level, and had few or no numerical concepts. On the *Wechsler Intelligence Scale For Children* she achieved a verbal I.Q. of 62, a performance quotient of 68, and a full-scale I.Q. of 66. These test scores were in agreement with similar I.Q.'s achieved on Form L of the 1937 *Stanford-Binet* intelligence test and on the *Grace Arthur Scale of Performance Test*. A reading readiness test indicated that Jeanne was far from ready to begin her reading experience. Further evaluation indicated that she had exceptionally poor visual-motor abilities. The personality evaluation indicated that she was a very immature child, who clung to childish ways of behavior, and who was very much threatened by her school experiences. It was felt that she was unable to profit from the experiences of the first grade, and that, rather than being retained in the first grade, she should be transferred to a special class for retarded children.

The results of the evaluation were discussed with the father and mother at a conference attended by the school principal and Jeanne's teacher. The results were catastrophic! Jeanne's father became highly insulted at the possibility that his girl was a mentally retarded child. He stated (or, rather, shouted): "It's just an impossibility! No one in my family has ever been accused of being dumb. I got good grades all through school, and all of the children did. My father is a successful businessman, and my mother is a college graduate too, so this thing is absolutely absurd! The whole family is bright, and so it just can't be! If there were someone in the family like that it would make more sense, but there just isn't anyone who didn't get along in school."

Jeanne's father also presented a large number of reasons to "explain" why she could not achieve in school. He stated: "I know that she hasn't been doing her school work properly. But I also know why she doesn't. The whole trouble is because of her mother. Her mother just babies her all the time. She takes her part when I tell Jeanne it's time to do her homework, and many times when I tell her to do something that she doesn't want to do then her mother always steps in and sees that she doesn't have to do it. Just the other night, I sat down and gave her some real simple addition in arithmetic to do. She couldn't even add 8 and 6 right. So, I told her that she couldn't watch television any more or go out and play until she could do all her arithmetic correctly. Then the very next night, when I came home from work, I found Jeanne outside playing. I grabbed her up and was going to give her a few slaps but her mother interfered again. She says that the girl is trying hard and doing as well as she can, but I don't see that at all. What she needs is somebody to sit down on her very hard, and see to it that she does her work. The way her mother handles her she never will get anywhere. Jeanne's got the idea now that she can just slip by and not do a thing, and that if I try to make her do anything that she can go to her mother and get her own way. But that's going to change. From now on I'm going to put my foot down and see to it that she does learn. I think that you are making a big mountain out of a molehill. You're making a problem where there really isn't any at all!"

In regard to Jeanne's low test scores he stated: "There's lots of people that just can't do well on a test at all. I had trouble with tests too; I knew the stuff, but when I used to take a test I wouldn't do too good. It's the same way with Jeanne. I know that she can do a lot better on things than she did on the tests. She probably didn't want to try anyhow, so they don't mean too much."

Jeanne's father refused to consider the possibility that Jeanne would do much better if placed in a special class. He felt that such a course of action would be shameful to the entire family. "What in the world would I tell my relatives if you did that? They would think that she was a real dummy or something. How could I explain it to them and what would all the neighbors think about it? That's out!"

Upon being informed that Jeanne just could not do the work, he said that he would employ a tutor in the summer months, so that Jeanne could then be promoted to the second grade at the beginning of the next school term. At a second conference Jeanne's father still maintained the same opinions. He said that he had "been sitting down on Jeanne," and that he felt she was making some progress.

Following the second conference, Jeanne's mother visited the school by herself, and talked to the principal. She said that she knew that Jeanne could not possibly keep up with the work of her grade, and that she had observed that Jeanne was crying a great deal and that it was difficult to "get her off to school" in the mornings. The mother also stated that she and her husband were in frequent disagreement over ways to handle Jeanne, and said that: "It seems that we are always fighting about something. It has gotten so bad that I hate to see my husband come home in the evening. He is grouchy, and he is always complaining about things. Our whole family is entirely up in the air. He finds fault with everything I do, and it seems that he is always picking on Jeanne."

The emotional reactions of the parents in the case of Jeanne were, as in the case of Bobby, maladaptive. In particular, the father could not accept the reality of Jeanne's retardation, and tended to view her limited capacities as a reflection upon his own abilities. He reacted toward Jeanne with strong hostility, and tended to blame the girl for her inability to achieve. As the situation became progressively worse, he then began to displace his feelings upon his wife.

Feelings of guilt and shame were pronounced, and Jeanne's father was particularly concerned about the attitudes and feelings of his neighbors, which were perceived as being derogatory to the family. The father's reactions only tended to make the situation deteriorate even more, since he insisted upon placing pressures on Jeanne to achieve at levels which were completely beyond her capacity (the pressures of extra tutoring, lengthened study periods, and the like).

This case also illustrates the beginnings of the breaking up of the family unit. There were increasing disagreements between the parents, with the father "placing the blame" on the mother for Jeanne's short-comings. Neither the mother nor the father had insight into the fact that their problems were not so much in relationship to each other, but, rather, stemmed from their continuing frustration in being unable to cope with the stress of Jeanne's problems.

Dynamic considerations

As we have seen from the preceding cases, there are many different ways in which a parent can react emotionally to the fact that his child is mentally retarded. The resulting patterns of behavior may vary from a more constructive form of adjustment (such as a realistic acceptance of the child's condition) to a more destructive and maladaptive form of adjustment (as in rejection or denial of the retardation). The multitude of individual parental reactions may be grouped into a number of major categories of behavior, according to the type of acceptance of the child's retardation. In one such categorization scheme, Kanner states that the parent may react to the stress situation of the child in one of three major ways.[1] He may *accept, deny,* or *reject* the child's mental retardation. Although parental reactions to retardation may be categorized in this manner, this is done for didactic purposes only. Each parent reacts in his own unique manner to the stress situation created by the child's retardation. We shall consider typical parental patterns of behavior in the following paragraphs.

THE ACCEPTING PARENT. One category of parental reaction which may be regarded as being constructive and adaptive is that one in which the parent acknowledges and accepts in a mature manner the reality of the child's disability. Such an acceptance of the child leads to many positive benefits for both the child and the parent, as well as for the family unit and, in the last analysis, of course, for society as a whole. Such a parent eventually comes to a full acceptance of the child, and loves the child *as he is.* He does not attempt to substitute a fantasied picture of the child for the way he is in reality, and, in fact, there is

---

[1] Kanner, L., "Parents' feelings about retarded children," *Amer. J. ment. Defic.,* 1953, *57,* 375–383.

little disparity between the two images. He perceives clearly his own role as a parent, and recognizes that he has an identity of his own which must be preserved. Therefore, the accepting parent deals with the problems of the child in a realistic manner, and does not make a "slave" of himself in his relationships with the child. He assumes responsibility for the many other roles which are demanded of him by society, such as those of father, husband, breadwinner, companion, and the like.

An accepting parent has no undue anxieties either in regard to his own needs and capacities or in regard to the disabilities of the child. His behavior is essentially that of the problem-solving type. As in the case of all persons, he may have anxieties from time to time, but essentially they are anxieties of the *object* type. These anxieties are based on particular situations that cause difficulties, and since the cause of the anxiety is thus known, it is dealt with in a rational and problem-solving manner. Such objective anxieties are in contrast to the *objectless* type of anxieties which the psychoneurotic person experiences, and in which the feared situation is not consciously known.

The parent who shows this type of positive emotional reaction may be characterized, from one point of view, as a person who is able to bring himself to acceptance of an unpleasant reality situation, one which is possibly quite threatening. This acceptance is by no means an easy task, and its achievement is dependent upon the psychological maturity of the parent, and also upon appropriate guidance. It may be postulated that, to the degree that the personality structure of the parent is psychoneurotic, logical thought processes are inhibited, and so the perception of the reality situation, as well as its acceptance, is distorted. Fenichel has pointed out the prerequisite for logical thinking.[2] He states that such a type of thinking demands a strong ego which is capable of postponement of immediate gratifications, an ego that is able to control basic drives in an adequate manner, and also one that is ready to judge reality in accord with its experience. Thus, if the parent is not sufficiently psychologically mature, then the full acceptance of the child by him becomes a difficult task indeed.

However, the acceptance of the reality situation by the parent is not an all-or-none affair; a parent's reactions may fall at any point within a *wide range* of the total scale of adjustment possibilities. As we shall see, the attainment of a high degree of reality perception based on acceptance of the mentally retarded child comes about as the result of a

[2] Fenichel, O., *The Psychoanalytic Theory of Neurosis*. New York: W. W. Norton & Company, Inc., 1945, p. 51.

gradual process of growth within the parent. Fortunately, it is one that may be fostered by proper learning and guidance experiences, which we shall delineate in detail later.

Thus, the parent initially may rank at the lower end of the scale of acceptance of the child, but through appropriate growth experiences may acquire more insight and understanding until he reaches a relatively much higher and more mature kind of acceptance. In addition, the full acceptance of the situation is not only a logical or rational one, but it is also an *emotional* one. A concept or situation may, on the one hand, be accepted intellectually, but be rejected completely on emotional grounds. For instance, a parent may react in a manner similar to this:

John's mother stated that she was quite well aware of the fact that her 7-year-old son should be encouraged to do things for himself to the extent that he was able. As she said: "It is in this way that he will grow." Yet, in discussion it developed that the mother completely dressed the child each morning, and usually accompanied him to school. The reason she gave was: "John has such a tough time."

At one level, the mother was aware of John's needs, but emotionally she was unable to behave toward him in a mature and growth-stimulating manner.

The accepting parent, then, needs to be aware of the nature of his own emotional relationships to his retarded child. He must be aware of what *needs of his own* are threatened by the child's condition, and he must be aware of the extent to which these needs determine his own behavioral reactions.

One of the primary goals in the counseling and guidance of parents of mentally retarded children is to develop full acceptance of the child in both emotional and intellectual spheres. Such acceptance leads to many beneficial results. First, the child himself is made more secure in his relationships with his parents. As a consequence, he is likely to be more secure in his relationships with other children and with the world as a whole. His percept of himself is more positive, and he is stimulated to achieve maximum growth in all areas. The demands he makes upon his parents and others tend to be more realistic and pertinent, and he is better able to achieve his potential growth levels.

Second, the parent reaps many direct benefits. His own self-percept is also more positive, and he too is more secure in his relationships with his family, with other people, and with the world in general. Energy is not consumed in dealing with neurotic, internal problems in regard to the retardate, and consequently can be devoted more to dealing with other important factors in real life. He is able to function more adequately vocationally, and to form more adequate and satisfying social relationships. Marital discord and strife are not so apt to occur, and greater satisfaction can be achieved in marriage and family life in general.

THE DISGUISING PARENT.   Another major category of parental reactions to mental retardation includes those modes of behavior which attempt to *disguise,* in some manner, the child's condition. Not only are such attempts made in order to hide his condition from other people, but, more important, they are made in order to attempt to hide it from the parents themselves. In general, the disguising parent does perceive, to some extent, that there is "something wrong" with the child. But he is unable to recognize or admit the fact that the child's inability to perform adequately tasks which are ordinarily done by other children of the same chronological age is due to a state of limited intellectual capacities.

As Kanner points out, the disguising parent searches very hard for some reality factor to which the child's retardation may be attributed. Consequently, medical consultations may be frequent. At one time or another, for instance, the child's condition may be attributed to "bad tonsils," or to "infected teeth," or to "dietary insufficiency," or to some similar cause. The child is given one medical examination after another, each time with the hope that a specific remedial cause for the retardation will be discovered and corrected.

In many instances, the parent may see the child himself as being at fault. In such an event the child may be seen as lazy, as uncooperative, as "not wanting to try," or as being punitive to the parents. For instance, Mr. Roe stated:

"Bob is just plain lazy. He could do much better if he tried. He goes to school and just sits there, and doesn't want to get anything out of it. If he would get it into his head that he has to do better, he would—that's his real trouble— he just doesn't want to learn." This despite the fact that Bob has an I.Q. in the low sixties, and that several attempts have been made to interpret the situation to Mr. Roe.

Or, as another example of attempts to disguise the child's condition:

"Jack has some real problem somewhere. We thought sure that it was his eyesight that was the trouble. We took him to an eye doctor, and he found that Jack really had a severe astigmatism in the right eye. He prescribed glasses, and Jack has been wearing them now for about six months. His school work hasn't improved very much, though, so there must be something else wrong. We have made an appointment to get his hearing gone over, and he is to be seen in about two weeks."

Frequently the child's academic disabilities are seen as being the fault of inadequate instructional methods. The parent, in such an instance, is able to see that the child is seriously retarded in school, and, possibly, may even acquiesce to the placement of the child in a special class. But the "disguising" parent is unable to accept the real function of such a class. Shortly following such a placement, the parent may begin to make strong demands upon the child for academic progress. He may frequently visit the school and complain to the teacher about his progress. Such forms of behavior may be interpreted as being indicative of the parent's misperception of the situation. Despite interpretation to the parent to the effect that the special class is designed to meet the unique needs of the retarded child, the disguising parent may tend to see it as essentially a tutorial or remedial class, where the child will receive instruction so as to quickly bring him to the academic level of more average children. These feelings are clearly demonstrated in the following example:

Joe is a ten-year-old boy, who is of borderline intelligence. Following consistent failures in the regular grade, he was transferred to a special class. After about six months in the class, the parents visited the school and talked with the teacher. His father stated: "Joe isn't doing any better than he did in the regular class. He still isn't able to read. I don't know why. He is over here with you and there are only 12 children in the class. With all that attention he should be making good progress. In his other class there were over 30 children, and he did not get the attention that he needed. But now, with just a few children, he should be able to learn much faster. I don't see why his reading hasn't improved."

THE DENYING PARENT. A severe emotional reaction to the stress situation resulting from the mental retardation of the child is shown by the type of parent who feels the need to deny, both to others and to himself, the reality of the child's disabilities. This mode of defense is called *denial* (see Chapter Six). It is said that the ostrich, when faced with a threatening situation, attempts to avoid it by burying his head in the sand. In such an action it is as if the mere fact of blocking out the visual perception of the situation which presents the threat is sufficient to remove the threat itself. But this is not true, since the ostrich, even though it buries its head and so does not see the danger, is still vulnerable (and even more so!) to the threat. It still is very much exposed!

This particular form of defensive behavior is often manifested in the behavior of children. Frequently a child, when exposed to a threat of some sort, may shut his eyes, or cover his eyes with his hands so as not to see the threatening object or situation. Symbolically, the same type of reaction is shown by the parent who denies the reality of the child's retarded condition. Such a person does not, of course, close his eyes, but he does avoid perception of the actual reality of the situation. In effect, the person believes: "What I refuse to see does not exist." An example of this type of behavioral reaction is that shown by Mr. White in discussing the problem of his son, a mildly retarded child.

"There's nothing at all wrong with Jack. This whole thing is just a passing phase in his growth. I had a lot of problems when I went to school too, but I got over them in pretty good shape. I had a rough time until I was about 14 years of age, then I straightened out and didn't have any more real trouble. Jack will do the same thing. One day he'll wake up and then go ahead. So why make all this fuss about this thing? It isn't going to do any good to hold him back in school again. I'll talk to him, and next year he'll get along fine. I don't see anything at all to get worried about, and I can't understand why you seem to think that it's so important."

As in the case of the parent who attempts to disguise the child's condition, the denial is a defense reaction upon the part of the parent to the threat of the stress situation to which he is subjected. Attempts to disguise or to deny the mental retardation of the child are by no means rarely encountered. However, they should not be seen as deliberate and conscious efforts of the parent to avoid the situation. Rather, they should be recognized as reactions of the parent to a situation which is threatening to him and which provokes defensive reactions upon his part. The utilization of a psychological defense is not a deliberate or planned conscious reaction on the part of a parent, but, rather, is a more automatic and an unconscious reaction to a stress situation. The particular defense utilized is a function of the general maturity level and life history of the individual, and, as we have seen, the more immature the parent, the greater is the stress of the situation and the more extensive are the defensive reactions and consequent maladaptive behavior.

Characteristic personality reactions of parents

The parent may react in a variety of ways to the stress situation resulting from the child's retardation. As we shall see, parental reactions are functions of many complex interacting variables, and are unique to the particular parent. But there are some general parental reactions which are encountered so commonly that they warrant detailed attention. These include: distortions in the parent's perception of the capacities and qualities of the child, rejection tendencies, marital discords, narcissistic involvements of the parent, unwarranted reactions to the community, and feelings of guilt in regard to the mental retardation. These specific psychodynamic problems are discussed in the following pages. In addition, there is considerable evidence to indicate that the parent usually progresses through a well-defined process of growth in arriving at a full acceptance of the disability of his child, and of his own feelings. This growth process is discussed in the final pages of this section.

DISTORTED PARENTAL PERCEPTIONS. It is not unusual to find that the parent of the retardate is unable to perceive the reality of his child's retardation. He often sees the child as being quite different from what he actually is. As a consequence, many family problems arise which are based on such faulty perceptions. In a recent symposium it was concluded that parental difficulties in dealing with retarded children included: (1) the setting of unrealistically high goals for the young child; (2) overprotection of the child; (3) overindulgence of the child; and (4) maladjustment of the parents, manifested in alcoholism or emotional disturbance.[3] It was found that the most frequent stumbling block in attempts to deal with these problems is the unrealistic perception by the parents of the child's disabilities.

Many studies have demonstrated the fact that such faulty parental perceptions may occur. For example, Schulman and Stern conducted a study of parents' estimates of the intelligence level of their retarded children.[4] They asked 50 parents to estimate the developmental age of their retarded children *prior* to the time that psychological tests were administered. These estimates were then compared with the obtained intelligence test scores. They found that the mean obtained I.Q. was 55.5, and that its standard deviation was 16.6. The mean estimated quotient was 57.2, and the standard deviation was 17.4. Thus, there was *no* statistically significant difference between the two mean scores. Four parents overestimated the intellectual level of the child by more than 20 points, and 7 parents overestimated the I.Q. by 15 points or more. Twenty-three parents *overestimated* the I.Q. by an average of 12.6 points, while 19 *underestimated* it by an average of 10.7 points. The correlation between

[3] Symposium, "Counseling the mentally retarded and their parents," *J. clin. Psychol.* 1953, *9*, 99–124.

[4] Schulman, J., and Stern, S., "Parents' estimate of the intelligence of retarded children," *Amer. J. ment. Defic.*, 1959, *63*, 696–698.

the actual obtained I.Q. and the estimated quotient was + .67, indicating that the two measures were moderately correlated.

This study has some important implications. In the first place, it indicates that the parents of retarded children, as a group, are quite aware of the disabilities of their offspring. Too often the generalization is made that the parents are unaware of the child's intellectual retardation. This study does not support such a generalization. In the second place, even though the parents, *as a group*, are quite accurate in their assessment of the degree of mental retardation, there is considerable variation from one individual estimate to another. Some parents *underestimate* the child's capacities to a marked degree, while others inordinately *overestimate* the intellectual level. The degree of insight into the extent of the child's deficits thus may vary significantly from one parent to another.

Some attempts have been made to relate the parent's estimate of the intellectual ability of his child to various specific attributes of his own. Such attempts have not, in general, been too successful. An example of such a study is that conducted by Ewart and Green.[5] These researchers looked for relationships between the mother's ability to estimate the age level of the child's behavior and data in regard to the personality traits of the mother. They made the fundamental assumption that the accuracy of the mother's perception of the retardation of the child was, to some extent, a measure of her acceptance or rejection of the child's condition. The validity of this assumption was not demonstrated in the study. They also obtained data on 50 retardates who did not have any serious physical pathology and on another 50 who had organic brain lesions. In each instance, the mother was asked to estimate the age level at which the child was currently functioning. This age was then transformed into an estimated I.Q. for comparison purposes.

Ewart and Green then divided the mothers into two groups: in Group 1 they placed those mothers whose estimates were within 15 points of the obtained I.Q.'s, and in Group 2 the mothers whose estimates were more than 15 points, or more deviant from obtained quotients. The two groups were then compared by certain personality characteristics. Ewart and Green found that the presence or absence of physical anomaly in the retardate child was not related to the validity of the estimate, and neither was the sex of the child. It is surprising to note that there was no relationship between previous psychological evaluation and correctness of the

---

[5] Ewart, J. C., and Green, M. W., "Conditions associated with the mother's estimate of the ability of her retarded child," *Amer. J. ment. Defic.*, 1957, *62*, 521–533.

estimate. There was a slight tendency for a more correct estimate to be made for the younger children, but this was a trend only. Neither educational level nor the occupation of the father was related to the validity of the estimate. The significant relationship demonstrated was with the educational level of the mother—the higher her educational level, the more accurate was the prediction.

It should not be concluded that there are no factors related to the accuracy of the prediction of the intellectual abilities of the child made by the mother, since it may well be that important variables were not explored in the Ewart and Green study. For instance, other personality characteristics of the mother (such as her dependency needs, hostile and aggressive impulses, need for dominance, and the like) may be of importance in determining the accuracy of her perception of the limitations of her child.

Another such study is that of Worchel and Worchel, who explored some attributes of the way in which the parents perceived the child.[6] They asked parents from 22 families with at least one retarded child to rate the child on several different variables. It was found that the parents rated the retarded child less favorably on many personality traits than they did their non-retarded children. Further, the retarded child was seen as deviating more from the concept of an ideal child than was the non-retarded one. Worchel and Worchel interpret their findings as indicating that there is a greater degree of parental rejection of the retardate child than there is in the case of the more average child.

Zuk has studied *autistic* distortions in parents of retarded children.[7] (Autism, according to Zuk, is the process which causes a person "to see what he wishes to see.") He formed two groups of retarded children, one without significant motor impairment, and the other with serious motor disabilities. The parents were then asked to give information about the child, and this was compared with information gathered by more objective means. Zuk found that the information furnished by parents of the children without motor disabilities had a high degree of autistic distortion, while that furnished by the parents of the children with motor disabilities was not found to be as highly distorted.

Zuk feels that a more realistic perception of the child's disability is held by the parent when there is a motor disability present, since the perceptual ambiguity is less in such an instance. He states that "the

[6] Worchel, T., and Worchel, P., "The parental concept of the mentally retarded child," *Amer. J. ment. Defic.*, 1961, *65*, 782–788.

[7] Zuk, B., "Autistic distortions in parents of retarded children," *J. consult. Psychol.*, 1959, *23*, 171–176.

realistic process" operates in a stronger manner when there are objective evidences of the child's lowered level of functioning manifested. Further, Zuk states that, in the case of the retarded children with motor disabilities, the unconscious wish for normalcy held by the parents lacked an external factor to which it could be attached and so be reinforced. The same unconscious wish for normalcy of the child was present in both groups of parents, but in one instance (the motor-disabled group) there was less opportunity available for conscious expression of the wish.

The situation is further complicated by the fact that other children readily adopt the attitudes and feelings of the parents (*identification*) toward the mentally retarded child. This is illustrated quite well by the experiment conducted by Caldwell and Guze, who were primarily concerned with investigating the adjustment difficulties of the parents and siblings of institutionalized and non-institutionalized retardates.[8] They compared the adjustment patterns of the mothers and siblings of 16 institutionalized children with those of the mothers and siblings of 16 non-institutionalized children. No important differences were found between the mothers of each of the groups. However, the siblings of the institutionalized child felt that it was much better that he was away from home, while the siblings of the non-institutionalized child felt that it was much better that he was at home. Caldwell and Guze stated that, without exception, the siblings of retardates mirrored the attitudes of their parents, and that they molded their value systems so as to conform to the family *status quo*. This is another reason why it is so important that the parent perceive realistically the assets and liabilities of his retarded child.

REJECTION. It is likely that the emotional maladjustment of the parent is reflected in his behavior toward the retarded child. In many instances, this behavior is essentially rejecting in nature. As Fried points out, when this rejection of the child occurs, the rejecting parent then is unaware of the child's hurt "sensibilities."[9] Fried feels that the parent tries to adopt patterns of rigid and persistent discipline and training at home because he feels that such actions will help the child. He cannot see how this blocks off the possible fantasy life of the child, and leads to the consequent development of many severe emotional disturbances in him. Such a rejecting parent frequently has great concern over the

[8] Caldwell, B., and Guze, S., "A study of the adjustment of parents and siblings of institutionalized and non-institutionalized retarded children," *Amer. J. ment. Defic.*, 1960, *64*, 845–861.

[9] Fried, A., "Report of four years work at the Guidance Clinic for Retarded Children, Essex County, New Jersey," *Amer. J. ment. Defic.*, 1955, *60*, 83–89.

sexual development of the child, but this concern is essentially a projection of his own particular fears and disturbances in this area.

Because the parent's rejection of the child is frequently unconscious, the parent is not aware of the basis of his own feelings toward him, and consequently he experiences severe conflicts. These, of course, depend upon his own personality characteristics. If, due to his own dynamics, the parent is an anxious person, the added anxiety due to factors brought about by his relationship with the child may be sufficient to precipitate a severe psychoneurotic reaction. This condition would again react in a circular fashion on both the child and the parent.

MARITAL DISCORD. Marital difficulties often arise due to parental anxieties. Each may blame the other for the child's condition and his behavior (either consciously or unconsciously), and may displace some of the feelings toward the child on each other. In addition, the restrictions that the parent may perceive in his social interrelationships may result in further hostility and anxiety. These may also be displaced upon the other marriage partner, producing further marital discord and occasionally resulting in a needlessly broken home.

It is true that the mentally retarded child, particularly at a younger age, does demand a more than usual amount of attention and care. It is usually the responsibility of the mother to provide this. However, the father may often resent the fact that his wife pays more attention to the child than she does to him, and so he tends to react with hostility toward both his wife and child—toward the wife for rejecting him, and toward the child because of his demands upon the mother. Such a reaction is more apt to occur when the husband tends to be immature and infantile.

NARCISSISTIC INVOLVEMENTS. Every parent tends to see a great deal of himself in his children. He tends to see the child really as an extension of himself, and displaces upon him many of his own feelings and needs. Too often the parent is so closely identified with the child that he cannot see the child as having any separate existence in his own right. When the child does something that is approved, the parent takes pride in the child's performance, and when the child fails at some sort of task, the parent feels undue grief and anger. For example, Johnny brings home a poor report card from school. The parent who is overly identified with his child may feel aggrieved because he perceives the failure as his own—it is *he* who has failed and not the child. It is *he* who is responsible for the poor grades. The problems of the parent are the ones that are foremost in such instances, not those of the child. The parent has a picture of himself—a self-image—which is confused with that of his child. Thus, any blow to the child, any shortcoming, failure, or censure by other individuals is perceived by the parent as a blow to his own narcissistic (self-love) pride. When the child is diagnosed as mentally retarded, then such a parent feels that he himself is in some way being described in a derogatory manner.

DEPENDENCY REACTIONS.   In some instances the parent may be a dependent person who leans very heavily for emotional support upon other individuals. The presence of a retarded child often serves to intensify his conflicts in this area. It might well be that, prior to the birth of the retarded child, such a parent's psychological defenses were relatively adequate in dealing with his dependency conflicts. However, the retarded child needs to lean more heavily, and for a longer period of time, upon the parents. He *demands* a great deal from the parents. This demand upon the dependent parent to give more than he is able often precipitates further conflict within him, and the dependency needs, which otherwise would be handled marginally, break through, frequently with catastrophic results. Severe emotional reactions and maladaptive reactions on the part of the parent may then be expected. In a similar way, other problems of the parent may be aroused by the problems of the retarded child. For example, the weaning or habit training difficulties of the retarded child may serve as "triggers" to his own severe problems in these areas, and re-arouse problems within him that were, up to that point, controlled in a relatively adequate manner.

The parent of the retarded child is also prone to a fear that is continually with him. Even though the child may be making good progress, maturing both physically and psychologically as well as could be expected, the parent is faced continually with the reality of the child's limitations. He then begins to wonder: "What will happen to my child when I am no longer here to help him?" This type of fear is persistent, and constantly plagues the parent. Some relief follows when the parent realizes the fact that the child can often profit from vocational training, that he can be helped to become a self-supporting individual, and that continuing help from social agencies will probably be available to the child. If the fear is too persistent and too anxiety-producing, then the parent will need some form of treatment to alleviate his own anxieties.

REACTIONS TO COMMUNITY. The parent reacts emotionally not only to the retardate, but also to the community's perception of and reaction to the problem of mental retardation. As pointed out earlier, society has many stereotyped attitudes and prejudices about mental retardation, and the parent, being himself a member of society, is often affected by them. Let us look, for example, at Mrs. Brown's feelings about her son:

Mrs. Brown brought her five-year-old child to the clinic for examination. She said: "You know it is very hard for me to do this. I knew that there must have been something wrong with him even when he was a little baby, but I did not want to really find out. People have a lot of ideas about retarded children, and I didn't want them having them about my boy. But then I found out that there were a lot of other children like this, and I talked to some of the other mothers and I decided to bring him in. I still feel awful funny about it, though, and I don't want other people to know. I guess it can't be helped, though, and you can't hide it all the time."

Let us look at a similar reaction to social forces, as expressed by Mr. Smith:

"All right, I can see that the boy is a retarded child. But what in Heaven's name am I going to tell the neighbors? They have been asking me what is wrong with him, and some of them know that I brought him in for examination. Now I'm not going to tell them that he is a retarded child—they have too many funny ideas about that. Don't you have some other kind of name that you can tell me, then I'll give them that instead? It's none of their business anyhow, but I've got to tell them something. You've got to live with people, you know."

As Weingold and Hormuth so clearly point out, the presence of a mentally retarded child accentuates the personality problems of all members of the family.[10] The attitudes of the parent are, in part, reactions to the fact that he is often rejected by the various community groups of which he is a member. Group pressures, whether real or merely perceived by the parent, often force the family to withdraw from their normal social contacts. The family tends to become isolated. Due to this increasing social rejection and isolation, the parent then tends to focus intently on every minute activity of his child. This increased attention to the shortcomings of the child further serves to accentuate the personality difficulties of both parent and child. As Weingold and Hormuth point out, the final result is an increase in the parents' feelings

[10] Weingold, J. T., and Hormuth, R. P., "Group guidance of parents of mentally retarded children," *J. clin. Psychol.*, 1953, *9*, 118–124.

of shame and guilt and the development of attitudes of rejection and overprotection toward the child.

GUILT FEELINGS OF PARENTS.   Frequently the parent of the mentally retarded child feels, in some way, that the child's condition is due to some past action of his own. Such a reaction stems directly from the guilt feelings of the parent which may be aroused by the disabilities of the child. As we have seen, guilt is a special form of anxiety which stems from overly strong superego factors. It is generally directed by the person toward some past actions. "I have done something wrong," or "What I did was not right." The person who constantly feels guilty has a lowered self-percept, and tends to see himself in an unfavorable light. When guilt feelings are strong, the person feels insecure and unprotected. In short, his *self-esteem* is lowered. The greater the existing guilt feelings of the parent, the more readily he tends to blame himself for the disabilities of the child.

A guilt-ridden parent asks, in effect: "What have I done to deserve such a terrible thing?" or, "What sin have I committed to be punished in this way?" He may berate himself, and constantly ruminate over events in his past life in an attempt to uncover his defection or sinful behavior. Very often no specific act is discovered. But in many instances some "wrong" act is seized upon and made the focus of the guilt reaction. The following statements made by parents are illustrative:

1. "It is my fault that my child is retarded. It is a punishment on me for giving up my religion. When I married my husband I changed faith, and this is my punishment for sinning."

2. "This is all my doing. Before I was married I ran around a lot, and twice I had premarital sexual relationships. I always felt very badly about that, and now I have to pay for what I did."

Human nature being what it is, there is no lack in any life of experiences which the person regrets, nor of acts for which he feels some degree of shame or guilt. Consequently, such experiences are easily "discovered," and may then serve as the focus of the guilt reaction aroused by the presence of the retardate.

Mrs. Murray, in her moving discussion of the needs of the parents of such children, is deeply concerned with the theological conflicts which so often arise.[11] She states that death, physical illness, loss of job, eco-

---

[11] Murray, M. A., "Needs of parents of retarded children," *Amer. J. ment. Defic.*, 1959, *63*, 1078–1088.

nomic insecurity, and other misfortunes are familiar to every adult, and are within the realm of possibility of occurrence. But the presence of a retarded child often places the parent "outside the providence of God's mercy and justice." If such a parent has been reared in a puritanical environment, then he is overwhelmed by guilt. Mrs. Murray feels that any event which destroys or permanently damages one's concept of a "loving and merciful God" presents a problem which must be resolved by skilled help. We have repeatedly noted such feelings in our clinical treatment of parents of retarded children.

Throughout the ages, concern with sin and guilt has been interwoven inextricably into the basic tenets and concepts of all religious creeds. For this reason the religious background of the parents may be an important factor in determining the degree to which the retarded child is accepted or rejected. Zuk has explored this hypothesis in studying the relationship between religious factors and the role of guilt in the parental acceptance of the child.[12] He studied the religious backgrounds of 76 mothers of retarded children, and compared them with various measures of acceptance of their children. The results of this study showed that mothers of the younger children were more accepting of the child's disability than were the mothers of the older ones. As Zuk points out, this is somewhat a characteristic parental reaction, since initially it is not the child but, rather, the diagnosis of mental retardation that is rejected.

Zuk found significant differences between the degree to which Catholic and non-Catholic mothers accepted their retarded offspring, with the Catholic mothers being more accepting than the non-Catholic mothers. He offers, as an explanation for this, the hypothesis that Catholic mothers are given greater emotional support by their religious faith, in that they are explicitly absolved from parental guilt in the birth of a retarded child. As a result, the Catholic mother is less subject to a process of searching self-examination which often results in feelings of guilt. Zuk states that she accepts the fact that the child's condition was the "result of a decision made by a high spiritual authority," and that this enhances the possibility of the acceptance of the child.

Such a point of view, according to Zuk, is also embraced by the Hutterites, who do not socially reject the defective, but, regardless of his age, view him as a child who therefore is incapable of sinning and so, in each instance, attains automatic salvation. Zuk emphasizes the fact

---

12 Zuk, G. H., "The religious factor and the role of guilt in parental acceptance of the retarded child." *Amer. J. ment. Defic.*, 1959, *64*, 139–147.

that the parents are caught between strong feelings of love and hate for the child. The conflict between these opposing feelings results in the arousal of guilt reactions. Then, since the parents cannot admit the guilt, it is manifested in such reactions as rejection, fostering of overdependency, or putting too great a pressure on the child to achieve.

Laufer and Denhoff have explored the genesis of the guilt feelings of parents of retarded children.[13] They state that, normally, childhood is a period of disorderliness and disorganization in any event. But if the child is mentally defective, then his behavior may become unbearable for the parent. Due to the mental defect, the child has a low degree of frustration tolerance, .and consequently makes a poor response to its mothering. The mother's percept of the child then becomes distorted by her own feelings of inadequacy, since she cannot placate or satisfy the needs of the baby. These feelings of inadequacy are then displaced onto the father and other members of the family. According to Laufer and Denhoff, a vicious "cycle of childhood" ensues, and a behavior problem develops with the family, as "parental guilt displaces dislike and overprotection superimposes itself on realism."

In light of the available evidence, it seems reasonable to assume that the religious background of the parent may have a considerable bearing upon the acceptance of the retarded child. It may be concluded that if the religious background is such as to predispose the parent to a feeling of personal sin and guilt, without explicit absolution, then it is more likely that guilt related to the birth of the child will be experienced. The greater the feeling of guilt, the greater will be the difficulties of the parent in fully accepting the child, and the more probable that intrafamily problems will arise.

Development of insight

There appears to be a developmental process through which the parent usually passes before adequately recognizing and accepting the problems of his child. Rosen points out that there is a pattern of growing comprehension on the part of the parent as he gradually becomes aware of the problems of his child.[14] He postulates five levels in this process. There is, first, a phase of *awareness*, when the parent perceives the child as being "different" in some way from other children. The mean age of the child at the time of this perception is about two years and eight

---

[13] Laufer, M., and Denhoff, E., "Hyperkenetic behavior syndrome in children," *J. Pediat.*, 1957, *50*, 403–474.

[14] Rosen, L., "Selected aspects in the development of the mother's understanding of her mentally retarded child," *Amer. J. ment. Defic.*, 1955, *59*, 522–528.

months. This is followed, when the child is about five years of age, by a *recognition* upon the part of the parent that the child is retarded. Following such a recognition of the problem, the parent then seeks anxiously for the *cause* of the retardation.. More than half the mothers in Rosen's study felt that there just *had* to be a specific physical basis for it. Next, there is a phase in which the parent seeks for a *solution*—the child is taken from person to person by the mother and she talks to all whom she perceives as possibly being of help to her. Finally, there is the phase of *acceptance*, when both the child and his problem are accepted by the parent. The progression of the parent through these phases is not an automatic matter. The adequate growth of the parent—and it is really a process of growth—depends not only upon the basic emotional maturity of the parent himself, but also upon the guidance that he receives in coping with the problems involved.

We have pointed out many of the more *usual* emotional reactions of the parent to his retarded child, but there are many other *possible* reactions that may occur. However, the point of primary importance that we wish to make is that *the emotional reactions of the parent of the mentally retarded child are essentially a function of his own personality characteristics.* As Morris points out:[15]

To some the mentally retarded child comes as an additional family member, to be loved and cherished, subject to the same privileges and restrictions as his siblings, geared to his sameness and differences. To others, he comes as a pawn or added burden in interpersonal conflict.

It is important that the emotional problems of the parents be treated, since the well-being and emotional maturation of the child depend to a great extent upon the nature of his relationships with his parents. Cianci has pointed out that only a very small percentage of all retarded children are placed in either state or residential schools.[16] It has been estimated that only ten per cent are so placed, which means that *ninety per cent of retarded children are cared for at home.* Their future psychological growth is thus dependent to a great degree upon the care, training, and emotional climate provided within the home by the parents. Parental emotional reactions are, therefore, of paramount importance, since they can so seriously interfere with the proper emotional development of the child.

[15] Morris, E., "Casework training needs for counseling parents of the retarded," *Amer. J. ment. Defic.*, 1955, *59*, 510–516.
[16] Cianci, V., "Objectives of home training," *Train. Sch. Bull.*, 1953, *50*, 23–29.

TREATMENT OF PARENTAL PROBLEMS

We have discussed some of the patterns of the emotional reactions of parents to their retarded children. It should be emphasized that the reactions cited are not unusual or rare phenomena, but occur commonly. In fact, problems such as these are so usual that we may safely state that *all* parents of retardates need some help in order to deal more adequately with their own problems, let alone those of the child. It is our conviction that all such parents should receive frequent and continued opportunity to discuss their problems with appropriate professional personnel. Further, they should all be acquainted with the fact that their problems are not unique, but that they are common to most parents of retarded children, and so are shared by a very large group of persons.

The emotional problems of parents may be thought of as falling into two major categories. The first group of parental reactions stem from a lack of adequate knowledge concerning the retarded child. Parents need to know a great deal about the condition of mental retardation; too often they have a large amount of faulty information that needs to be corrected. There may be, in such instances, no deep-seated personality changes in the parent, and no severe maladaptive behavioral reactions on his part. In such an event the parent essentially needs a very carefully designed *educative* program (or guidance), but, at the same time, attention must be paid to his feelings and emotional reactions. In the second broad type of parental reactions, the parent does develop significant personality changes and resultant maladaptive behavior. He may, for example, develop a severe psychoneurotic reaction. In such an event an educative or guidance approach is not adequate to help him resolve his problems. More intensive help, such as that offered by psychotherapy, is needed. We shall now discuss each of these major treatment approaches.

Parental treatment through education and guidance

We usually fear the unknown, but, fortunately, with understanding there often comes a relief from tension. The major objective of the education and guidance of parents of retarded children is to provide an amelioration of stress by imparting knowledge and correcting misinformation in an emotionally appropriate climate. Often the parent will be drawn by his internal needs to read many articles concerning mental retardation that are difficult for him to assimilate. In his reading, because of his own problems, he may attend selectively to certain areas and focus upon particular points that are not applicable to his problems. Such activities upon his part may only serve to increase his anxieties and induce further fears.

The educative process should be initiated as soon as feasible following the establishment of the diagnosis of mental retardation in the case of the child. Such an action helps to prevent excessive and undue anxieties in the parent, and reduces the probability of subsequent severe emotional reactions. Rose has found that uncertainty about the child's future has a severe impact upon the mother-child relationship.[17] He states that any problem which results in uncertainty in regard to life or death, or in regard to normal or defective capacities, influences the mother's feelings toward her child. Once such a suspicion is aroused, she *must* know. The longer time it takes her to find out, the greater is the internal conflict.

A similar point of view is expressed by Denhoff, who studied the emotional reactions of parents of exceptional children.[18] Denhoff concluded that the mothers of children who learn about the condition of their offspring early tend to be more free and easy about the child. On the other hand, the mothers of children who have a more mild or a more hidden disability and are so informed later, are more difficult to treat.

Morris has pointed out that there are many levels within such a counseling or educative process that may be offered to parents.[19] He postulates four such levels, based upon the emotional reactions of the parents. At one level is the *emotionally mature* parent who has accepted the reality of the child's retardation. However, even such an accepting and understanding parent as this is in need of continual help, to aid him in redefining both the child's needs and his own objectives in dealing with the problems of the child and himself. He needs guidance in regard to specific events, such as, for example, problems of adolescence, vocational training, and the like. At another level are those parents of the pseudoretarded child, who are usually faced with the results of an intense, *poor parent-child relationship*. Then, there are the parents of a retardate who experience great difficulties in their management and treatment because of a *lack of knowledge* concerning the effect of lowered intellectual capacities upon behavior in general. Finally, there are the parents who *exert pressures* upon the child to force him to perform at levels that are really beyond his capacities of achievement. The extent and depth of the educative program provided for the parent will depend upon the nature of the problems that he presents.

---

[17] Rose, J., "Factors in the development of mentally handicapped children: Counseling with parents of children with mental handicaps," *Proceedings of the 1958 Woods School Conference,* May 2-3, 1958.

[18] Denhoff, E., "The impact of the parents on the growth of exceptional children," *Except. Child.,* 1960, *26,* 271–274.

[19] Morris, *op. cit.*

But, regardless of the level at which the counseling or educative process is undertaken, it is important that the needs of the parent and the child be kept paramount. Too frequently the needs of the counselor intrude into the situation, and when this occurs, it is then highly probable that a more serious situation will arise. In many instances, the counselor, motivated by his own anxieties, is unable to communicate the reality of the situation to the parent. On the other hand, he may be carried away by his own feelings of omnipotence, and may seriously minimize the extent of the actual defect of the child. An example of this follows:

Joe was referred to the school clinic for psychological evaluation, following a history of failure in the first and second grades. Following extended study, it was clearly evident that he was a child of borderline intellectual capacities. This information was imparted to the school principal, who assumed the responsibility of interpreting the findings to the parents. But the parents were told, in effect: "Joe is a slow-learning child. But he will probably be able to do his school work if he gets a lot of special help. We will make arrangements to do this next year." The principal told the clinic staff: "I think Joe might get along next year a lot better than he did last year. *I hate to give up on a child*, and I think I should make an all-out attempt to work with him next year before I tell the parents that they have a retarded child. You don't want to rush these things." Fortunately (as does not happen in all instances), it was possible for the school counselor to intervene so as to deal with the situation in a more adequate manner, and to give Joe's parents a realistic appraisal of the child's abilities.

Zwerling states that persons dealing with the parents of retarded children are often prone to make three major errors: (1) there is too great a delay in defining the problem; (2) false hopes for the recovery of the child are encouraged in the parent; and (3) too much direct advice is offered.[20]

What are some of the more common educative needs of the parents? Many persons have attempted to spell them out in detail,[21] but such needs, of course, vary in accordance with the particular needs of the individual parents.

[20] Zwerling, I., "Initial counseling of parents with mentally retarded children," *J. Pediat.*, 1954, *44*, 469–479.
   [21] These include:
      (a) Wolf, S., and Lourie, R. S., "The mentally retarded child," *J. Pediat.*, 1953, *42*, 521–524.
      (b) Cianci, *op. cit.*
      (c) Fried, *op. cit.*
      (d) Popp, C. E., *et al.*, "Helping parents understand their mentally handicapped child," *Amer. J. ment. Defic.*, 1954, *58*, 530–534.

Kanner states that the parents of retarded children have five "curiosities," which should be answered in a straight-forward manner, and answered, in each instance, without evasion.[22] There are: (1) questions in regard to the diagnosis of the child's condition; (2) questions relative to the etiology of the retardation; (3) questions about the family structure; (4) concerns in regard to prognosis and future guidance of the child; and (5) questions about therapeutic planning.

Parents themselves have indicated what they feel their needs are. For example, Mrs. M. Murray has summarized the needs of parents of retarded children.[23] The points she has stressed are somewhat different from those ordinarily emphasized by many guidance authorities, but they have been observed quite commonly by the authors in their clinical practice. According to Mrs. Murray, the most pressing needs of the parents of retardates are: (1) an acceptance of the fact that the child is retarded; (2) a solution of the financial problems involved, so as to use available income intelligently in relation to the child; (3) an easing of the emotional tension resulting from carrying a burden that cannot be shared with one's fellow-man; (4) a resolution of the very severe theological problems which usually arise; (5) some answer to the need for lifetime care of the child; and (6) a way of dealing with the problems stemming from inept, immature and ill-timed professional advice. The parent must learn to "sift the wheat from the chaff."

According to Mrs. Murray, the chief need of the parent is a continuing and adequate counseling at various stages in the child's life. She points out that an adequate guidance program enables the parent to find answers to individual problems, which, of course, in turn, benefits the child.

ETIOLOGY OF MENTAL RETARDATION.   As discussed in previous paragraphs, the parent needs to be given a thorough understanding of the etiology of mental retardation. As we have pointed out, lack of understanding promotes the development of feelings of shame and guilt within the parent. Further, it frequently leads to disturbances in the social relationships of the parent, and, consequently, he withdraws from groups, activities, and interactions.

CAPACITIES OF THE CHILD.   The parent should be made aware of the fact that, regardless of the treatment program developed for the

---

[22] Kanner, L., "Parent Counseling," in *Mental Retardation*, Rothstein, H. (ed.). New York: Holt, Rinehart & Winston, Inc., 1961, pp. 453–461.
[23] Murray, *op. cit.*, 1078–1088.

child, probably no startling changes will occur in his abilities to function in many different areas. He should be aware of the fact that the child usually will mature gradually over a period of time, but that, at best, his capacities will be below those of the "average" individual. There should be careful interpretation to the parent of both the limitations and assets of the child, so that total planning can proceed in a more realistic manner. The parent should have a clear idea of what may reasonably be expected of the child. The need for a detailed, complete, and continuing assessment of the child's capacities should be stressed.

FAMILY AND SOCIAL RELATIONSHIPS. There should be discussion with the parent of the relationships of all family members with the retarded child. The effect upon the siblings should be stressed. Relationships of the child with neighbors and social groups should also be an important topic. The parent should have opportunity to discuss the cultural stereotypes of the mentally retarded child, and be made aware of the fact that he himself often shares such attitudes. There should be discussion of the feelings of the parent toward the attitudes of neighbors and other persons with whom he interacts.

EMOTIONAL NEEDS OF PARENTS. Great stress should be placed on discussing the emotional reactions of the parents themselves. Often parents lack insight into their own conflicts, and this area needs to be handled very delicately. The parents should be brought to an awareness of their own particular psychological defenses, and be helped to grow to the point where they accept both the child and their own emotional reactions to him. This involves a very careful study by the parent of his own particular way of life; that is, how the retarded child influences his own life and actions. It is important that there be thorough clarification of the role of the parent in the etiology of the child's condition, so that his fault-finding and guilt reactions will be alleviated. The parent should see that he is not alone, but that many other persons have problems similar to his own. He should be encouraged to interact with such groups of parents. There should be awareness of the fact that help is available to the parent from many sources if he wishes to avail himself of it. Further, there should be development of the point of view that seeking for help is not an indication of "weakness" on the part of the parent, nor does it necessarily indicate that he is an emotionally disturbed person. (Many parents do not discuss their problems or seek help for such reasons.) Rather, he should be helped to see that if he perceives and acknowledges his problems, and then does something about them by seeking help, both he and the child may profit. Seeking for help is, therefore, an indication of a maturing point of view on the part of the parent, and an indication of the fact that he is not continuing to deny his problems (as well as those of the child).

EMOTIONAL CHARACTERISTICS OF THE CHILD.   The parent must be given a thorough knowledge of the way in which the personality of the child develops, and what his unique needs are from time to time. This will enable the parent to anticipate future problems of the child, so that the problems will not be as serious as they otherwise might be. It will also help him to deal with his problems in a less anxious manner. This entails an understanding of the fact that intellectual functioning is but one aspect of the total personality of the child, and that many factors other than intelligence are important in the determination of his total adjustment patterns. The parent should learn about the various unique problems that the child will encounter at his different developmental levels, and should be aware of the ways in which they may be handled.

TREATMENT PROCEDURES FOR THE CHILD.   The parent should know how mental retardation may be treated, and what the limitations and expectations of treatment programs are. This means that: (1) his own role in the treatment of the child should be made very explicit; and (2) he should be informed of all available community resources and how they may be utilized.

WAYS OF APPROACH.   The parent may be given guidance and education on the problems involved in mental retardation, either individually or in a group with other parents who have similar problems. If the parent has severe emotional reactions, individual sessions may be more desirable at first. In our experience we have found that group sessions are highly effective for educative and guidance purposes. Such groups provide the parent with an opportunity to interact with other persons who are experiencing the same difficulties as himself; they provide him with an opportunity to identify with a group; they serve as a clearinghouse where valuable procedural methods may be passed along from parent to parent, and experiences shared; they enable the parent to gain, from his association with others, a sense of positive achievement and hope. In our practice, we have held group sessions on a once-a-week basis, each session lasting for approximately one hour. The group is most effective when it is not too large (that is, not more than ten persons, and probably not less than five or six). We believe it is important, also, to provide the parents with an opportunity for individual sessions in addition to the group sessions when the need for such an individual approach is indicated.

Parental treatment through psychotherapy

As stated earlier, the parent's emotional reactions to the retarded child may be so severe as to result in a psychopathological reaction. However, the *primary* cause of such a parental reaction is not the condition of the child *per se*—but, rather, the primary cause of the reaction is the severe problems of the parent himself. The added stresses to which the parent is subjected, and the additional problems created for him by the child, are burdens that serve to intensify and to precipitate his own severe emotional problems. Of course, it might well be that, if it were not for the added stresses in connection with the child, the parent might be able to defend himself adequately enough to hold the psychopathological reaction in abeyance. The more conflicted and unstable the parent is (due to his own internal problems), the more apt he is to react in a maladaptive way to the additional problems created by the child. The degree and severity of the resultant emotional reactions of the parent are proportional to his own emotional stability. The most usual maladaptive reaction is the development of a psychoneurosis, but a psychotic reaction may occasionally develop. (See Chapter Eight for a discussion of the characteristics of psychoneuroses and psychoses.) An example of a psychoneurotic reaction in a parent of a retarded child follows:

Mrs. Doe, the mother of a severely retarded girl, developed extensive symptoms. She complained of many gastrointestinal disturbances: "I throw up just about every morning, and I get cramps real often." She also had difficulty in going to sleep at night, and often had nightmares in which she dreamed that she was being run over by a car. At times she got dizzy: "It's just like I was going to faint, and I get shaky and weak and feel that I'm going to pass out. I don't, though, but I feel like I'm going to faint." She had many conflicts concerning her own abilities and capacities, and the psychoneurotic symptoms she presented were related to her relationships with her parents during childhood. The responsibilities of caring for her retarded daughter served to revive and intensify her own conflicts. She responded fairly readily to psychotherapy, her anxiety symptoms disappeared, and she adequately assumed the responsibilities for caring for and relating to her child.

The individual developing a type of psychoneurotic reaction such as this usually cannot be adequately treated through education or guidance alone. He is in need of treatment specifically directed toward relieving his basic emotional problems. Such treatment is known as *psychotherapy*. We shall now discuss some of the forms of psychotherapy.

INDIVIDUAL PSYCHOTHERAPY. Individual psychotherapy is, as the name implies, a form of psychotherapy in which just one person is seen by the psychotherapist at one time. (This is in contrast to *group* therapy, in which the therapist deals with several individuals at one time.) There are many misconceptions commonly held about psychotherapy. One such belief is that, in psychotherapy, the therapist "finds out what is wrong" with the patient, and then tells him "what to do about it." Although there may be some therapists who operate in this fashion, this type of behavior is very far from what is commonly done in psychotherapy. Another misconception is that the therapist can "make the patient over"; that is, he can change him at will. There are a number of things wrong with this belief: in psychotherapy, as in most other forms of learning, the patient's motivations and his active effort and cooperation are important factors in his psychological growth and resultant change; moreover, psychotherapy is not a process in which the therapist's will is pitted against that of the patient—psychotherapy is a *joint* undertaking by both therapist and patient. There is the misconception that only "crazy" people or psychoneurotic persons receive or ask for psychotherapy. More and more individuals, such as college students and industrial workers, to give merely two examples, are increasingly seeking psychotherapeutic help, although they may not be suffering from any recognizable psychiatric disorder. They may seek such help simply to improve their over-all emotional adjustment, so as to live richer and fuller lives. In fact, this last statement might be taken to describe one of the general aims of psychotherapy.

There are many aims of psychotherapy. The specific aim in a given case, of course, will depend upon the problem for which the individual seeks help, the circumstances of his life situation, the nature of his personality structure, and the kind of help that he wishes to have. These are factors that are dependent upon the person who comes in for help. The aims of psychotherapy will also depend upon the training and the personality of the therapist, the time and energy he has available in a given case, the estimation of possibilities for and dangers of change in the patient by the therapist, and an estimation by the therapist of how much help, as well as what kind of help, seems advisable. Thus, in a given instance with a given therapist, there still may be considerable variability in the selection of the aims of psychotherapy.

In general, however, psychotherapy seeks to help the individual to achieve at a more adequate level and to improve his adjustment. Sometimes this may mean only the elimination of a symptom or a reduction in its severity, although an evaluation will have to be made as to whether or not the individual will profit or lose by such a modification. (Symptom removal without consideration of its meaning and cause can be quite dangerous.) The aim may be to help the individual achieve better insight into his conflicts and their causes, in order to lessen their severity. Another aim of psychotherapy may be to help the individual become less sensitive to or less disturbed by his conflicts and symptoms. This may mean that he learns to tolerate his symptoms and to live more effectively even though his problem remains unchanged. (For example, this is sometimes done in certain cases of homosexual reactions.) The aim may be, again, to offer emotional support to the patient during critical periods in his life and thus enable him to master a painful situation. The most ambitious aim of psychotherapy is a reorganization of the total personality, so that the individual is eventually freed from all major conflicts, and can lead a more spontaneous and effective life.

We may ask how these aims can be achieved. In order to answer this we must know something of the nature of psychotherapy. Psychotherapy may be viewed as a process of self-realization. In emotional maladjustment, unconscious factors have too great a role in the determination of behavior. By this, we mean that the ego is overwhelmed, or its functions interfered with by forces over which it has lost some control. Self-realization implies that, in the course of psychotherapy, the individual becomes more aware of these unconscious determinants of his behavior, perceives himself differently as a result, and then begins to change the means and goals of adjustment. He can then be freer to lead a well-disciplined life, in which he utilizes his capacities in a more spontaneous manner. This process of self-realization goes on between two people, the subject and the psychotherapist. The major "currency" of this interaction is *verbalization;* that is, the patient talks, telling about himself, his complaints, his feelings, and the like. There are other "currencies": the motor behavior of the patient (since he may communicate thought and feeling by gesture, movements of the body, postural tonus and adjustments, and other means); the attitudes of the person as revealed by his forms (as distinguished from the content) of communication (since he may show "slips of the tongue," he may come late or he may miss an appointment, he may be unable to think of anything to say, and he may say things in unusual ways); and there may even be unconscious communications between the individual and the psychotherapist.

There are many unique characteristics of the therapist as distinguished from all other persons to whom an individual may go in his search for help. The therapist is not a moralist, he does not presume to function as a superego representative of society. Unlike parents, teachers, friends, or other people, he does not judge the "goodness" or "badness" of the person. Instead, the therapist tries to understand, accept and help the individual to a more effective emotional adjustment. Moreover, the therapist retains his own integrity as distinct from that of the patient. This means that he does not become confused in his role, he does not permit his own private problems or conflicts or value systems to obtrude themselves into the therapeutic situation. By this means he attempts to help the patient *differentiate* himself more adequately from the roles of his parents, siblings, peers, and superiors. He enables the person *to become himself* more fully.

Learning processes play their part in psychotherapy, but the central feature is an emotional one. As a result of the emotional "reliving" done by the person in psychotherapy, factors that were formerly in the preconscious and unconscious are brought into conscious awareness more completely. They can then be dealt with and integrated more adequately into the functioning of the ego.[24]

There are many different psychotherapeutic approaches, or "schools" of psychotherapy. Examples of these are: client-centered therapy, Meyerian therapy, neo-psychoanalytic therapy (Jung, Adler, Horney, the Chicago school, and the Washington school), eclectic therapy, and Freudian psychoanalysis. These approaches differ somewhat in their methods of treating the person. Despite the variety of such approaches, however, they have many points in common. These common elements are summarized in the following paragraph.

All psychotherapists attempt to establish an *emotional relationship* with the individual in treatment. This is sometimes referred to as *rapport*, an intense relationship in which the individual not only becomes emotionally involved in the therapeutic task, but also with the therapist. The therapist offers *emotional support* to the individual and helps him feel understood and accepted. In all forms of psychotherapy the individual becomes *identified* to some extent with the therapist, and "takes in" many of his attributes (either consciously or unconsciously). All forms of psychotherapy involve and encourage the *release of emotional tension*. To some extent, all psychotherapists *interpret* the individual's

---

[24] For a full discussion of psychotherapy see: Hutt, M. L., and Gibby, R. G., *Patterns of Abnormal Behavior*. Boston: Allyn and Bacon, Inc., 1957.

behavior. They also, through such interpretation, develop *emotional insight* into the subject; that is, the subject develops an understanding of the complexities of the causes of his reactions, in terms of both emotional and intellectual elements. Finally, all psychotherapeutic approaches attempt *integration* of the personality.

As we have said, in the treatment of the parent who is in need of psychotherapy, both the goal and the therapeutic approach will vary with the specific nature of the problems involved. Generally, however, the treatment is directed toward relieving the problems of the parent that the child *precipitated* but did not *originate*. As the parent responds to psychotherapy his relationships and reactions toward the child will change. This will, in turn, initiate a change in the adjustmental and behavioral reactions of the child. The effects of psychotherapy are thus much broader than those occurring in the parent, since they spread to the child and to other members of the family.

GROUP PSYCHOTHERAPY.   By group therapy is meant any organized program of psychotherapy in which more than one person is treated simultaneously by one or more psychotherapists. In most group therapy approaches the therapist behaves as he would in individual therapy, except that he has to deal with several persons at one time. Emotional experiences and the gaining of emotional insights are stressed, and there is active interaction between members of the group and the therapist.

The purposes of group therapy are varied. It was at first thought that group therapy could produce only minimal changes in adjustment. For some time group therapy was thought to be a palliative measure only, and was considered by many persons as a supplement to individual therapy. Another purpose of group therapy was, simply, to treat large numbers of persons more economically than could be done by individual therapy. As group therapy became more widely used, it was believed that it was applicable to only certain types of individuals, such as those in need of socialization experiences, or those who found individual therapy to be too threatening. Some group therapists believed that psychotic persons could not be helped significantly by group therapy. However, there is now evidence to lead us to believe that all types of persons can profit considerably from group therapy if the nature of the group and the competence of the therapist are appropriate. Certainly parents who develop emotional problems can usually profit readily from such a therapeutic approach. The aims of group therapy may vary. Some group programs may be aimed at symptom relief only, whereas others may be aimed at deep reconstructive therapy.

Modern approaches view group therapy as a process of dynamic interactions between the therapist and group members, as well as among the members themselves. They stress the importance of the emotional reactions between individual group members, and the therapist interprets the behavior (both words and deeds) of the participants in much the same way as he would in individual psychotherapy.

We have found group psychotherapy to be an effective method of treating the emotional problems of the parents of retarded children. Of particular importance are the interactions that take place among the parents themselves, and the support they offer to each other, which, of course, does not occur in individual psychotherapy.

Group therapy differs from usual group education (as discussed in the previous section). In the educational group, attempts are made to induce changes in the parents through imparting information, and we have stressed that this is the primary purpose of such a group, even though the emotional reactions must also be considered. Primary attention is not paid, as it is in group therapy, to the resolution of the personality problems of the parent, since the parent in such a group should not present sufficient psychopathological reactions to warrant such an approach. If he does, then he is in need of psychotherapy. Whether or not a parent is in need of group guidance and education or group psychotherapy depends upon the nature and extent of the psychopathology he shows. The determination of the treatment program for the parent thus demands that the psychologist (or other professional therapist) must carefully assess not only the problems of the child, but also those of the parent.

PARENTAL PROBLEMS DIFFICULT OF RESOLUTION. As we have repeatedly stressed in this chapter, the emotional adjustment and the consequent behavioral reactions of the young retardate are determined, to a significant degree, by the nature of the parental relationships, and, in particular, by his relationships with the mother. If such interactions are not wholesome, then the adjustment of the child may be affected in an adverse manner. The President's Panel on Mental Retardation has focused on several highly undesirable patterns of maternal behavior which directly affect the welfare of the child.[25] As previously discussed (see Chapter Eight), any separation of the child from the mother, regardless of the reason, is of importance, in that it may induce severe

[25] President's Panel on Mental Retardation, *A Proposed Program for National Action to Combat Mental Retardation.* Washington: Superintendent of Documents, 1962.

emotional reactions, usually characterized by depressive and somatic symptomatology. One of the reactions that commonly accompanies the separation of mother and child has been termed the *"Unavailable Mother"* pattern by the Panel. Here, the mother is, literally, not available to the child. An example would be that of the *working mother*.

The importance of this is underlined by the following comments of the Panel:

There are 15 million children whose mothers are working or not otherwise available, of whom approximately four million are under the age of six years, while five million are between the ages of six and 11 years of age; further, a survey conducted in 1958 showed that there was no plan of care for 400,000 children under the age of 12, and that they were expected to take care of themselves without adult help or supervision, while their mothers worked full time.

Another type of mother (unfortunately, too often encountered) is the one who is unable to meet the emotional needs of the child due to her own problems. She is herself emotionally unstable. According to the President's Panel, such mothers would include those who are extremely possessive or lethargic, deeply depressed, highly rejective, or mentally ill.

A third type of maternal behavior is that of the parent who, in the words of the Panel, produces the *"Battered Child Syndrome."* We share the dismay of the Panel that this is: ". . . an incredible occurrence in our society—various injuries to young children, including brain damage, resulting from frequent or severe beatings on the head by parents or others who care for small children." As told to one of the authors by such a father:

"That one child of ours—God knows why I did it, but he was the one that is slow and was born prematurely. I beat him black and blue, and he is only a baby. Then I made him go to bed with me and lie there during the day when he had been asleep all night. I got the urge to beat him and I did." [He has been arrested twice for his assaults on his infant son.]

We do not know the incidence of this type of abuse of the child by the parents, but, from our clinical experience, we would like to emphasize the deplorable fact that such cases are by no means rare.

To these three severe patterns of undesirable parental behavior, we should like to add a fourth. Frequently, a parent of the retardate is also mentally retarded himself, and so may be unable to deal effectively with the child's needs, and sometimes is even unable to provide him with the absolute necessities of life. Of course, in such instances, psychotherapy or educational guidance will be of little value.

Thus, in some cases, the problems of the parents may be too severe to be ameliorated by any type of usual psychotherapeutic approach. In such cases, the most appropriate solution (and, indeed, perhaps the only humane one possible) may be to remove the child from the situation which is so deleterious to his welfare. Placement in a foster home or in an appropriate institution may then be warranted. Such action may prove to be best not only for the welfare of the child, but also for the welfare of the parent, and for society.

ch. 11

EDUCATIONAL

MANAGEMENT AND

GUIDANCE

THIS AND THE FOLLOWING CHAPTER ARE CONCERNED WITH THE education, training, and guidance of the retarded child. In the present chapter we shall focus our attention on the more general problems which confront the teacher and the school administrator in such programs, while, in the next chapter, we shall deal with more specific aspects of such programs, particularly with respect to educational methods. Much of what we shall have to say will be introductory and orientational, so the reader is directed to other works in which more detailed accounts of problems and procedures are available.

Two general points should be emphasized at the outset, however. The first is that relatively little sound research evidence is available concerning the long-term effects of various types of programs; it is still in the stage in which recommendations are based, to a considerable extent, on generalized findings emanating from specific learning experiments. The second, and related point, is that much of the content of suggested programs is based on long and considered experience with varying educational programs, and, therefore, represents some distillation insofar as it has been reported.

332

AN HISTORICAL PERSPECTIVE

The history of special educational programs for the mentally retarded in this country is only a little over 100 years old, and the history of special educational classes for such children in the public schools is even shorter, the first one reportedly having been established in Springfield, Massachusetts in 1897. Prior to that, various sporadic efforts were made, especially in Europe, to deal with the problems of the retarded. Thus the history of public education for these individuals is quite brief. It will be helpful to see how the present programs of education gradually came into being.

In ancient times the attitude toward mentally retarded persons can best be characterized by the use of the then prevalent term *idiot* (from the Greek, meaning "peculiar"). This attitude was deprecatory and hostile. Gradually, a more tolerant attitude developed; during the medieval period it was highly ambivalent, ranging from amused tolerance to hostility and persecution; in the 13th century the first colony for retardates was established in Belgium; in later centuries other custodial places were sometimes established, but almost never for training purposes.

The modern period in the education of retardates had its beginnings in the work done in the retraining of the blind and the deaf. Various attempts were made in the 18th and 19th centuries to teach individuals who were severely deprived in these sensory areas, and a great deal was learned about special methods and techniques suitable for their education. It was on the basis of these prior experiences that the now-famous experiment was conducted by Itard on the so-called "Wild Boy of Aveyron" in 1798.

This 11- or 12-year-old boy was discovered in southern France and seemed, at the time, to behave like an animal. He wore no clothes, walked on all four limbs, was unable to speak, selected his food by smell, and was largely uninhibited in his behavior. Itard, who was a physician in an institution for the deaf in Paris, thought that this boy's condition was essentially the result of his severe social-cultural deprivation, and that intensive sensori-motor training, the stimulation of his social needs, and the teaching of language and thinking through intensive tutoring would overcome his socially derived handicaps and enable him to function in a normal manner.

He devoted five years of extremely intensive tutoring to this boy, but finally gave up in severe disappointment when the boy *failed to respond according to Itard's expectations.* That his efforts were not entirely unsuccessful may be seen from such facts as the boy did learn to read a little, could recognize many objects, did become socialized to a great extent, and seemed to improve in many aspects of his thinking processes. Itard was even commended by the French Academy of Sciences for his contribution to educational methods. He was able to demonstrate that even an extremely low-grade mental retardate could profit considerably from an intensive program of individually tailored educational stimulation—by the so-called *clinical method*. Perhaps his greatest contribution, however, was in stimulating others to develop and try out special methods for training and educating mental retardates.

One of Itard's pupils (Séguin) developed his methods more explicitly. In 1837 Séguin opened the first school in Paris for the education of mentally retarded children. Later he came to this country and helped to organize special institutions for such individuals. He emphasized the importance of neurophysiological training through muscle training, especially of the hands, through sensory training by discriminatory exercises in audition and vision, through speech training and later by writing and reading, and through individualized programs adapted to the specific needs of each child. Later followers of Itard and Séguin developed special educational methods based, in large part, on this earlier work, making adaptations in both materials and methods of instruction. Almost all of them focused attention on the pedagogical rather than the medical problems involved in training mental retardates.

It was the work of these early pioneers that led to the establishment in 1832 of the first state-supported institution for the handicapped, the Perkins School for the Blind, in Massachusetts. Some three years later New York State followed with its own "experimental" institution, now known as the Syracuse State School. But it was only in the last few years of the 19th century that public school classes specifically intended for retarded children were established in this country.

It was in the public schools that significant shifts in educational philosophy, as well as in pedagogical methods, were introduced. Hungerford and his co-workers have reviewed the major shifts in the basic educational philosophies for retarded children.[1] At first, the objective of such programs was to relieve the stress upon normal children and their teachers by removing the retardate from regular classes and placing him in a special class. This approach, called a *relief philosophy*, entailed a negative attitude and pessimistic expectations toward the retarded child. Later, the concern for him was that he should be happy. He was

---

[1] Hungerford, R. H., DeProspo, C. I., and Rosenzweig, I. E., "Education of the mentally handicapped child in childhood and adolescence," *Amer. J. ment. Defic.,* 1952, *57*, 214–228.

placed in a special class so that he would not have to compete with normal children and suffer unnecessary frustration. This has been termed the *happiness philosophy*, but it involved a negative and sterile orientation, in that little other than the removal from a frustrating situation was suggested by it.

The next phase, termed the *salvage philosophy*, emphasized the teaching of academic skills, sometimes at a watered-down level, more often at levels beyond the child's actual capacity to achieve. In any case, excessive emphasis was placed upon the need to achieve. There followed a compensatory reaction, embodied in the *handiwork philosophy*, in which stress was placed upon manual activities. The implication was that the retarded child *could not learn from books but could learn to do things with his hands.*

The *modern philosophy* emphasizes the worthwhileness of the child. It assumes that the child can become a contributing member of society. Although it accepts the essential dignity of the child as a human being, it recognizes that the retardate lacks certain skills and talents. Education represents an attempt to evaluate carefully the specific capacities of each child and to assist in developing them to the highest degree of which he is capable. It attempts to be both humane and realistic. It often emphasizes the vocational goals of the educational process.

The present orientation toward education of retarded individuals seems to be represented in the opening sentence of the section of the 1962 President's Panel on Mental Retardation, which states, "Every human being has potential for *useful* activity [italics ours]." This report also alleges, "Modern science and action by our social institutions have demonstrated that many of them (retarded individuals) can become self-supporting and self-reliant if provided adequate education, rehabilitation, and training services, including counseling, guidance, and placement." Thus the broadly conceived goals of education now embrace *both* vocational adequacy and self-reliant behavior. The Panel sees the need for more teachers of special classes and for more adequate training of these teachers.

Another recommendation which indicates something of the modern conception of education for the retarded child states, "It is *essential* [italics ours] that adequate opportunities for learning of intellectual and social skills be provided such children through *formal pre-school education programs* [italics ours] designed to facilitate adequate development of intellectual skills such as language development, abstract reasoning, problem solving, and other cognitive processes, and to effect desirable patterns of motivation and social values." Despite the tremendous strides which have taken place in programs for the mentally retarded, it is still true, as the President's Panel reports, that only ¼ million of the 1¼ million retarded children of school age in this country are enrolled in public special education programs.

GENERAL OBJECTIVES IN THE EDUCATION OF THE RETARDED

Although there is no clearly established consensus concerning the general objectives of education of retardates, at least in the general public's orientation, educators and scientists concerned with these problems seem to be emphasizing certain goals. We shall now discuss some of the most important of these objectives.

Self-actualization

Present educational philosophy emphasizes the maximization of each individual's potentials as they are uniquely manifested. The outcome of any process which maximizes the self-actualization of children will necessarily be different in the case of *educable retarded** children as contrasted with *trainable retarded†* children. But, in both cases, education should attempt to stimulate the maximum development of abilities and skills of which the individual is capable. One of the major difficulties in realizing this objective in education is that it requires very careful and detailed assessment of the individual at many points in his detailed assessment of the individual at many points in his development and *adequate evaluation of all the relevant factors*—physical, emotional, intellectual, and social—which may affect, especially adversely, the development of the individual.

This objective in the education of the retarded individual is not different from that proposed as the first of the four general objectives by the Educational Policies Commission.[2] In the case of retardates, however, its attainment is far more complicated. As we have noted throughout this book, retarded individuals are more likely to have been blocked in their development by virtue of special physical handicaps, subcultural conditions in the home, and emotional withdrawal, among

---

* The *educable retarded* child is usually defined as having an I.Q. between 50 and 75, and as being capable of *minimal* attainment in academic work, social adjustment and occupational skills.

† The *trainable retarded* child is usually defined as having an I.Q. between 25 and 50, and as being capable of learning self-care and limited social and economic usefulness, but as not being capable of learning academic subjects.

[2] Educational Policies Commission, *Policies for Education in American Democracy*. Washington: National Education Association, 1946.

other conditions. By the time such children reach school their own expectancies, as well as society's expectancies of them (as reflected in the school's orientation and evaluation of them), may very well have been considerably lowered.

Such children need, therefore, not only intensive assessment, but *continuing* assessment in order to discover possible assets which adverse experiences may have covered or inhibited. They need special attention in terms of their needs for acceptance by teachers, peers, and others. They also need a school climate which is both accepting and appropriately stimulating. In some cases they may need highly individualized programs of training, guidance, or psychotherapy.

Some research studies have shown that, generally speaking, retarded children have more fear of failure than normal children. Other studies have shown that such children who are placed in special classes feel less rejected than those who are placed in regular classes. In all of these studies there are significant individual differences. Hence, no matter what type of program is planned for retardates, special effort is needed to evaluate the kinds of progress of which the individual is realistically capable, and the effort must be made to maximize such progress.

Social competence

We include under this heading both the ability to maintain effective relationships with peers and others and the ability to maintain an internal harmony within oneself. Thus we are referring to *interpersonal* relationships as well as to *intrapersonal* adjustment. These related objectives are combined here for several reasons. In the first place, intrapersonal adjustment is markedly dependent upon interpersonal adjustment, as we have shown elsewhere in this text. In the second place, it is universally recognized by authorities that one of the school's functions is to foster social competence, but it is not so widely accepted that the school also has a basic responsibility in the sphere of personal adjustment. Yet, if the two are so inextricably linked, how can we attain one objective if the other is neglected? In the third place, the retarded child has unique problems in his personal adjustment—some of them unnecessary consequences of society's unfortunate attitudes toward him—and so special emphasis needs to be placed by the school on the simultaneous and complementary processes leading to over-all general social competence.

Lloyd M. Dunn, chairman of the department of special education at George Peabody College for Teachers, points out that the goals for the trainable retarded have to be somewhat different from those for the educable retarded.[3] Since, as he states, the former will not be able to live independently as adults, special stress must be placed in their education programs upon ". . . the development of minimal skills for living and working in sheltered environments." The latter group, however, will be able to make an independent adjustment and will be able to maintain itself effectively in the community. Numerous studies have shown that most retardates are, in fact, able to adjust at least reasonably well when conditions are favorable. As Kirk puts it, ". . . the educable retarded are able to adjust to society and lead a normal life in the community if the social conditions of the community are conducive to their adjustment."[4]

The school must make special provision, however, to teach personal and social skills to the retarded, not only because of their retardation, but also because they are often socially and culturally handicapped by their home and community environments. Even when they do not suffer such social privations, the attitudes of their school peers as well as other school personnel may make the attainment of social competence a more difficult task than for others who are more nearly normal. And, in general, the greater the degree of mental and social inadequacy, the greater the emphasis must be upon teaching simple social skills and adjustments as a base for effective relationships within the environment. In the case of the trainable retarded such skills must include self-care, methods of communication, eating habits, and habits of dress and personal cleanliness.

We shall discuss elsewhere the arguments relating to the relative merits of placing retarded children in special classes as opposed to regular classes. The evidence to date indicates that such children exhibit special problems in both types of settings, but they are able to make relatively better adjustments in special classes, where they are more likely to be accepted and attain a higher self-regard.[5] But, here again, placement in such special classes does not, by itself, solve the problem. In either case, adequate provision for improving social competence is needed.

[3] Dunn, Lloyd M. (ed.), *Exceptional Children in the Schools.* New York: Holt, Rinehart & Winston, Inc., 1963.

[4] Kirk, S. A., *Educating Exceptional Children.* Boston: Houghton Mifflin Company, 1962, p. 115.

[5] Johnson, G. O., "A comparative study of the personal and social adjustment of mentally handicapped children placed in special classes with mentally handicapped children who remain in regular classes." Syracuse, N.Y.: Syracuse Research Institute, 1961.

Development of general and special skills

Many retarded children will be able to learn to read reasonably well and to do simple computational work, while others will be able to make only minimal progress along these lines. Similarly, many retardates will have little difficulty in communicating with others, while some will have considerable difficulty along these lines. Thus, not only will there be significant differences for this general objective of the development of skills between educable and trainable retarded children, but within each group there will also be considerable variability. The educational program, taking into account these significant differences in ability and skill, will need to provide for the *appropriate* training along academic lines, when this is feasible, and along special lines when needed.

In general, retarded children will need more training in specific activities which, in the case of normal children, can be taken for granted. Such skills will include habits of safety, habits in motor and sensory behaviors, habits in the arts and crafts, and the like, as well as the more general work habits involving learning to attend, to persist in working at a task, to avoid distraction and distracting others, and the like. The particular pattern of general academic and specific skills taught, as well as the *emphasis and sequence* within which they are taught, will have to be geared carefully to the special needs of the particular class and the particular individuals in it. A number of guides for preparing such specialized objectives have been published and will offer the teacher considerable help in planning a suitable course of study for the group under consideration.[6]

It should be emphasized that, especially when children enter school or preschool programs with limited previous experience in language, communication, sanitation, and interpersonal skills, considerable training along these and related lines will need to be provided before any significant progress along more general lines can be expected. And, again—as was indicated in our discussion of the objective of social competence—arousal and maintenance of interest, meeting the needs already present, and an attitude of a high degree of acceptance will be especially important for such children.

Vocational and economic competence

Whether the expected outcome will be complete or relatively complete economic independence, or whether it will be living under sheltered

[6] See for example, the following: Thiel, E., "Design for daily living: A framework for curriculum development for children and youth with intellectual handicaps." Tallahassee, Fla.: Florida State University, 1960; and, Goldstein, H., and Seigle, D. M. (eds.), "A curriculum guide for teachers of the educable mentally handicapped." Springfield, Ill.: Illinois State Dept. of Public Instruction, 1958.

and protected conditions, a major objective for all retarded individuals, educable and trainable, will be the attainment of some degree of vocational competence and economic productivity. Increasingly, the accumulated evidence has shown that a far higher proportion of mentally retarded persons are able to become productive and work in gainful occupations than was previously suspected (see Chapter Eight). The whole trend in dealing with this population has been toward placement in and involvement with society in normal patterns of employment, rather than in institutionalization and in a welfare status. As suitable training programs have developed at both elementary and secondary school levels, increasingly larger percentages of the mentally retarded have become part of the nation's work force.

In general, the higher the mental level of the individual, the higher the complexity of vocational training which is possible for him.[7] It must be remembered that other factors than mental ability enter significantly into the kind of work which an individual is capable of performing under reality conditions. The economic status of the community at the time of possible employment is one such factor.[8] The social skills—especially ability to get along with others and to take and follow directions—constitute another. It is also true that retarded individuals are capable of performing many complex manual and technical operations if they are given appropriate training.

Vocational training not only enables such individuals to participate meaningfully in society, but it also leads to a higher self-regard and contributes to improved social adjustment. It is also important to note that vocational training can include, above and beyond the specific occupational skills which are involved, many social skills such as punctuality, courtesy, cleanliness, and reliability. Some studies have indicated that traits such as these are of primary importance in getting and holding many types of jobs.

One of the most intensive follow-up studies of retarded individuals (in Lincoln, Nebraska) who had been enrolled in special classes but who had not necessarily been given the kind of vocational training which we have been discussing, found that more than 80 per cent of these "graduates" of the special class program were gainfully employed.[9] Although

[7] Collmann, R. D., and Newlyn, D., "Employment success of mentally dull and intellectually normal ex-pupils in England," *Amer. J. ment. Defic.,* 1957, *61,* 484–490.

[8] Heber, R. F., and Stevens, H. A., *Research in Mental Retardation.* Chicago: University of Chicago Press, 1963.

[9] Charles, D. C., "Ability and accomplishment of persons earlier judged mentally deficient," *Genet. Psychol. Monogr.,* 1953, *47,* 3–71.

most held laboring types of jobs, some held much higher-level positions, including managerial positions. A few even lived in expensive homes. It is also interesting to note that Charles found that, although more than half of the men had been involved in some law violation, *none* had committed any serious offenses, the usual offense being that of some minor traffic or civil infraction!

Although not all follow-up studies paint such a favorable impression as this one, the general finding is that the mentally retarded individual, except for the lowest grades, is employable, is able to hold a job about as

"Filling Out Blanks" Is an Important Part of Vocational Education (Reproduced by courtesy of The Special Education Service, Virginia State Department of Education, Richmond, Va.)

well as the rest of the population during times of reasonably good or very good employment, and is essentially a good law-abiding citizen. With improved vocational training and with the availability of good and continuing employment counseling, there is every reason to believe that this record can be improved upon.

Our discussion of the general objectives of education for the retarded has centered around four main issues. There are many other sub-issues, and some other types of issues which some writers have suggested. We shall deal with many of these in the next section, on more specific objectives of educational programs.

SOME SPECIFIC OBJECTIVES OF THE EDUCATIONAL PROGRAM

Let us start at the beginning of the educational ladder and focus our attention on the objectives of a possible preschool program for retardates. We shall discuss briefly some of the more important considerations in planning the total school program, beginning with the preschool program; then we shall look at the teaching of skills in various areas, then view the total program from inception through the secondary level; and, finally, we shall examine special aspects of school planning in relation to home experiences, as well as in relation to other school programs.

Carrying on an effective preschool program

In considering the school program for retarded individuals, especially the *educable* group, the first question that may arise is: "When should the school program begin?" There was a time when the school training of such pupils was delayed well beyond the usual beginning of six years. Retarded pupils often were withdrawn, or even expelled, from school if they had been enrolled at six years, because they were often unable to adapt to regular class instruction and routine, and, even when placed in special classes for the retarded, were often unable to adjust to school conditions. Yet, as we have seen, so many retarded children suffer from deprived social-cultural stimulation or have special handicaps in perceptual and motoric skills that for a great many, at least, educational training ought to begin even earlier than that for the more nearly normal child. Certainly, a large number of retardates can benefit greatly from appropriate preschool training, whether in residential or community schools. Of course, careful assessment of each child is needed *before* placement is attempted, but, for many, placement in a special school program at five years is not only entirely possible but may yield rich returns.

A recent study by Kirk, who compared the subsequent development of educable retarded children who had been given enriched preschool training with others who had not had this opportunity, revealed that the former group benefited considerably from their experience.[10] Naturally, provisions other than school placement may be needed for those children who present special problems such as a very unstable home environment or very serious physical handicaps.

Although many of the usual facilities of the regular kindergarten

[10] Kirk, S. A., *Early Education of the Mentally Retarded: An Experimental Study*. Urbana, Ill.: University of Illinois Press, 1958.

are useful in the preschool programs for the retarded, additional special equipment and facilities are needed. These children will usually need special training in such matters of self-help as dressing and undressing, washing and drying oneself, the use of the toilet, and eating. For these functions special equipment may be quite necessary— facilities designed with an eye toward utmost simplicity. Adequate room for conducting these activities and individual attention are more important for such youngsters than for others.

Similarly, this preschool program will need to emphasize beginning skills in speaking, simple interpersonal communication, language development (especially for those from deprived environments), the use of the gross muscles, eye-hand coordination, and perhaps, above all, sensori-motor functioning. Recent research evidence has emphasized the importance of training in perceptual visual and auditory skills, in which these children are likely to be severely retarded—proportionately even more than their general cognitive development would indicate. It can be expected that at least two years will be needed for the usual, educable retarded child to attain the level of the beginning skills of the normal, first-grade child, and even more than this for the severely retarded. The whole emphasis must be on teaching the readiness skills in these areas before anything like more formal school training is begun.

We have noted the importance of individual assessment. The teacher can gather much useful information from the mother before the child gets to school. An inventory of the kinds of skills which the child can perform at home can be very important in planning the first individual and group activities at school. Questions such as these should be asked: what are the child's linguistic skills; what are his usual patterns of communication; what kinds of activities concerning self-help has he mastered; what kinds of physical skills does he have; and what are the patterns of his social skills? These kinds of information can be carefully catalogued and the approximate developmental levels in each area can be evaluated with some degree of accuracy by means of reference to developmental norms. Of course, more formal assessment of intellectual level, physical condition, and the like will be the province of the specialist, but these informal findings can be most useful to the teacher.

Just as important as the specific skills which are to be taught are the methods to be employed in their teaching. The whole approach should be geared to the development of *enjoyable* and *successful* training experiences. Two of the essential general principles which need to be kept constantly in mind are: (1) enjoyable and successful experiences can do much to encourage self-confidence and a positive self-concept; and (2) successful experiences can produce proper habits of attention and concentration, which are so important to learning for these children. Most authorities suggest that activities at this level be offered in the spirit of *games,* so as to enhance interest and participation by the children. Units for learning and detailed activities are proposed by Perry, and can be adapted or modified as needed.[11]

Developing basic readiness skills

The major portion of school time, both for the preschool program and perhaps for another year beyond this, will be spent on the development of *readiness skills.* The aim at this level for the educable retarded child is to prepare him for later academic and pre-vocational training, while that for the trainable retarded child is to help him to become at least minimally self-sufficient, if at all possible.

For both of these groups, it may be assumed that the young retarded child has "missed out" on many normal elements of experience in preschool years, even when the home environment has not been a particularly deprived one. He has not been able to profit as much as other children from the everyday experiences that youngsters have, because of his retarded perceptual and motoric development, in particular. As a consequence, his abilities to attend, to communicate, to understand language, to coordinate in physical activities, and to engage in creative thinking (and especially in fantasy) are likely to be quite limited. The school program must, therefore, focus on the development of a variety of basic readiness skills which can be taken more or less for granted in the case of the normal youngster. When the retardate has additional physical handicaps, other special problems are created.

There is controversy about how well retarded children can learn in comparison with normal children of comparable mental age (that is, younger and more normal children). Some researchers maintain that retarded children learn less well and forget more rapidly what they do learn. Retarded children are thought of, from this viewpoint, as having "leaky buckets." Although there is evidence to substantiate this conclusion, the reason for the finding may lie, not so much in the fact of mental retardation, as in the conditions under which the retarded usually learn. Because they need more time to master material than their normal peers, because they so often meet failure in a society geared for normals, and because they have had insufficient learning in basic skills and have not been properly prepared to learn what they are exposed to, they tend to

[11] Perry, N., *Teaching the Mentally Retarded Child.* New York: Columbia University Press, 1960.

develop poor learning attitudes, and they may also forget more rapidly than they should.

Recent research indicates that retarded children can learn as well as normal children of comparable mental age, can retain as well, and can even transfer this learning to other related areas, *providing* they are not handicapped by previously poor learning of basic skills or by poor attitudes toward the learning task.[12] These findings suggest that retarded children need to be given ample time, originally, to learn—and even to overlearn—basic skills that are within their "current" grasp. As for the average child, the level of the learning must be geared to their current ability, the tasks must be presented simply, and they must be *thoroughly mastered (i.e., overlearned)*.

All of these considerations point up the importance of sound training in readiness skills. What are some of these skills? In the first place, *skills in controlling the body* should be considered, such as coordination in walking, drawing, eye-hand coordination, balancing, tumbling, and running. Studies have indicated that retarded children are one or more years behind the norms in both gross and fine motor coordinations.[13] In the second place, as we have stated so often, retarded children need *intensive training in perceptual skills,* many of which normal children master as a function of incidental learning in everyday experiences. They need training, therefore, in visual and auditory memory skills, in form perception, in the use of each eye as well as both eyes in looking at objects, and in focusing on details of visual objects. The teacher can provide a wide variety of games which emphasize the learning of these basic perceptual skills. A by-product of such activities, when taught properly, may be *learning to attend*.

Then, of course, special training is needed in *basic language skills:* vocabulary; simple sentence structure; articulation; asking and answering questions. They also need training in *basic number concepts:* size; shape; numbers; and the simplest concepts involved in adding and subtracting. And, finally, because they have so often been denied opportunity to gain this experience in normal social interaction, they need to learn basic *social interaction* skills: learning to listen; learning to communicate; learning to share and cooperate; learning simple forms of inde-

---

[12] Ellis, N. R., *Handbook of Mental Deficiency: Psychological Theory and Research.* New York: McGraw-Hill, Inc., 1963; and, Vergason, G., "Retention in Educable Retarded and Normal Adolescent Boys . . ." Unpublished doctoral dissertation, George Peabody College for Teachers, 1962.

[13] Francis, R. J., and Rarick, G. L., *Motor Characteristics of the Mentally Retarded,* Coop. Res. Bull. No. 1, USOE 35005. Washington: Government Printing Office, 1960.

pendence; learning to respect the rights of others; learning simple games; etc. Skills such as these not only provide a foundation for many other types of learning in school situations, but they also help to improve self-confidence and self-assurance, and so, indirectly, to improve realistically one's aspiration level. (See Chapter Twelve for some details on specific methodology.)

Organizing an effective total school program

We shall reserve for discussion in the next chapter some of the specific plans for organizing education for the retarded child, but we would like to take a general look, now, at the over-all school program. We have emphasized the importance of preschool education, especially for the educable retarded. Such training appears to be vital to the development of readiness skills, constructive attitudes toward school and learning, and the development of self-attitudes which are both realistic and positive. *But a good beginning is not enough!* It is likely that the educational program will be more productive if the terminal goals are clearly perceived and implemented. Toward what end is the total school program geared? What may be expected of the educable and of the trainable retarded?

Recent research evidence has made it abundantly clear that a large majority of the educable retarded can become entirely self-supporting, and that many others can become at least partially self-supporting if provided with some guidance and support during the early adult years.[14] Some of the trainable retarded can become partially self-supporting and most can learn to get along in their communities if provided with guidance and counsel, following their formal school period. And we have learned, in previous chapters, that a significant number of those who have been diagnosed as retarded are able to maintain themselves very effectively in their communities.

If, therefore, we view two of the important goals of schooling for these groups as (1) vocational competency and (2) effective social living, the total school program should be organized toward these and related objectives. There are those who argue that such a program places too heavy a burden upon the schools, but, in rebuttal, it should be noted that while this problem is more easily arguable in the case of normal pupils, the retarded present a special problem, and neither the home

---

[14] Mackie, R. P., Dabelstein, D. H., and Heber, R. F., *Preparation of Mentally Handicapped Youth for Gainful Employment.* Washington: Government Printing Office, 1959.

nor the usual community resources other than the school can provide an effective program along these lines.

Viewed from this perspective, the total school program should provide: preschool preparation, when necessary; training in basic readiness skills; preparation in academic skills related to specific concurrent aspects of living and to pre-vocational training; vocational training and counseling; and post-school training and especially guidance. The program should span the chronological age range from 5 years through 18 years, with follow-up facilities after this. (In some cases, training may begin at 4 years.)

Thus, the program may be divided into five major phases: preschool, primary, intermediate, secondary, and post-secondary. The emphasis in each phase of the program would shift, taking into account both the physical and psychological maturity of the individual. The program would also provide for considerable flexibility, since some pupils will be able to transfer to regular school programs, while others will need continued placement in some phase of the total educational program. In general, however, placement in each phase should be governed, within the limits of mental maturation and acquisition of skills, by the chronological and physical maturity of the individual more than by any other single factor. And it should hardly be overlooked, that effective mental hygiene for each pupil, in each phase of the educational program, should be a central concern of the teacher and the school.

Relating the school program to other experiences

In some European countries special boarding schools are being utilized for retarded school children, in the belief that special education in the normal school program is insufficient in both scope and intensity. In these programs intensive training is offered during school hours *and* after school hours. Not only is educational training provided, but training in social skills, often by specially trained personnel, is also an *intrinsic* part of the program.[15] Such programs have the advantage—whatever their disadvantages may be—of coordinating the total-life-experience of the child during the critical years of his training.

If, as seems indicated by present educational trends, we are to continue, by and large, to provide special instruction only during regular school hours, we must, nevertheless, be alert to the need for integrating and coordinating these experiences in school with the concomitant experiences these children are having at home and in the community.

[15] Dunn, L. M., and Kirk, S. A., "Impressions of Soviet psychoeducational service and research in mental retardation," *Except. Child.*, 1963, *29*, 299–311.

Otherwise, the possible gains achieved in school may be offset by antagonistic or traumatic experiences elsewhere, or, at the least, such gains are not likely to be reinforced by such experiences. This lack of coordination of the school program with other experiences may be one of the reasons for the inadequate success which some of the special school programs have achieved.

At the center of these other-than-school experiences is the milieu of the home. When it is at all possible, careful and continuing relationships with the parents should be maintained by the school. Even when special classes for the retarded are quite small in size and the teacher is able to find sufficient time to maintain regular and frequent, personal contact with at least one parent, the assistance of the visiting teacher or of the social worker may prove to be indispensable. The parents need to be appraised of the specific and current goals of the school program, so that they may reinforce them with appropriate and related experiences in the home and community.

This is not to suggest that the parents be encouraged to teach their retarded child, but, rather, to encourage them to provide the kinds of experiences in the home and outside which may supplement those of the school. The parents will also need help in understanding their child more deeply, and will need guidance in providing their children with appropriate social experiences (see Chapter Ten). There will also be situations in which the parents will need guidance in finding additional help for their child, such as speech therapy, psychotherapy, and physical therapy—which the school may be unable to provide.

We should like to consider another important point. We have stressed the fact that the general attitudes of society are significant factors in determining the behavioral reactions and personality growth of the child. What is so often overlooked in connection with this is the fact that the *school itself* is a part of society, and so shares the attitudes of the culture in which it is embedded. Moreover, the special class is part of a larger institution—the public school system, and within this system there are negative or even hostile attitudes toward mental retardation that need to be recognized and, where necessary, modified appropriately. Administrators, teachers, clerical workers, janitors, and all other personnel have attitudes toward the child that often reflect the unfavorable cultural stereotypes that we have previously discussed. Further, other pupils may have similar unfortunate attitudes, and so do the *retarded children themselves*. There should, therefore, be awareness of these undesirable attitudes, and attempts should be made to provide for their modification. The special class teacher needs to be one of the "spark plugs" fostering more positive developments. This responsibility has often been ignored. In the same way as attitudes within the family structure itself often hinder the total growth process of the child, so do attitudes of the school interfere with the growth of the retarded child. The school is a community, and, as such, can be used as a positive force in helping the child to achieve his maximum self-actualization.

LEARNING CHARACTERISTICS OF THE RETARDED CHILD

We have presented various comments about the learning characteristics of retarded children at a number of previous points in this book. Now, we shall attempt to summarize and integrate the major findings in this area.

The variable effects of slow learning ability

We have stressed the fact that the degree of mental retardation cannot be represented adequately by I.Q. alone. Children with the same I.Q. or M.A. scores vary significantly in many aspects of cognitive functioning and vary tremendously in most other factors associated with learning ability. Nor have we meant to imply, in discussing the differential learning experiences necessary or the different goals in education for the educable and trainable retarded groups, that these groups have little overlap in learning level or characteristics. The fact is that there is tremendous overlap in the characteristics of these groups, and their separation for educational purposes does not mean that each individual in one group is distinctly different from each individual in the other.

Our previous review of some experimental studies of learning characteristics (see Chapter Six) indicated that, in some areas, retarded individuals functioned disproportionately below their own levels of general mental development. We highlighted the significance of anxiety in producing unnecessary impairment in learning. In turn, as we also noted previously, failure in learning tends to reduce aspiration level and, therefore, impedes subsequent learning still more. We have also emphasized the relative lack of sufficient *incidental* learning experiences of retarded children, especially in those coming from sub-standard or culturally deprived homes. All of these and other factors tend to combine to produce quite variable learning characteristics of children with the same level of general mental development. Not only do retardates have different learning characteristics from children with normal mental development because of the difference in mental maturity, but retarded children have *learned to learn* in quite different ways from each other as well as from more superior children.

Recent studies on *discrimination set*[16] and on *transfer of training*[17] in retarded children indicate that, although retarded children are likely to be different in these characteristics from other children with higher I.Q.'s who are matched with them in mental age, these differences are *not inherent or immutable.* Slow learners seem to have developed different kinds of learning sets, expectancies, attitudes, and capacities for generalization than normal learners of comparable mental age, because of different experiences during the learning process: more frequent failure, inadequate preparation, too rapid pace in learning, and lack of sustained attention. When such factors are compensated for by proper remedial instruction, the resulting learning characteristics of the retarded do change.

On the basis of known facts, we may make the following general conclusions:

1. Retarded children learn less rapidly than do children of comparable chronological age, but of superior mental development, in most learning situations.
2. When retarded children are compared with normal children of comparable mental age (and, therefore, of lower chronological age), the results are quite variable: the retarded are equally competent in some tasks, better in some, and poorer in others.
3. Retarded children, as compared with normal children, tend to be inferior in ability to attend, to remember, to discriminate, to transfer, and to conceptualize, even when the groups are equated for mental age, but these differences are probably less significant for new types of learning situations (as in laboratory experiments such as those described by Johnson and Blake); moreover, these differences are not necessary and intrinsic concomitants of the phenomenon of retardation.
4. Slow learners, like all other learners, show marked variability in learning capacities, and their potential for specific learning situations must be assessed on an individual rather than on a collective basis.

General learning characteristics

Keeping in mind the qualifications we have stressed in the preceding section, can we offer any more specific generalizations concerning the learning of the retarded child?

[16] Barnett, C. D., and Cantor, G. N., "Discrimination set in defectives," *Amer. J. ment. Defic.*, 1957, *62*, 334–337.
[17] Johnson, G. O., and Blake, K., *Learning Performance of Retarded and Normal Children.* Syracuse, New York: Syracuse University Press, 1960.

We should begin with the findings of Jordan and DeCharms,[18] confirmed in some other studies, that the *achievement motive* in retarded children is inferior to that of normal children. This means that special motivational methods must be employed by the teacher to compensate for this deficiency, if learning is to be effective.

Also of basic importance are the findings that the behavior of retardates tends to be highly rigid, so that they find great difficulty in shifting learning procedures to new tasks.[19] However, when special training is given to improve precise discrimination in the learning problem, *i.e.*, to improve discrimination set, retardates can improve significantly in this respect.[20]

Retarded pupils have shorter memories for recent events than do their contemporaries of comparable mental age, but here, too, intensive overlearning can compensate fairly adequately for this limitation.[21] Ellis, who proposes a "stimulus trace theory" to account for the relatively short-term memories of the retarded, believed that this disability was due to some central nervous system dysfunction. However, the theory that poor memory is itself a functional result of previous poor learning experiences is probably more tenable.

Retarded pupils have less ability to attend. Here, again, inferior attention may itself be a function of previous learning, with inattention a defensive maneuver learned by the retarded.[22]

These represent the most important generalizations about the learning of retardates which differentiate them from the non-retardates. So far as is now known, the general principles of learning which have been developed over the years with normal individuals apply, in most respects, to the retardate as well. Such findings indicate the desirability of preparing the child carefully for the new learning situation by motivating him effectively, proceeding in small steps from the known to the unknown, using positive affect to reinforce learning, reinforcing learning by appeal to various sense modalities, avoiding failures as much as possible—so as to reinforce learning by successive success experiences—and providing for ample overlearning if long-term retention is sought for.

[18] Jordan, T., and DeCharms, R., "The achievement motive in normal and mentally retarded children," *Amer. J. ment. Defic.*, 1959, *64*, 457–466.

[19] Shepps, R., and Zigker, E., "Social deprivation and rigidity on the performance of organic and familial retardates," *Amer. J. ment. Defic.*, 1962, *67*, 262–268.

[20] Cantor, G. J., and Hottel, J. V., "Discrimination learning in mental defectives as a function of magnitude of food reward and intelligence levels," *Amer. J. ment. Defic.*, 1955, *60*, 380–384.

[21] Ellis, *op. cit.*

[22] Zeaman, D., and House, B. J., "An attention theory of retardate discrimination in learning," Progr. Rep. No. 3, Nat. Inst. Ment. Hlth, Bethesda, Md., Nov., 1962.

QUALIFICATIONS OF THE TEACHER

The teacher plays a very important role in the emotional growth of the child. In the lower grades especially, the classroom teacher is a powerful figure to the child, one toward whom he may develop intense feelings. The child tends to behave toward the teacher in the same way as he does toward his own mother, at least in the prepubertal years. He tends to identify with her and, thus, the teacher is likely to be an important influence in the later superego development of the child. Since the child learns many emotional habits from the teacher, she is likely to be an important positive or negative force influencing his personality development. The following illustration will make some of these points more concrete:

A child, who was in psychotherapy, developed unusual insight in regard to his relationship with his teacher. He had been rather withdrawn, but had made excellent therapeutic progress. As a result, he had begun to perceive his need to be close to his teacher, and had begun to develop a good emotional relationship with her. The teacher was accepting of his needs for closeness to her, up to a point. The relationship between them continued to develop until the child finally reached the point at which he was able to express some of his hostility toward her in the classroom situation. (This was based on unconscious feelings the child had toward his mother, and which were displaced upon the teacher.) This was really good development as far as this particular child was concerned, but these hostile expressions resulted in a severe emotional reaction by the teacher. She was made extremely anxious by the child's expressed hostility, due to her own emotional immaturity. Instead of perceiving and dealing with the problem as a manifestation of growth on the part of the child, the teacher referred him to the principal for disciplinary action. This destroyed the relationship of the child with the teacher.

In the case of this child, the nature of his family relationships was manifest in the school. The teacher was cast in the role of the mother, the principal (the authority figure) in the role of the father, and although it was not brought out in the case material just presented, the child's classmates were essentially perceived as siblings.

Even more than the average child, the retarded child tends to cast his teacher in a parental role, and the special class teacher must be aware of this almost automatic reaction. She must also be aware of her own emotional reactions in such a role, and learn to accept *her own* feelings as well as those of the child. She must learn to be able to understand how different children *perceive her,* and how each child differs in his basic demands of her. Despite her own emotional characteristics and personal integrity, as a unique individual, she is a different person to each of her pupils, depending upon their particular needs. It is important that she not only recognize the emotional demands made of her, the feelings that each child displaces or transfers upon her, but that she also learn how to use the relationship that exists between herself and the child to promote his emotional growth. This last point is of crucial significance; not only must there be feeling for the child, but there must be *adequate knowledge of what to do about it.* This demands of the teacher that she know something of personality dynamics, of child development, of human relationships and group structures, of her own emotional needs and reactions, and of the basic elements of psychotherapeutic relationships. As Bettelheim puts it in the title of his book, "love is not enough."[23] More than affection and good intentions toward the child are needed. Of course, it is basic that the teacher have feelings of warmth, acceptance, and love for the child, but without the technical "know-how" the child becomes buried in a "sticky" morass of feelings of pity, which eventually may prove to be a detriment to his growth.

Fields chaired an excellent discussion on the topic of the desirable characteristics of the teacher of mentally retarded children.[24] The following is a summarization of some of the major ideas developed by the group. The discussion stressed that the teacher should:

1. Be in sympathy with the philosophy of education for the retarded child.
2. Be an emotionally well-balanced person.
3. Have certain specific traits, such as humor, tact, vitality, patience, sympathy, good personal appearance, originality and creativity, good physical health, and have skills in planning and organizing.
4. Be accepting and understanding of children.
5. Have good interpersonal relationships with others.
6. Be willing to both look for and accept help.
7. Have adequate training.
8. Know the following specific things: the nature of mental retardation, the nature of the world in which the retarded must live, the things necessary to live in such a world, and the way to teach these things effectively.

There have been some very interesting studies of special class teacher-child interactions. One of these was done by Harris.[25] This was partly a methodological study in which three types of teachers' attitudes toward retarded children were explored: *persuasive,* in which the teacher

---

[23] Bettelheim, B., *Love Is Not Enough.* New York: Free Press of Glencoe, Inc., 1950.

[24] Fields, H. (chairman), "Who makes the best teacher of mentally retarded children?" *Amer. J. ment. Defic.,* 1953, *58,* 251-267.

[25] Harris, L. M., "A method for studying and treating behavior problems in the school room," *Amer. J. ment. Defic.,* 1955, *59,* 595-600.

feels and expresses understanding of the child's problems and returns kindness for his negative behavior; *suggestive* and *rational*, in which the teacher attempts to objectify the pupil's behavior and find reasons for her own behavior; and a *disciplining* attitude, a more restrictive and punitive approach toward the child. Harris suggests a method for studying the effect of each approach on the child, and concludes that the special class teacher should vary her attitudes in a deliberate manner, and note the effect of each approach upon the individual child. The Wayne County Training School studies on self-determination of controls of behavior are also pertinent.[26] In these studies, the children themselves determined their rules of conduct. These studies indicated that the retarded child is able to assume responsibility for his own behavior if given adequate guidance. Kirk and Johnson summarized a position with respect to the best teaching approach to mentally retarded children in the statements that follow:[27]

1. Teaching procedures should be organized in harmony with good mental hygiene principles.
2. The child's attention should be focused through positive suggestions and a positive classroom atmosphere of acceptable social behavior.
3. The retarded child should be allowed to plan activities within the range of his interests and abilities.
4. Techniques such as sociodrama should be used for the purpose of developing insights in practical life situations.
5. Self-determining activities should be organized to give children practice in the independent management of their affairs.

We agree with these statements wholeheartedly, but would stress the fact that the basic function of the special class teacher is to promote the development of the *whole* child, and that this entails attention to his emotional and behavioral adjustment.

TYPES OF EDUCATIONAL PROGRAMS

As might be inferred from our preceding discussion, schools in this country, as well as abroad, are trying out quite a variety of educational programs for the retarded. In some schools the retarded are kept in regular classes, whereas, in others, they are placed in special classes or even in special schools or community centers. Various types of groupings

---

[26] Kephart, N. C., "Group autonomy in a children's institution," *Ment. Hyg., N.Y.,* 1938, *22,* 585–590.

[27] Kirk, S. A., and Johnson, G. O., *Educating the Retarded Child.* Boston: Houghton Mifflin Company, 1951, pp. 357–358.

of pupils are being attempted and various educational procedures are being experimented with. Such variety is indicative both of our lack of adequate knowledge concerning the most effective methods for educating this population, as well as of the healthy interest in "experimenting" with new approaches to the education of the retarded.

In some larger communities special schools are organized for retarded children, and possibly for other atypical children. In other school systems retarded children spend some of their time in special classes for the retarded and some in regular classes. Advocates of plans such as this stress the importance of the social interactions of the retarded and normal child. Other schools use consultants with specialized knowledge and experience to assist the special class or regular class teacher in coping with the problems of the retarded. In some areas severely retarded pupils are given instruction at home by selected teachers. Such programs are most often utilized in connection with physically handicapped and/or bedridden cases. And, of course, there are residential schools for the retarded, often of very high educational quality, but these are usually restricted to children whose parents are financially very well off, or at least reasonably so.

Organization of special classes

We shall limit our discussion to the organization of classes for the retarded in school systems which can provide special classes for these pupils. Although there is still controversy about the desirability of placing retarded pupils in special classes rather than regular classes, the strong trend, supported by fairly good evidence, is toward special class placement when at all possible.[28]

It is generally agreed that chronological age is an important criterion for grouping pupils in such classes, although it is rarely used as the sole criterion. The argument is that children of similar chronological age are likely to have similar social and physical needs and characteristics, and can, therefore, be more easily handled in a group and will interact more effectively. Wallin, who has had extensive experience with programs of special education, argues that homogeneous grouping by age is not necessarily desirable. He states: ". . . it is not necessarily socially undesirable to educate children of different ages together, as has been done from time immemorial in the one-room rural schools, since children of all ages must learn to live, play, and work together at home, on the streets, on play-

[28] *Organization of Special Education for Mentally Retarded Children,* Publ. No. 214. Geneva: Intern. Bureau Educ., 1960.

fields, and in the community."[29] The issue is certainly arguable, but, from a *learning viewpoint*, there appear to be important advantages to having children of similar ages grouped together.

If, in addition to age, mental maturity is also used as a criterion (or M.A. as estimated by a psychologist on the basis of appropriate tests and observations), then the grouping will insure some general homogeneity in both present general learning potential as well as in general life experience. But these two criteria, together, will not insure a reasonable degree of actual homogeneity in specific learning capacities and skills —an homogeneity which makes it possible to minister to the needs of each pupil through both group and individual instruction. The evidence presented in other portions of this book has made it quite clear that even children with the very same M.A. may differ significantly in specific learning abilities. Evaluation of specific skills of which the child is capable is, therefore, needed as an additional set of criteria. This kind of evaluation may be very difficult before the child has actually been enrolled in and observed in a classroom situation by a competent teacher or educational expert. Thus, for the preschool program, other kinds of evaluations are especially important, such as assessment of the child's physical skills, his social maturity, his linguistic and perceptual skills, and the like.

Other factors guide the placement of the child in modern programs for the retarded. These include such things as physical or sensory handicaps, special problems in emotional adjustment, and limitations in previous social-cultural experience—all of which may place special handicaps upon the child, and for which special placement or special remedial instruction may be necessary.

For the most part, however, chronological age, mental maturity, and educational maturity are the concomitant criteria which may be used for grouping children into preschool, primary, intermediate, and secondary classes. Some schools use a committee, composed of a teacher of special classes, a psychologist, a school administrator, and a medical expert (often a nurse when a physician is not regularly available) to screen each child individually before placement is decided upon. The committee evaluates the evidence available and recommends appropriate placement. When needed, other expert opinion is called upon to assist in the judgment. In such schools re-evaluation of the child's placement is made from time to time, and the child may be shifted into a different group whenever this appears to be desirable.

[29] Wallin, J. E. W., *Education of Mentally Handicapped Children.* New York: Harper & Row, Publishers, 1955.

It will be noted that the sex of the child was not mentioned as a criterion for placement. Usually, special classes for the retarded have included both sexes in groups below the secondary level. It is more common to separate the sexes at the secondary school level, primarily because of the differing emphases in vocational education for the sexes at this level.

When schools provide separate programs for the educable retarded and the trainable retarded, pupils in the I.Q. range of about 50 to 75 are included in the former programs, and those with I.Q.'s in the range of about 25 to 49 are included in the latter program. Some experts argue that trainable retarded children should not be educated in the public schools.[30] The major arguments advanced to defend this position are: (1) schools should not be concerned with pupils who will not be able to learn academic subjects, and (2) schools should not assume the burden of training those who will not be able to become economically independent. Those who advocate public school placement in classes for the trainable argue that (1) the parents of these children pay taxes and schools are publicly supported, (2) each child deserves the best opportunity to develop his potentialities, and (3) no other agency is as well equipped as the schools to provide this training.[31]

Grouping pupils into classes for the educable retarded by means of C.A. and M.A. can provide groups that are reasonably homogeneous in these respects, at least, if there are separate groups for preschool, primary, intermediate, and secondary levels. For example, the preschool group would vary in age from about 4 or 5 to about 6, with a variability in M.A. from about 2 to 3 years. Educationally this group would be at the nursery level. The primary group would range in age from about 6 to 10 years, in M.A. from about 3 to 6 years, and would be at the kindergarten level educationally. The intermediate group would range in age up to about 13 years, in M.A. up to about 9 years, and in education it would range in level from about the 1st grade to 3rd or 4th grade. The secondary group would begin at about 13 to 14 years and attain a maximum M.A. level of about 12 years, and be able to reach academic achievement, in many cases, at about the 6th- or 7th-grade level. (We are not implying, of course, that the content of the academic program would be the same as that of the regular classes at these levels.)

None of our previous discussion should be taken to indicate that placement in a given level for the educable retarded should be based

---

[30] Goldberg, I. I., and Cruikshank, W. M., "Trainable but non-educable," *Nat. Educ. Ass. J.*, 1958, *47*, 622–623.
[31] *Ibid.*

on rigidly specified criteria. The problem of placement requires careful
and individual assessment and evaluation, with consideration for both
the capacities of the child and the requirements of the group. Flexible
application of the general criteria and principles requires planning and
sound educational judgment, based on the nature of the problems involved. The time has surely passed when administrative decisions for such
children can be based upon I.Q. or M.A. alone, no matter how competent
the mental examiner whose results are used may be!

It remains to say a word concerning the optimal size of the class.
Unfortunately, crucial research data on this problem are lacking, and
are, indeed, difficult to obtain. We must be guided, instead, by the cumulative experience of teachers of retarded children and by administrators.
Current practice in the various states, often defined by law, usually sets
the *minimum limit* for such classes at 10 (occasionally 15) and the *maximum* at 20 (more often 15). The optimal size for effective teaching purposes is affected by the relative degree of homogeneity of learning level of
the pupils (since less individualized teaching is then necessary), and by
the general level of maturity of the pupils (since more mature pupils are
more easily capable of engaging in independent activity and can take
care of themselves). Other factors that should be considered are: the
degree and frequency of severe physical handicap or limitation; the social adjustment of the children; and the degree of inadequacy in previous cultural, linguistic and perceptual skills. All of these considerations
suggest the need for both *flexibility* in determining the size of a particular
class, and *careful pre-assessment* of each child, as well as continuing
assessment after placement.

As a general guide to the size of special classes, Kirk suggests that
"The younger the children, the smaller the class."[32] The preschool group
should probably be no larger than 10 pupils, and a size of six or eight
in the class can be defended from both pedagogical and economic view-
points. These pupils will need intensive teaching and evaluation; relatively little is known about them when they enter school. The teacher
will need ample time for individual attention to these children. The
size of the class may be increased gradually as the children mature,
reaching the maximum number of about 20 at the secondary level. When
children are enrolled in both special and regular classes at the secondary
level, the size may even be slightly larger.

The nature of the curriculum

In broad terms, the curricula for the educable retarded and the
trainable retarded, as viewed in contemporary educational practice,

---

[32] Kirk, *op. cit.*

may be divided in terms of the major emphases which are provided. The former program is designed to insure minimal and practical competency in basic tool skills involving reading and number work, adequate skills in physical activities, practical skills in interpersonal relations and self-care, and vocational skills to provide for economic independence as far as possible. In contrast, the program for the trainable retarded is designed to insure self-help in taking care of personal and physical needs, social adjustment to home and community, and some degree of economic usefulness which does not imply economic independence. These differing curricular aims are based on both experience and research with these two broad categories of pupils.

The curriculum for the trainable retarded is spelled out in considerable detail in such books as those by Baumgartner[33] and Perry.[34] The self-help aims are directed toward teaching the child to do such things as dress himself, eat by himself, wash and groom himself, take care of his toilet needs, and follow simple directions. The social skills aims are directed toward being courteous, obeying rules, getting along with others, using language in interpersonal situations, and sharing in activities with others. The economic aims are directed toward learning to be useful in the home or in other sheltered work situations, and they include such things as running errands, washing dishes and cooking, homemaking, sewing, using the telephone, getting around the community, and using tools. Most of these skills can be taught to the older trainable groups in play and social situations both in the classroom and in the nearby community.

Hudson made an extensive study of the techniques used in implementing these aims, and was able to determine, as part of her analysis, the major lesson areas currently employed in these programs.[35] She found, for example, that language development occupied by far the most important place in the program. Next came motor development, followed by mental development and sensory training. Teaching arithmetic concepts occupied about one-third of the time devoted to language development, and occupational concepts about one-fourth of the time. The modern curriculum for the trainable retarded is returning many children to useful lives in the community, under at least partially sheltered conditions, rather than relegation to institutional living.

The curriculum for the educable retarded, nowadays, emphasizes the

---

[33] Baumgartner, B. B., *Helping the Trainable Mentally Retarded Child*. New York: Bureau of Publications, Teachers College, Columbia University, 1960.

[34] Perry, *op. cit.*

[35] Hudson, M., "An exploration of classroom procedures for teaching trainable mentally retarded children: Final report," CEC Res. Monogr., Series A, No. 2. Washington: Council for Exceptional Children, 1960.

unit approach to teaching. It is questionable how well retarded pupils do in academic work in special classes as compared with regular classes, as we have indicated above, but studies do show that they make better social adjustments.[36] The unit approach stresses meaningful, concrete and, usually, social learning situations. It includes short- and long-term projects, and tends to stimulate interest in the activities involved. The curricular aims are to develop: practical skills in reading and number work; effective use of language in interpersonal situations; industrial, musical and art education (although these areas now constitute less than one-third of the total school time,[37] whereas they occupied about one-half of the time just a few decades ago); physical education; "core skills" such as health habits and the like; and, in later years, skills in inter-personal relations and in vocational areas, usually in relation to each other. The reason for the inter-relationships of the last two items is that it has been found that retarded individuals more often lose jobs due to poor interpersonal relationships than due to poor vocational skills. Kirk presents a very useful summary of curricular practices for this group.[38]

MENTAL HYGIENE IN THE CLASSROOM

Our next concern is the broad question of how to implement the emotional well-being of all retarded pupils. We shall be concerned with various aspects of this question in the following paragraphs.

The general role of the school

The broad objectives of the educational program for the retarded child are not different from those established for all children. Fundamentally, they are concerned with enabling the child to lead a happy and effective life. Such goals have been specifically suggested by the Educational Policies Commission of the National Education Association in four principles that apply to all children.[39] They are summarized in the following statements: (1) the need for *self-realization*, which involves development of the child's capacities to use basic educational (or academic) "tools," and promotion of his health, cultural, and recreational interests; (2) development of a full awareness of *human relationships*,

[36] Johnson, G. O., "A study of the social position of the mentally handicapped children in regular grades," *Amer. J. ment. Defic.*, 1950, *55*, 60–89.

[37] Erdman, R. L., *Educable Retarded Children in Elementary Schools*. Washington: Council for Exceptional Children, 1961.

[38] Kirk, S. A., "Research in education of the mentally retarded," in *Mental Retardation 1961: A Review of Research*. Chicago: University of Chicago Press, 1963.

[39] Educational Policies Commission, *op. cit.*, p. 47.

which involves an appreciation by the child of his role as a member of society; (3) education for *economic sufficiency,* which involves vocational training, placement, and follow-up; and (4) education for an assumption of as high a degree of *civic responsibility* as the child is able to attain. We need to examine the frequently quoted objective of "helping the individual to lead a happy and effective life" a little more closely. We would like to ask the question: "When?" Too often this objective is interpreted as applying to some time in the distant future, when the child has grown up. "Living" goes on every day, however; it is a here-and-now affair. Even though this interpretation is true for all children, it is particularly applicable to the mentally retarded, who need concrete and realistic help *daily.*

Although the basic objectives listed by the National Education Association are relevant for the retarded child, there are, nevertheless, large and real differences in what can specifically be accomplished for the retardate as opposed to the average or superior child. These differences are reflected in the more specific educational objectives of programs developed for him. As Kirk and Johnson point out, the retarded child is generally slower in most things than the average child.[40] He does better in physical and social areas than he does in academic tasks. He has greater success in hand skills than he has in those functions that depend upon academic training. Vocationally, he usually functions best at an unskilled or semi-skilled job, rather than at a highly skilled job, although some retarded children often develop high degrees of skill in a particular area. For these reasons, we believe that the educational objectives for the retarded child should stress occupational and personal adequacy, as well as social competence. The educational objectives for the retarded differ from those for other children chiefly in that they focus more on specific and differentiated goals. This is because the retarded child is not as flexible in his adjustment to life, and cannot contribute to society as extensively as does the more normal child. As Ingram points out, the primary aim of education is to "help the child react as a growing child to situations both in and out of school and to establish habits and attitudes that will continue to operate as life goes on."[41] This is also one of the primary aims for the retarded child.

More specifically, the goals of the educational process of the retarded individual should be oriented toward the daily life activities. This principle should be applied in all areas of instruction. The child should

[40] Kirk and Johnson, *op. cit.*
[41] Ingram, C. P., *Education of the Slow-Learning Child.* New York: The Ronald Press Company, 1953, p. 61.

be helped to develop habits of physical health that are directly relevant to his current status and capacity. Similarly, the teaching of basic academic subjects should center upon their direct applicability in daily life. Stress should be placed upon socialization experiences, upon developing within the child understanding of the responsibilities of group living, and upon ability to participate as fully as possible in community life. The mental health of the child should be fostered.

There is still another important objective in the education of the retarded child. The child has to learn a realistic evaluation of his own limitations and assets, in order to help him avoid continual frustration. If his unrealistic aspirations are beyond his actual capacities, resulting frustration may lead to the production of severe anxiety. This problem presents special difficulties for the special class teacher. On the one hand, she must provide stimulation to enable the child to develop his capacities as completely as possible, and yet she must not expose him to situations that lead to frequent discouragement and frustration. The successful teacher must gauge the child's assets and liabilities accurately.

In considering the goals of special education for the mentally retarded child, we can do no better than state a principle that Dr. Henry Goddard, long a champion of the cause of such children, has repeatedly stressed: *The happiness of the child is first—everything else is second.*

THE TEAM APPROACH

The great difficulties and complexities of the task in dealing with the problems of the mentally retarded child have so many interrelated facets that, at times, one almost despairs of finding any solution to them. Yet, the success that is achieved keeps our hopes alive and indicates that much can be done. As we have seen, human behavior is exceedingly complex; it is affected by an infinite variety of internal and external forces that cannot be isolated. At the same time, the complexity of human behavior offers hope that improved care of the mentally retarded child will result in his improved behavior.

The fact that the problems of the mentally retarded child are intricate and extensive—that they cover the whole range of possible human behavior—is clearly evident. How, then, can a single discipline assume responsibility for the total management and treatment of such a child? Let us take another glance at some of the facts that we have stressed. Mental retardation is not an entity—it is a complex of factors. It involves a vast range of somatic processes, internal psychological reactions, social and cultural forces, and intricate interpersonal relationships.

Evaluation and treatment for all these factors, therefore, should not be the responsibility of any single discipline. It seems more reasonable that they should be shared by *all* disciplines that are capable of effectively assuming any portion of the total burden. At the same time, within a specific area, one profession may be able to contribute more than another. The mentally retarded child has medical problems, psychological problems, educational problems, vocational problems, social problems, and the like, and needs the appropriate specialized professional services for problems in each of these areas. Such problems as these do not occur in isolation; each usually involves the others. They are problems within a unitary organism. Further, we should be aware that no single discipline has evolved a solution to the specific treatment of the mentally retarded child, and we still do not know from where the *best* solutions—for there may be many—will eventually come.

The problems of the retardate must, therefore, be attacked upon as many fronts as possible. Any individual who can make a contribution should be welcomed with open arms, regardless of his professional membership. There should be no room for either inter- or intra-professional jealousies. There must be *teamwork* in the attack on the basic problems of mental retardation itself and in dealing more adequately with the problems of the retarded child.

Who should be members of the team? Traditionally, the team has consisted of a physician, a psychologist, and a social worker. However, this team membership needs to be expanded, and, fortunately, it *is* being expanded in all progressive approaches to mental retardation. The team may include: teachers, parents, and specialists of all types, such as psychiatrists, neurologists, physical therapists, occupational therapists, recreational workers, vocational guidance workers, sports leaders, physiologists, internal medicine specialists, and the like. Although only a few retarded children will need the services of all these types of individuals, the service of the total team should be available, to be called upon as needed.

When De Prospo accepted the 1955 Education Award presented by the Association for the Help of Retarded Children, he stressed the need or such professional unity. He said:[42]

When we realize the enormity of our problem, extending from the cradle to the grave, we should see the importance of being unified, whether we be physicians, psychologists, parents, or teachers. When we realize that only through the coordination of all concerned, at every level of society and government, can

[42] De Prospo, C. J., "Unity," *Amer. J. ment. Defic.*, 1955, *59*, 378–379.

we achieve a complete program for our children, it becomes imperative that no part of us be divided, either within a particular discipline, or among the various disciplines.

The team concept thus implies more than a mere physical interaction of individuals. It implies that the team should be a group of individuals bound together by a concern for the welfare of the retarded child, and that each member hold the fundamental belief that the problems of such a child can best be solved and his needs best met by a cooperative and integrated team approach.[43] Hubbard in discussing the underlying implications of the team approach, stated, in effect, that the team member must be a well informed individual in his own right, with a good capacity to see himself in relationship to his co-workers. He should allow others to do those things that they can do better than himself, and do those things that are the best for all, even though he is reluctant either to assume or give up responsibilities. He must have the strength to withdraw from those activities in which he feels himself to be not as well prepared as others. It is only then that maximum team cooperation can be achieved.

Further, the team concept is being extended beyond the problems of treatment and management of the retarded child alone. It is being utilized in the training of personnel.

STIMULATING GROWTH

As we have repeatedly stressed, the mentally retarded child has many assets, and can profit from help in many ways. There are two chief sources from which such help usually comes: the public school system and the home itself. In addition, in many instances, the effects of community clinics and other organized groups are also being felt.

The contributions of the parents are, of course, of paramount importance for the adequate growth of all children, but are of particular importance during the preschool years when so much can be done.

We have previously discussed the role of the parents in fostering the social and emotional growth of the child, and have emphasized its central significance for him. There are many highly specific areas in which the parents can be of great help in stimulating the more adequate growth of the child.

In the *emotional area* the parents can foster a more adequate percep-

---

[43] Hubbard, R., "The nurse and the healing arts team," quoted in part in *Social Work Practice in the Medical and Psychiatric Setting*. Pittsburgh: University of Pittsburgh Press, 1954, p. 79.

tion and appreciation of reality factors by the child. They can help him gradually to develop traits of independence and feelings of confidence. Through careful programs of management they are able, in many instances, to forestall many of his problems before they rise to serious proportions. The parents can help the child become aware of reality factors—the "do's and don'ts" of the particular society or community in which the child is living. At the same time that the parents *protect* their "slower" child, they can encourage him to assume more *independence* in coping with such problems. Tolerance for the child's slower recognition and acceptance of such responsibilities is needed, while, at the same time, overprotection must be avoided.

The parents have the responsibility of helping the child develop *basic skills* and appropriate *attitudes*. Such skills include: proper eating skills and habits, toilet training habits, habits of personal cleanliness, skills in dressing, ways of playing, and the essentials of social relationships with other people. It should be noted that the retarded child will

LEARNING TO PLAY HELPS TO DEVELOP MANY SOCIAL SKILLS (Reproduced by courtesy of The Special Education Service, Virginia State Department of Education, Richmond, Va.)

need *much more practice* in developing such skills than the average child, so the parents will have to learn to develop tolerance and patience.

Another major area in which the parents can be of great help is in the development of the *communication* abilities of the child. This includes the development of speech, reading, and writing. For example, speech development is frequently hindered in retarded children when the parents are too eager to respond to the gestures of the child. Even though the parent may not actually teach the child to read and write himself, he may be able to provide the basic groundwork for such skills to be more easily taught at a later date.

In all of these areas it is necessary that the parents know thoroughly the capacities and limitations of the child, through evaluations made by the appropriate specialist, and by continued observation. In addition, they must be made aware of the *developmental* rate of the child, that is, the rate at which he matures, so that they can provide proper experiences at the right time (pacing). If attempts are made to develop a skill before the child is ready, then he may develop anxiety and maladaptive forms of behavior. He should be *encouraged* to learn a task, rather than be pushed.

Cutting across all these areas is the general factor of the emotional maturity of the parents, and their wholehearted acceptance of the child (see Chapter Eight). Parental attitudes and feelings are important factors in the child's growth. The parents should realize, however, that they cannot do the job alone. They need the continuing guidance of experts to deal most adequately with the problems of the retarded child.

As the child grows older the role of nursery school and public school becomes more and more important, and the teacher becomes a most important figure in promoting his appropriate maturation.

PSYCHOTHERAPEUTIC APPROACHES

It may seem a bit unusual to include a section in this volume on psychotherapeutic approaches for the mentally retarded child. Psychotherapy is a technical procedure applied by experts who have had special training in this area, and is not considered to be within the province of the classroom teacher. Nevertheless, many retarded individuals who have emotional problems which interfere with learning or adjustment can profit from psychotherapy; for some it is essential. The classroom teacher should understand the role of psychotherapy and should know something concerning its characteristics. Only then can she be expected to be alert to its possible use for some of her pupils, and only then can she cooperate fully in the total therapeutic program—which frequently involves some degree of contact, direct or indirect, with the psychotherapist. And her understanding of this field will assist her in her general mental hygiene work in the classroom. The school administrator, too, can benefit considerably from knowledge of this kind.

It has been assumed, erroneously, that the mentally retarded child is unable to benefit to any great extent from psychotherapy. Sarason states that some of the reasons underlying this belief are:[44] the retarded child cannot tolerate strong emotional states; he cannot view the behavior of other individuals in an objective manner; he has difficulty in relating to other people; he cannot see the results of his maladaptive behavior. He also believes that one of the reasons that the usual methods of psychotherapy are not effective with the retarded child lies in the child's inability to communicate verbally in an adequate manner with other people. The retardate has difficulties in using language, for example; he cannot either generalize or readily express himself. Therefore, it is not surprising that the usual psychotherapeutic techniques based on verbal interactions are not too effective in his treatment. We agree with Sarason's feeling that the pessimism expressed concerning psychotherapy with retarded children has been based upon theoretical deductions rather than upon specific research considerations.

Abel also believes that one of the reasons it is thought that the mentally retarded child does not profit from psychotherapy is that he does not have an adequate degree of verbal understanding necessary for this type of treatment.[45] Abel points out also that there is too prevalent the concept that the mentally retarded individual cannot profit from techniques designed to result in re-education and character changes. Further, it is felt that the whole process of psychotherapy is colored by the cultural attitudes of rejection of this type of child. But, Abel points out, these concepts are not necessarily valid, and many studies have shown that the retarded child *can* profit from psychotherapy.

We believe that, in many instances, retarded children can benefit from both group and individual psychotherapy, as studies that we will cite clearly show. Further, as we have previously stated (see Chapter Ten), the "currency" of the psychotherapeutic situation is the interaction that occurs between the subject and the therapist, but this "currency" can be non-verbal as well as verbal. Moreover, interactions occur

[44] Sarason, S. B., *Psychological Problems in Mental Deficiency.* New York: Harper & Row, Publishers, 1949, p. 263.

[45] Abel, T., "Resistances and difficulties in the psychotherapy of mental retardates," *J. clin. Psychol.*, 1953, *9*, 107–109.

in many ways *other* than at the verbal level. For example, a child may communicate feelings and thoughts by postural adjustments, play activities, drawings, and so on. Inability to verbalize may be a limiting factor in some phases of therapy, but is not necessarily a complete block to all psychotherapeutic work.

Intelligence is also considered by many authorities to be significantly related to psychotherapeutic progress, and it has been stated that little progress in psychotherapy can be made by individuals with limited mental capacities. For example, Rogers believes that the subject must have adequate capacities for dealing with life situations, and that he must have at least dull normal intelligence to profit from psychotherapy.[46] Fenichel states that the mentally retarded individual cannot profit readily from psychoanalysis, since the ego does not have the capacity to "face its conflicts." However, even though Fenichel rules out the use of psychoanalysis with such persons, he states that they might respond to psychoanalytically oriented psychotherapy.[47] Psychoanalysis is a special form of psychotherapy that may not be applicable to all types of individuals.[48] Whether psychoanalysis is, in fact, contra-indicated for all mentally retarded cases is a moot question.

The pessimism that many persons express may be warranted for the *particular psychotherapeutic approach that they employ,* but there may be other psychotherapeutic approaches from which the mentally retarded child *can* profit. It is a major error to generalize that, since *some* psychotherapeutic approaches may not be applicable to defective children, *all* such approaches are not applicable.

Let us examine a few of the studies of the effectiveness of psychotherapy with mentally retarded children. Thorne reported upon psychotherapy with institutionalized children.[49] His approach involved: complete acceptance of the retarded child, expression of emotional reactions, an attempt at teaching emotional controls, teaching acceptable ways of behaving, building up feelings of self-confidence, and training the child to seek help when faced with severe problems. He studied the therapeutic responses of 68 retarded individuals. Of these, he felt 45 improved, 16 were unchanged, and 7 appeared to be less well adjusted following the

[46] Rogers, C. R., *Counseling and Psychotherapy.* Boston: Houghton Mifflin Company, 1942.

[47] Fenichel, O., *The Psychoanalytic Theory of Neurosis.* New York: W. W. Norton & Company, Inc., 1945, pp. 576–577.

[48] For a discussion of psychoanalysis, see: Hutt, M., and Gibby, R., *Patterns of Abnormal Behavior.* Boston: Allyn and Bacon, Inc., 1957.

[49] Thorne, F. C., "Counseling and psychotherapy with mental defectives," *Amer. J. ment. Defic.,* 1948, *52,* 263–271.

course of psychotherapy. Thorne concluded that retardates *could* profit from psychotherapy.

Heiser studied 14 retarded children who were given psychotherapy.[50] They ranged in I.Q. from 44 to 75. The diagnoses varied: one was diagnosed as familial, 6 were diagnosed as organic, and 7 as psychogenic mentally retarded children. Each child had from 11 to 58 hours of psychotherapy. Twelve children improved in social and environmental improvement; only one of the organic and one of the psychogenic children did not improve. Heiser felt that psychotherapy was definitely of benefit to retarded children.

Astrachan carried a number of mentally retarded females in group psychotherapy.[51] It was felt that they responded to such treatment, and that group psychotherapy was particularly valuable to those who were passive, depressed, or who had mild paranoid feelings. In particular, Astrachan reported that, as a whole, these individuals were better able to recognize their dependency needs following psychotherapy. There was a reduction in feelings of isolation, shame, and fear. He also felt that they were able to solve many of their conflicts concerning authority figures and siblings.

Fisher and Wolfson treated 12 mentally retarded girls, ranging in age from 10 to 13 years, with group psychotherapy.[52] They concluded that eight of these showed definite improvement in their behavior and attitudes. It was felt by these workers that there was an initial shift from ego-centered behavior to in-group–centered behavior. Finally they developed out-group–centered interests. They showed more alert attitudes and were, in general, more receptive to learning experiences. Fisher and Wolfson felt that the keynote to the success of their group psychotherapy was their permissive attitude. They stated that the group therapist should move slowly, and that, eventually, the group members themselves would show him their ultimate levels, which the therapist should not attempt to exceed.

This permissive approach has also been stressed by Harris, in dealing with mentally retarded children in classroom situations.[53] It was found that a permissive atmosphere produced good results.

[50] Heiser, K. F., "Psychotherapy in a residential school for mentally retarded children," *Train. Sch. Bull.*, 1954, *50*, 211–218.

[51] Astrachan, M., "Group psychotherapy with mentally retarded female adolescents and adults," *Amer. J. ment. Defic.*, 1955, *60*, 152–156.

[52] Fisher, L. A., and Wolfson, I. N., "Group therapy of mental defectives," *Amer. J. ment. Defic.*, 1953, *57*, 463–476.

[53] Harris, L. M., "Reactions of adolescent, mentally deficient girls to a permissive atmosphere in an academic schoolroom," *Amer. J. ment. Defic.*, 1953, *57*, 434–446.

Not all attempts at psychotherapy with retarded children have been successful, and it is unfortunate that these attempts have not been extensively reported, for we can learn as much from our failures as from our successes. Vail has reported upon his attempts to use group psychotherapy with mentally retarded boys.[54] The group was composed of 14-, 15-, and 16-year-old boys, who ranged from 35 to 70 in I.Q. Vail stressed verbal techniques in his approach. Even though no significant improvement was shown by the group, Vail felt that, paradoxically, those subjects who had attended the fewest sessions showed the greatest amount of improvement. He drew an important conclusion from this unsuccessful attempt at group psychotherapy: the psychotherapist cannot be only a listener and observer, regardless of his sincerity, but, rather, he must be alert to provide repeated gratification of the needs of the subjects as they arise.

What, then, can be accomplished by psychotherapy with mentally retarded children? It is unlikely that psychotherapy will raise the innate intellectual capacities of retarded children (although it may enable emotionally disturbed ones to make more adequate use of their mental capacities). It will not transform them into intellectually normal children. Psychotherapy may enable them to solve their emotional problems and conflicts, however. It may help them to grow in desirable directions, and alleviate many of their maladaptive behaviors. It can promote their adjustment in the community, and help them to lead a happier and often more productive life, both in the present and in the future.

We may conclude from the available evidence that the mentally retarded child *can* profit from psychotherapy. As Wiest points out, the general goal of psychotherapy is not only to develop a fuller utilization of the child's capacities, but also to effect changes in the home or family situations.[55] He stresses the fact that education reduces the stigma of retardation. In part as a result of such educative and psychotherapeutic approaches, institutions for the mentally retarded are undergoing a slow change in their purposes and functions. Institutionalization for the moderately retarded child is beginning to be perceived as a temporary measure—as an aid to the child until he can be returned to the community. Wiest has developed a frame of reference in regard to his therapeutic approach to the mentally retarded child. He points out that a child may be psychotic because he has never left an infantile state,

[54] Vail, D. J., "An unsuccessful experiment in group therapy," *Amer. J. ment. Defic.*, 1955, *60*, 144–151.

[55] Wiest, G., "Psychotherapy with the mentally retarded," *Amer. J. ment. Defic.*, 1955, *59*, 640–644.

and that, from one point of view, infancy may be conceived of as a state of psychosis. He feels, as we do, that the unconscious of the retarded child may be modified without the use of verbal interactions, and that the retardate can profit from psychotherapy. He stresses the fact that it is possible to make reality so appealing to such a child that he will grow toward it.

It is also evident that traditional psychotherapeutic approaches are not very effective when applied to the mentally retarded child, and that new approaches are· needed. Those approaches that lean heavily upon verbalizations and intellectual processes are probably not effective, and cannot be utilized successfully.

The goals of psychotherapy with the retarded child need to be reconsidered. They need not involve complete reorganization of the total personality, nor is it likely that such goals are feasible in the vast majority of cases. The goals set by the therapist must be realistic and readily within reach of the child's capacities.

It is our belief that one of the most important aspects of psychotherapy with such a child is the opportunity provided for him to identify with the therapist. This process of identification occurs at both conscious and unconscious levels (see Chapter Ten). One of the authors worked intensively with a group of 16 retarded adolescent boys for six hours a day over a period of eight months. It was brought to his attention by colleagues that the entire group walked in the same manner as he did. He was often told, to his dismay, by some of the boys: "I wish I could get heavy like you." This identification with the psychotherapist seems, to the child, to make the environment safer, and eventually enables him to achieve a more adequate perception of reality.

In addition to the major psychotherapeutic approaches, there are other valuable methods. *Occupational therapy* has been used with apparently considerable success. This approach involves creative activity on the part of the retarded child (such as simple woodworking, clay modeling, weaving, and the like). Occupational therapy enables the child to develop his interests and aptitudes, and provides a means through which specific disabilities may be corrected.

Music therapy is another valuable treatment approach. Knight and his co-workers, in discussing the effectiveness of music therapy, point out that, when properly used, it will enable the retarded child to inhibit his random muscular inpulses.[56] Further, it increases his abilities to

---

[56] Knight, D., Ludwig, A. J., Strazzulla, M., and Pope, L., "The role of varied therapies in the rehabilitation of the retarded child," *Amer. J. ment. Defic.,* 1957, *61,* 508–515.

shift more readily from one activity to another, and provides him with opportunities for growth in a group situation. Specific forms of treatment have been developed for children with organic brain injuries. These often center around sensorimotor activities, and have been extensively utilized by Strauss and Lehtinen.[57]

The role of the teacher in the treatment process

As pointed out in our previous discussion, the teacher is a very important member of the treatment team, and may play a significant role in the total treatment process of the retarded child. It is self-evident that the teacher bears the major responsibility for the growth-stimulating programs that have been detailed in the first sections of this chapter. The teacher should work closely with the parents of the child, interpret his progress to them, aid them in dealing with their own problems, and suggest ways in which they can further the development of the child. The teacher forms the link between the home and the school. She is primarily responsible for stimulating the growth of the child in many areas. The general mental hygiene of the classroom is her responsibility, and this entails an understanding of the needs and capacities of each child. She makes use of the interactions of the children to enable them to understand themselves better, to foster ego development, and to stimulate the growth of social skills. It is also the responsibility of the teacher to pace the educational and vocational tasks set for the child in accordance with his abilities, psychological needs, and specific maturational level. We should also consider the fact that the teacher has a direct therapeutic role. She continually interacts in both group and individual sessions, either on a formal or informal basis, dependent upon her training. It is for all these purposes that she needs to know more about personality development, guidance and counseling techniques, and psychopathology.

Even when the treatment program is centered around somatic methods, the role of the teacher is vital. She is in a position where she can observe the reactions of the child on a continuing basis, and can evaluate his possible progress and behavioral change. All pertinent behavioral reactions of the child should be discussed by her with the other team members, so that the somatic method utilized may be adapted to the child's changing needs. Further, as the somatic therapy continues, changes often occur in the child's needs. The teacher has to be alert

[57] Strauss, A., and Lehtinen, M. A., *Psychopathology and the Education of the Brain-Injured Child.* New York: Grune & Stratton, Inc., 1947.

to the possibility of such changes, and correspondingly introduce changes as necessary in her classroom program.

The following illustration of the teacher's role in the somatic aspects of the treatment program is pertinent:

Jerry, a nine-year-old retarded child, was receiving medication daily (chlorpromazine). The teacher noted that he showed marked behavioral changes in his classroom behavior. Formerly he had been quite active, and involved in all the class activities. Two weeks after his medication had been initiated Jerry was lethargic, appeared to be drowsy most of the time, and did not enter into the class activities. He "just sat." The teacher discussed these behavioral reactions with the child's physician, who then adjusted the medication to help the child maintain more alertness.

The teacher also can be of great help in the psychotherapeutic treatment of the child. She should consult regularly with the psychotherapist, in order to acquaint him with the progress and behavior of the child, and to find out how she herself can aid in implementing the goals of psychotherapy. For example, she might, with one child, allow him to lean very heavily upon her. In the case of another child, it might be desirable that she should not permit him to be too dependent upon her. Through discussing the progress of the child, and being an active participant on the therapeutic team, the teacher can play a vital role in the therapeutic process.

Specialized treatment methods

We may categorize treatment methods as being either *somatic* or *psychotherapeutic* in nature. *Somatic* methods are those that attempt to deal with the problems of the individual by effecting some *physical change*. *Psychotherapeutic* methods, on the other hand, do not aim at the modification of any somatic aspect of the individual (although such modifications may occur as a result of treatment), but, rather, attempt to effect changes in the child's behavior through modification of his personality. We shall discuss each of these approaches in the following paragraphs.

Many attempts have been made to treat the behavioral reactions of retarded children by various somatic methods. It has been hoped that such approaches would also serve to raise the intellectual capacities of the child. Two prevalent types of somatic therapies are *pharmacotherapy* (the use of various drugs) and *convulsive shock therapy*. We shall discuss each of these in turn.

In general, the utilization of various drugs in the treatment of mental retardation has not, to date, produced significant improvement in the child. (In such cases as cretinism, in which a *specific deficiency* has been the cause of mental retardation, the story is, of course, different. See Chapter Three.) In past years, a great deal of interest was shown in the possible beneficial effects of *glutamic acid* upon mental retardation. Because some observers felt that children treated with this drug appeared to function more adequately in many intellectual areas, experimentation was conducted upon the relationships of glutamic acid to the learning process. Many such experiments were performed on animals, as, for example, white rats.[58] The results of several of these studies indicated that there was an apparent increase in the rate of learning by rats when glutamic acid was administered to them. In studies on humans there were indications that scores on some psychological tests tended to rise after the administration of glutamic acid.[59] Sarason, who has reviewed many major experimental studies on the effects of glutamic acid on mental retardation, points out that there may be some relationships between an increase in psychological test scores and administration of glutamic acid, but he feels that the significance of their finding is in doubt.[60] He believes that such studies were not adequately controlled. Lombard, Gilbert, and Donofrio studied the effects of glutamic acid on the intelligence, social maturity, and adjustment of mentally retarded children.[61] A group of 28 retarded children were given glutamicol over a seven-month period. They were compared with a matched group of 25 other retarded children who were not given the drug. No statistically significant differences were found between the two groups on any of the factors that were investigated.

On the basis of all the evidence, the original enthusiasm for the use of glutamic acid as a cure for mental retardation cannot be maintained. Although glutamic acid does have some value in helping to control some undesirable behavioral reactions, it does not, of itself, produce improved intellectual functioning.

Newer drugs, the so-called "tranquilizers," have also been administered to retarded children. Two of the most prominent tranquilizers are

[58] Zimmerman, F. T., and Ross, S., "Effects of glutamic acid and other amino acids on maze learning in the white rat," *Arch. Neurol. Psychiat.*, 1944, *51*, 446–451.

[59] Zimmerman, F. T., Burgenmeister, B. B., and Putnam, T. J., "A group study of the effect of glutamic acid upon mental functioning in children and adolescents," *Psychosom. Med.*, 1947, *9*, 175–183.

[60] Sarason, *op. cit.*, pp. 198–203.

[61] Lombard, J. P., Gilbert, J. G., and Donofrio, A. F., "The effects of glutamic acid upon the intelligence, social maturity, and adjustment of a group of mentally retarded children," *Amer. J. ment. Defic.*, 1955, *60*, 122–132.

chlorpromazine and *reserpine*. Originally, these drugs were
to control the disturbed behavior of chronically overactive
The research literature in regard to their psychological (as w
somatic) effects is, at times, contradictory, but certainly mo
quately controlled studies do not substantiate the earlier beliefs ... the
drugs served to "cure" psychopathological reactions or mental retardation. It is true that the drugs do tend to "calm down" some extremely
anxious persons.

The tranquilizers have been given to disturbed mentally retarded
children, and there have been indications of an increase in their intelligence test scores when they have been so treated, but such an increase
does not necessarily mean that their *intellectual capacities have improved*. It is likely that the "calming" effects of the drug may enable some
children to focus more effectively on the test problems, and devote more
of their attention to adequate solutions of the items presented. Thus,
such children might, at least temporarily, function more adequately,
although no change might be effected in native intelligence. For example,
Rettig treated highly disturbed retardates with chlorpromazine.[62] It was
concluded that they were more receptive to training procedures. This does
not mean that the drugs made them "more intelligent." There is also
evidence to indicate that the tranquilizing drugs sometimes produced
impaired intellectual functioning. Kornetsky and his co-workers,[63] as
well as Primac and his co-workers,[64] found that chlorpromazine causes
impairment in the performance on a number of tests of intellectual and
psychomotor capacities in normal subjects. Such drugs have not proven
to be of value in the general treatment of mental retardation.

Another method that has been tried, in an attempt to improve the
intellectual functioning of mentally retarded children, is that of *shock
therapy*. Such therapies have long been thought to be of value in treating persons suffering from severe behavioral disorders. Modern methods
of shock treatment may be divided into three major categories: *insulin*
shock, *metrazol* shock, and *electric* shock. Since the use of metrazol shock
has been largely discontinued during recent years, we shall not discuss it.

Insulin shock is induced in the individual by an *intravenous* or *deep
muscular* injection of insulin. The patient shows a tendency to "doze off"

[62] Rettig, J. H., "Chlorpromazine for the control of psychomotor excitement in
the mentally deficient," *J. Nerv. Ment. Dis.*, 1955, *122*, 190–194.

[63] Kornetsky, C., Humphries, O., and Evarts, E. V., "A comparison of the
psychological effects of certain centrally acting drugs in man," *Arch. Neurol. Psychiat.*, 1957, *77*, 318–324.

[64] Primac, D. W., Mirsky, A. S., and Rosvald, H. E., "The effects of centrally
acting drugs on two tests of brain damage," *Arch. Neurol. Psychiat.*, 1957, *77*, 328–332.

and to sleep. Unconsciousness then follows and the individual is not responsive to external stimulation. Finally, a shock state occurs, in which there are spasms of the entire body, and violent contractions of the limbs and muscles. This convulsive reaction (which resembles the convulsive seizures of the epileptic) subsides after a short period of time, and the individual then lapses into a deep coma. He is awakened by an injection of glucose. There is a progressive breakdown in the integrative functioning of the brain. It has been hypothesized that there is a resulting re-integration of its functioning when the hypoglycemic reaction is relieved.

Electric shock therapy also produces a severe convulsive reaction. This shock is produced by passing a charge of electric current through the brain. It is applied by means of electrodes applied to the outside of the head, although, in some newer techniques, the current is applied directly to the brain itself. When the current is first applied, unconsciousness results. The patient then becomes rigid and all the muscles of the body become tensed. A convulsive stage then follows. This is then followed by a period of relaxation and deep coma. Often the individual is in fairly good contact with reality following shock, and is able to communicate better with other people. Many theories have been advanced to explain the possible beneficial results of electric shock therapy.[65] Some emphasize the possibility of physiological and anatomical changes in the brain, and the creation of new neural "pathways." Other theories suggest, for example, that electric shock is perceived by the individual as a punishment through which he "atones" for his guilt and "sins." There is no convincing evidence, however, for these or other theories.

The possible neuropathological results of shock treatments (either insulin or electric) are not definitely known. The question of whether there is any resulting damage to the brain from the shock has often been raised, but research to date is not conclusive on this point. Careful analysis of the clinical and research evidence indicates, however, that organic brain damage *may* result in some cases, particularly as a result of electric shock therapy.

Mentally retarded children have been treated with insulin and electric shock therapy. However, such treatment is *not* intended to raise the intellectual potential of the child, but, rather, is designed to alleviate severe behavioral reactions.

[65] For a detailed discussion of shock therapies, see: Hutt and Gibby, *op. cit.*

ch. 12

SPECIAL EDUCATIONAL

METHODS

Now that we have considered the general problems in the educational management and guidance of the retarded pupil, we shall turn our attention to some of the special methods which have been developed for his education. We can do no more than sample some of the more important of these methods, for separate volumes and handbooks would be needed to present in detail the methods and materials which have been utilized. We shall refer the reader to other sources for this additional detail, and would like only to present some concrete illustrations of the general methods and principles.

METHODS RELATED TO LANGUAGE TRAINING

The communication arts lie at the center of a great many interpersonal skills. Thus the proper development of communication abilities is a central task for the sheer mastery of *receptive* and *expressive* communication. They are also highly important because they are part of the essential base for "getting along with others" socially as well as on the job. They are basic, also, for the learning of abstraction and generalization, as well as for the learning of many academic subjects. Linguistic skills have been categorized into three major components: *receptive skills,* which include attending to and comprehending the linguistic communication; *associative skills,* which include relating ideas and symbols; and, *expressive skills,* which include speaking and writing.

There are a number of standardized tests of linguistic skills, as well as of readiness for training in these skills (see Chapter Nine) which the teacher can use profitably, but we should like to call special attention to a test developed by Kirk and McCarthy, the *Illinois Test of Psycholinguistic Abilities,* which can prove especially useful to teachers of the retarded.[1] This test provides measures of nine aspects of linguistic ability, including all of the major components we have previously enumerated, and, therefore, is useful in planning remedial teaching (when this is necessary), as well as in organizing lesson plans for the entire class.

Mental retardation and language development

It is well known that language development is highly correlated with general intellectual development, as currently measured. Aside from the fact that this result is biased by the very nature of our intelligence tests, linguistic development is a necessary precursor for, and concomitant of, most kinds of abstraction and generalization. Hence, it is understandable that, in general, retarded children are also retarded in language development. However, it is also noteworthy that the rate of the language development of retarded children is disproportionately slower than the rate of their intellectual development. This is probably because these children are *disproportionately* handicapped by factors other than lowered intellectual maturation. As Hutt and Gibby have shown, language development is affected by many external factors, even though the general rate of maturation is centrally important.[2]

In the case of many retarded children, such factors as general cultural deprivation, little motivation in the home for the use of language, decreased emphasis upon interpersonal stimulation, and insufficient or improper emotional stimulation combine to retard language development excessively. In particular, the development of speech in these children is excessively retarded, and various physical limitations and anomalies may also contribute to this condition.[3] It is also clear that improvement

[1] Kirk, S. A., and McCarthy, J. J., "The Illinois test of psycholinguistic abilities —an approach to differential diagnosis," *Amer. J. ment. Defic.,* 1961, *66,* 399–412.

[2] Hutt, M. L., and Gibby, R. G., *The Child: Development and Adjustment.* Boston: Allyn and Bacon, Inc., 1958.

[3] Hull, F. M., "Speech impaired children," in Dunn, L. M. (ed.), *Exceptional Children in the Schools,* New York: Holt, Rinehart & Winston, Inc., 1963.

in language ability positively affects intellectual development,[4] and that special programs of speech and language training may, in the early years, significantly improve these aspects of development.[5]

These considerations emphasize the importance of a solid program of language instruction for both trainable and educable retarded. Some of the training, perhaps most of it, will be provided by the teacher of the classes for the retarded. She will offer appropriate, enriched, and remedial programs of language instruction; some of it may be provided by a speech therapist, and some of it may require assistance by a specialist.

Special methods of language instruction

Language instruction must play a pervasive role in all school instruction, but especially so in the preschool and primary grade education of the retardate. Of central importance, perhaps, is the *climate* of the classroom, which should be structured so as to encourage communication. It has been shown that a classroom program fostering social communication is not only effective in overcoming defects of articulation, but may even be more effective than the usual program of speech therapy.[6] Thus, the school program should be designed to encourage speech, listening, and associating. These activities should be encouraged, not only as part of the unit on speech, but in connection with *all* school activities.

Listening requires that the child *learn to pay attention*, and for this purpose special games and devices can be utilized which make enjoyable and profitable, as well as successful, the "detective" art of attending carefully. Through such activities the child's life-space may be expanded and his involvement in activities may be increased.

Speaking requires motivation to speak! Again, if the child is provided with interesting activities which challenge his attention, and if ample opportunity and reward are given for talking about such activities, speaking can be greatly encouraged.

Learning to associate requires skillful direction by the teacher, so that pupils are encouraged to think of similarities and differences. For instance, the right kind of questioning about daily activities may do much to foster the growth of associative thinking in the retarded child. He may engage in games which require that he follow directions, learn

---

[4] Hunt, J. McV., *Intelligence and Experience*. New York: The Ronald Press Company, 1961.

[5] Smith, J. O., "Group language development for educable mental retardates," *Except. Child.*, 1962, *58*, 111-123.

[6] Lassers, L. R., and Low, G., "Symposium on assessing and developing communicative effectiveness in mentally retarded children," *Asha*, 1960, *2*, 377.

to associate verbal with behavioral cues, and analyze simple problems. The use of multi-sensory stimulation in learning appears, also, to be especially important in the language instruction of retarded pupils.

Now, let us look at some examples of activities and units of work which encourage the development of the language arts.

SELF-EXPRESSION. Self-expression is useful in facilitating the maturation of mental development, as well as that of language development. Since spontaneity in self-expression leads to effective emotional behavior, it serves a very important function in the earliest aspects of language development. In one technique of initiating the development of self-expression, the teacher can make use of any daily event in the lives of the children in order to encourage them to talk about it.

For example, the children come to school when it is raining or snowing. This experience may be utilized to provoke many kinds of self-expression. The teacher can ask each child what his experience was like in coming to school in the rain or snow. How did he prepare for coming to school? What special kind of clothing did he wear? What did the snow look like, feel like, and what did it make him think of? Then, too, children can be encouraged to make drawings about snow or rain: heavy or light snow; snow with strong winds; snow on top of a house; simple drawings of snow flakes; drifts of snow; and the like.

Self-expression along such lines can lead eventually to a unit about the snow or rain, once interest has been sufficiently aroused. For example, the unit might deal with the causes of snow, or the effects of snow on life, or with the seasons and snow. The unit can then become the base for learning new words, learning new expressive techniques—as in drawing, speaking or play-acting—and for learning simple generalizations or abstractions. The unit also can lead, in the later primary grades especially, to new words that can be read, and to reading materials related to the project at hand, to be read by the pupil, the teacher, or both.

Self-expression can be greatly facilitated if appropriate materials are at hand. For instance, water play and sand play are particularly important at both the preschool and primary levels for retarded children. The simple materials used, contained in basin and box, are sufficiently unstructured so as to provide emotional release. They are unlikely to encourage feelings of frustration, since there are no "standards" of success which cannot be attained by the child. Such materials have long been used in child guidance clinics, to encourage the expression of affect and underlying conflicts, but are also effective in the classroom. They can be used in combination with simple objects, such as blocks of wood, simple toys, sponges, pails and shovels, and the like.[7, 8]

Other materials useful in connection with self-expression include: crayons and paints; finger paints; clay; construction toys; mosaics; blocks of wood; and simple, toy musical instruments. A useful book stressing the general therapeutic aspects of play and self-expression has been prepared by Jackson and Todd.[9]

RECEPTIVE LANGUAGE. We have stressed repeatedly the importance of teaching the retardate *to attend* to various external stimuli. *Discriminal attention* is necessary if the effective learning of receptive language skills is to be encouraged. Most authorities agree that the retarded child needs concrete experiences to relate to his receptive language learning. These experiences should include stimulation of all sensory modalities—auditory, visual, kinesthetic, tactile, and olfactory—so as to insure overlearning and provide rich associative meanings. But all of these experiences, no matter how rich and how vivid, will yield pitifully small returns in long-term learning, unless the child also *learns to attend carefully* to the experience.

It cannot be taken for granted, then, that simply providing the experience will insure effective learning. But how can attention be fostered? First, the child must be encouraged directly to attend, even if this means saying, "Look at me," or, "Watch my face while I speak." Then the presentation by the teacher must be *dramatic* and *vivid*. Great care must be taken to insure full comprehension by the child of what is said or done. This means proceeding very slowly, repeating important ideas or words, explaining carefully and fully, and constantly checking to insure adequate comprehension.

It usually helps if the child is requested to *do something* to show that he really has understood, such as following a direction, obeying a command, or making something (a drawing, playing-it-out, or the like). But not only must the child do something concrete to insure his comprehension; the teacher must also give concrete illustrations, and must carry out activities to give varied examples of the idea or concept being taught.

[7] Lowenfend, V., *Creative and Mental Growth*. New York: The Macmillan Co., 1952.

[8] Perry, N., *Teaching the Mentally Retarded Child*. New York: Columbia University Press, 1960.

[9] Jackson, L., and Todd, K. M., *Child Treatment and the Therapy of Play*. New York: The Ronald Press Company, 1950.

Kirk and Johnson list several types of activities which are useful in developing language ability.[10] These are: (1) encouraging free expression about immediate experiences; (2) carrying out instructions; (3) using pictures for purposes of discussion—later, stories and books may be used for the same purpose; (4) using trips and excursions to encourage discussion and introduce new concepts; (5) re-telling of stories; (6) using games, rhymes and riddles; and (7) giving exercises in classifying ideas and concepts ("What things do you eat?" "How many animals do you know?").

Before reading is begun in a formal way, the child must have an adequate store of these and other varied experiences in order to make the reading experience enjoyable and meaningful. There are several good sources of additional suggestions for pre-reading programs, some of which are noted below.[11] All that we can do in this short account is to emphasize some of the essential elements in the learning of receptive language as a base for such reading programs: (1) an adequate store of rich, vivid and meaningful experiences; (2) an adequate store of words and concepts; (3) the association of the linguistic concepts in various sense modalities; and (4) appropriate habits of attending, discriminating, associating, and generalizing.

The formal teaching of reading should not be introduced until the child's linguistic readiness and visual-motor skills are fully adequate for this task. For most moderately retarded children this will mean that reading instruction will not begin until the chronological age of at least eight years, and a mental age of at least six years.

Authorities differ considerably on the values of different methods of teaching reading to retarded children, just as they do concerning teaching methods for normal children. Present evidence does not clearly establish the superiority of any one teaching method over the others. It is generally agreed, however, that retarded children need much more repetition and guidance in the learning process, that special remedial methods are required in individual cases, and that special reading materials need to be used. Regarding the last point noted, it should be remembered that retarded children are chronologically older than their normal counterparts of similar mental maturity, and hence their inter-

[10] Kirk, S. A., and Johnson, G. W., *Educating the Retarded Child*. Boston: Houghton Mifflin Company, 1951.

[11] Baskin, J. W., "Vitalizing experiences for ungraded pupils," *Chicago Sch. J.*, 1952, March–April; Curtis, E. L., "Building toward academic readiness in mentally deficient children," *Amer. J. ment. Defic.*, 1943, *48*, 183–187; Garton, M. D., *Teaching the Educable Mentally Retarded*. Springfield, Ill.: Charles C. Thomas, Publisher, 1961; Warren, D. M., "Reading needs of the mentally retarded," *Educ.*, 1951, 548-551.

ests are different, in many ways, from chronologically younger children who have already reached their mental age maturity. Since reading materials should be geared to current interests, special selections of reading materials, some of which will have to be developed by the classroom teacher who knows her children's interests, are necessary. There are specific guides for the selection of reading materials and special remedial reading methods which can prove quite useful.[12]

EXPRESSIVE LANGUAGE. This area of instruction includes speaking and writing, primarily. We have already discussed some of the values and methods of self-expression. In the preschool program and in the early phases of the primary grade program, free play, trips, rhythm games, and the like will prove helpful. To these may be added dramatic experiences, the use of music and musical games, and the use of arts and crafts. It has been found that, to a large extent, retarded children prefer to deal with concrete experiences they have had or are having in their homes and communities. Hence, such activities as housekeeping, simple cooking programs, and simple crafts programs may well be incorporated in the teaching units, especially as these children become older.

Retarded children will need special stimulation to become involved in some of these activities, they will need frequent repetition of the same and similar activities, and they will constantly need encouragement to complete even the simplest projects. Art work seems to attract such children to a high degree, probably because it can be engaged in with very little language and because some of it, like clay modeling and weaving, for example, is concrete and appeals to motoric and visual senses. Such work can be truly expressive and oral expression can be encouraged in connection with it. When children have acquired sufficiently adequate skills in using art media, they can be given models to copy, such as bowls, simple figures, and place mats. With careful guidance they can acquire considerable skill and enjoyment and will be interested in talking about their products, thus finding new words to use and new concepts to explore.

It is entirely possible, and quite useful, to teach educable retarded children to write. Either the *cursive* or the *manuscript* method of writing may be employed. The manuscript method seems to be easier to teach, since the individual letters are spaced and learned as separate units, and since such writing is more closely correlated with printed read-

---

[12] See, for example: Durrell, D. D., and Sullivan, H. B., *High Interest and Low Vocabulary Booklist*. Boston: Boston University School of Education, 1950; and, Smith, N. B., "Helpful books to use with retarded readers," *Elem. Sch. J.*, 1952, 390–397.

ing materials. However, some authorities prefer the use of cursive writing, especially for brain-injured children, because of the greater ease in perceiving the word as a total unit when the letters are not written and perceived separately.[13]

The teaching of writing can begin with instruction in writing one's own first name, an activity which enables children to label their own work and their own property, and an activity, therefore, in which they show interest. Additional training in writing should probably be delayed until formal instruction in reading is begun. Since this will happen at about eight or nine years of chronological age, educable retarded children, whose motoric development is not as greatly retarded as their intellectual development, will be able to learn more readily. The emphasis in teaching writing should be upon *accuracy*, and not speed.

Children will need instruction in correct posture for writing; probably learning to write at the blackboard should precede writing at the desk, since accuracy can be more easily assured when the letters are large and the large muscle groups are being employed in writing. Using paper with ruled lines, and even boxes, allowing much more space than in normal adult writing, has been found useful. It is also advised that children be encouraged to write in rhythm in order to assist them in the early learning stages.

As in other areas of learning, as many sense modalities as possible should be employed. Therefore, writing in trays with soft clay and following a model of the word in the clay may be used as one method of reinforcing the learning of writing. Similarly, having children feel and trace words that are raised above the surface of the material on which they appear can be quite helpful. One method that has been suggested is to place words whose letters have been formed from sandpaper on paper with a smooth surface, and have children trace the letters and words with their fingers. In all of the work with writing, as in other phases of teaching the retarded, the words that are learned should have meaning and interest to the child, and should be related to other current interests and activities.

METHODS RELATED TO PERCEPTUAL-MOTORIC TRAINING

Perceptual development generally proceeds at about the same rate as general cognitive development, so that retardates can be expected to be deficient in perceptual skills to about the same extent that they are

---

[13] Strauss, A. A., and Lehtinen, L. E., *Psychopathology and Education of the Brain-Injured Child*. New York: Grune & Stratton, Inc., 1947.

mentally deficient.[14] Retardates take longer than normals to develop perceptual meanings, their perceptual behavior tends to be more rigid (*i.e.*, less spontaneous and adaptive), and as a consequence, they have greater difficulty in "erasing" perceptions.[15] In the case of retardates with brain damage, much more severe perceptual problems are present, and such children may have great difficulty in perceiving accurately even the simplest geometrical forms or discriminating between somewhat similar forms. Hence, it is probably true that all retardates would profit from special perceptual training, and the lower the level of intelligence and the more severe the brain damage, the more important would such training become.

We have learned that retardates are not as severely retarded in motoric development as they are in cognitive development. However, they do have special problems in that: (1) their motor development is generally slightly lower than that of normals; and (2) they have special difficulties in very fine hand-eye coordinations, such as are involved in finding a place in a book, selecting a detail in a picture, and in dealing with moving objects. Retardates would, therefore, benefit from motoric training, and such training can be helpful in other aspects of their learning and adaptation. Since motoric and perceptual training tend to complement each other, and since motoric development is basic to many aspects of perceptual development,[16] we shall treat the special methods for their training together.

Perceptual-motoric training is, as can be inferred from what we have said above, especially important in the preschool and primary grade programs. It is probably more important for trainable retardates than for educable retardates. Along with training in these skills, training in attending, carrying out of simple tasks, and following directions should be part of the total program.

Three basic aspects of perceptual-motoric training relate to: the self-image; perception of space and form; and perception of time. In training the retardate in these three areas, physical movements of the body or parts of the body are very helpful in concretizing the experience and reinforcing the learning. The use of music and of rhythmic activities through games and exercises can be helpful in perceptual development.

---

[14] Leibowitz, H., Waskow, I., Loeffler, N., and Glaser, F., "Intelligence level as a variable in the perception of shape," *Quart. J. Exp. Psychol.*, 1959, *11*, 108–112.

[15] Spitz, H. S., and Blackman, L. S., "A comparison of mental retardates and normals on visual figural after-effects and reversible figures," *J. abnorm. soc. Psychol.*, 1959, *58*, 105–110.

[16] Strauss and Lehtinen, *op. cit.*

And, as with all other basic learning for the retardate, reinforcement of the learning by means of appeal to multi-sense modalities should be constantly encouraged.

A number of principles which seem to have considerable value have been developed in programs for such training. (1) The structuring of spatial perceptions can be greatly assisted by the manipulation of concrete objects. If the child is given objects to move about, to place ahead of, behind, below, or above something, especially in the form of games, he is more likely to learn basic elements of spatial perception, and, at the same time, he will begin to acquire conceptual terms that are basic in spatial perception. Usually, the teacher will start with simple objects, like blocks or balls, and try to keep the visual qualities (form, shape, and texture) constant while varying the spatial requirements of the activities. (2) To maximize attention and discriminal perception, it is wise for the child, and not merely for the teacher, to feel and manipulate the objects whose size or position he is exploring. Movement of the object by the teacher may be used to attract and hold attention, but manipulation of the object by the child is important in order to supply him with concrete and vivid sensory experience. (3) The retardate will respond to perceptual qualities before he can respond to conceptual abstractions about these qualities. He can be taught to match forms, colors, and sizes before he can name the abstract qualities of the objects with these characteristics. (4) Along with principle number 3, the principle that each perceptual quality should be taught separately should be kept in focus. This means that differences in form should be learned with objects of the same size and shape, rather than with objects differing in these characteristics. (5) The learning of perception can best proceed from the body outward to the external environment. The child should learn to distinguish the "body" from the "not body," then he can learn to distinguish parts of the body, as well as positions on the body; and, finally, he can learn to distinguish spatial, form, and other qualities of objects around him. In the progression from "body" to "not body" the child can learn to perceive important aspects of his body-image and learn to attach names to many aspects of his body. (6) The careful teacher will assess the specific perceptual assets and limitations of her pupils, and then arrange activities designed to train the children in terms of these specific needs. (7) Retarded children have special difficulties with axial orientation and with differentiation of figure and ground. They need special training to overcome these confusions.

(8) Special training is needed in the perception of time, and such training is likely to be most efficient when linked with concrete representa-

tion of time. Time and space, and time and size, can be correlated both visually and motorically by a variety of games in which these characteristics are concurrently present. For special exercises and teaching materials, the interested reader is referred to two recent books.[17]

METHODS RELATED TO NUMERICAL TRAINING

Almost all retarded children can learn basic numerical and mathematical concepts, and almost all will need some competency in these areas in order to function effectively in the community and on the job. Although research studies have indicated that, even for the educable retarded, such children have far more difficulty with arithmetic reasoning than with arithmetic computations in comparison with normal children of similar mental age, these findings are not necessarily intrinsic to the problem of retardation, as such, but may reflect: (1) *inappropriate teaching methods* used with the retarded; and (2) *inappropriate pacing* of arithmetic teaching, as, for example, when arithmetic reasoning is introduced before adequate concrete and vivid arithmetical experiences are utilized in developing basic concepts of space, size, and time. Another example of inappropriate pacing is the teaching of arithmetic reasoning before the linguistic, conceptual level is adequate to comprehend the necessary abstractions.

Trainable retarded children can learn basic quantitative concepts such as big and small, heavy and light, and tall and short. They can also learn to count sufficiently to handle small amounts of money, and they can learn to tell time (in many cases), remember street numbers, and tell their age.

Educable retarded children can learn all of the basic computational skills involved in the four processes of adding, subtracting, multiplying, and dividing. They can also learn more difficult mechanical operations, depending upon the level of their mental maturity. And they can learn many aspects of mathematical reasoning and generalizing, if these are taught after the basic concepts and computational skills have been well overlearned and their mental growth has attained the appropriate level. Too often, mentally retarded children become phobic about arithmetic, especially about arithmetic reasoning, just as many normals do, because their experience in learning has been attended by too early abstraction, too frequent failure, and too much traumatization.

[17] Perry, *op. cit.;* and, Baumgartner, B. B., *Helping the Trainable Mentally Retarded Child*. New York: Bureau of Publications, Teachers College, Columbia University, 1960.

Even in the case of the trainable retarded, as well as with the lower levels of the educable retarded, appropriate and vividly meaningful numerical experiences can lead to effective learning in these areas. There are available a number of sources which can guide the teacher in selecting tangible and meaningful basic, numerical experiences.[18] The general principle advocated by the Gestalt psychologists, that configuration learning precedes analytical learning of sub-configurational parts, can well be utilized in learning basic number concepts.[19] As an example of this kind of principle, before the abstraction of "5" is learned, the concept of "5" can be learned as the configuration, ⦂·⦂ , or five dashes, thus: / / / / / , or, — — — — — .

Learning problems of the mentally retarded

In addition to the general statements about the learning of arithmetic which are similar to the learning of language in the case of retardates, there are a number of special problems which need to be highlighted. Arithmetical work places a great emphasis upon careful attention to detail, persistence in working at a problem, accuracy in work habits, and capacity for transference and generalization from one experience to another and from the specific to the more general. Retarded children tend to be inferior in these respects, in comparison with normal children of the same chronological age, and even of the same mental age. These personality characteristics and behavioral attributes, whether indigenous or acquired, handicap them severely in learning skills and acquiring concepts in arithmetic. A comprehensive study by Dunn and Capobianco has shown that retarded children are relatively deficient in the verbal comprehension and generalization or abstraction required in some arithmetical work, in habits of accuracy, and in the elimination of "mechanical crutches."[20]

Probably more than in any other academic area, learning arithmetic, especially for the mentally retarded, depends upon two primary bases, other than level of mental maturity. One of these is the *meaningfulness* of the numerical and computational concepts and operations, in terms of the child's current needs and interests.

[18] See, for example: Dolphin, J. E., and Cruickshank, W. M., "Pathology of concept formation in children with cerebral palsy," *Amer. J. ment. Defic.*, 1951, *56*, 386–392; and, Stern, C., *Children Discover Arithmetic: An Introduction to Structural Arithmetic.* New York: Harper & Row, Publishers, 1949.

[19] Carrison, D., and Werner, H., "Principles and methods of teaching arithmetic to mentally retarded children," *Amer. J. ment. Defic.*, 1943, *47*, 309–317.

[20] Dunn, L. M., and Capobianco, R. J., "Studies of reading and arithmetic in mentally retarded boys," *Monogr. Soc. for Res. in Child Develpm.*, 1954, *19*, No. 1.

In a study by Costello, for example, three methods of teaching arithmetic to retarded children were compared.[21] These methods were named: *verbalization* (verbal explanations of the meanings and relationships of different measurements); *sensorization* (concrete demonstration of relationships); and *socialization* (learning by doing meaningful tasks, such as learning to bake a cake and doing the measuring, taking fractional parts of things, and the like). In general, the socialization method proved to be more effective than the other methods, and, especially, more effective than verbalization methods. However, in some respects the sensorization or concrete demonstration method was about as good as, or better than, the socialization method. It was found that teaching by the socialization method was most effective in improving such concomitant aspects of learning as attention, comprehension, and abstraction.

Although one may criticize the conclusions of this study in terms of their generalizability, since not all ways of applying each of the three types of methods were compared, and not enough attention was given to the effects of the experimental procedures on children differing in levels of mental maturity and in personality, the findings are generally in accord with other evidence concerning the effectiveness of teaching arithmetic to retarded children. When "need" is present, and when the teaching is conducted in terms of these needs, with ample attention to the concretization of the concepts, learning is likely to be maximal.

Closely related to this base is the base of learning in a *climate of emotional security*. Our review of the relevant research in previous chapters demonstrated the effects of failure experiences and of anxiety upon the learning process. The learning of arithmetic is too often attended by failure experiences. One of the reasons for this is that the child can easily tell whether or not he fails ("gets the wrong answer") in arithmetic, whereas this is not so easily the case in other subjects. Care should be taken, therefore, to insure repeated success in learning arithmetic and to avoid frustrating failure experiences.

Another reason is that "correctness" is so highly valued by schools and by society, and the retarded child has, so often already, learned that what he does is not correct. His slow rate of mental maturation, his poor habits of attention, and his poor work habits—involving accuracy and persistence—have combined to lower his expectation of success in arithmetic and to increase his fear of failure. For these and related reasons, he can become phobic about arithmetic, particularly when it in-

[21] Costello, H. M., "The responses of mentally retarded children in specialized learning experiences in arithmetic." Unpublished doctoral dissertation, University of Pennsylvania, 1941.

volves abstraction, generalization, and transference of learning. When a child has special problems in emotional adjustment, this complicates the learning of arithmetic all the more.

In this connection, the findings of the "Committee of Seven" should be of noteworthy interest to teachers of retardates.[22] Among the many other things which were reported, this committee summarized the minimal levels of mental maturity which were necessary for probable mastery and retention of fundamental processes in arithmetic. For example, a mental age of seven years and four months is necessary for learning to do sums over ten, a mental age of eight years and eight months is necessary for subtractions over fifty, and simple long division requires a mental age of ten years and nine months.

Facts such as these can be useful guides to the teacher. If the teaching of arithmetic is to be maximally successful, it should be based upon adequate readiness of the child for the learning involved: adequate mental maturity; adequate experiential background; adequate language comprehension, and adequate mastery of underlying skills in the specific instructional area.

Special methods of arithmetic instruction

We can do no more than illustrate some of the special problems, and methods for dealing with them, in the teaching of arithmetic to retarded children. As we have emphasized, one of the first problems confronting the teacher is to evaluate the readiness of the child for learning number concepts and, later, for learning basic arithmetic fundamentals. A number of publications will prove highly useful in this respect.[23] In addition to the more formal methods of evaluating readiness by means of tests of general intelligence and of specific skills, the alert teacher can learn much about each child's specific assets and limitations by observing him closely in the *informal situations* in the classroom which involve games and other activities requiring some degree of numerical conceptualization.

The basis for concrete experience which leads to effective, primary conceptualizations of quantitative concepts lies in activities involving the perception of size, form, space and weight. Color perception may be closely linked with these phenomena as a means of providing discrimina-

---

[22] Washburne, C. W., "The grade placement of arithmetic topics: a 'Committee of Seven' investigation," *Yearb. Nat. Soc. Stud. Educ.*, 1930, *29*, 641–670.

[23] See, for example: Brownell, W. A., "Arithmetic readiness as a practical classroom concept," *Elem. Sch. J.*, 1951, *51*, 15–22; Cruickshank, W. M., "Arithmetic vocabulary of mentally retarded boys," *Except. Child.*, 1946, *91*, 65–69; and, Spitzer, H. F., "Techniques for evaluating outcomes of instruction in arithmetic," *Elem. Sch. J.*, 1948, *48*, 21–31.

tory and differentiating experiences. The general principle in teaching such primary perceptions is to make the experience as clear and vivid as possible. Of course, the experience must also be meaningful in the immediate life space of the child. A secondary principle is the importance of the utilization of multisensory experience to reinforce the tenuously forming perceptions.

Perry suggests a number of specific activities which appear to have considerable promise for trainable retarded children;[24] they are also highly useful in the preschool and early primary group experience of educable retarded children. Play with blocks, beads, and balls which differ in size, weight, and color is pleasurable for young children and enhances positive affective responses. A variety of games involving these and similar materials which require the use of sight, touch, and hefting can be employed. Gradually, the child can be taught to make simple discriminal perceptions of objects of different perceptual attributes.

Many of the games can resemble "playing detective" and finding the object which is *"like* this one," or is *"different* from this one," or is "the *opposite* from this one." These activities may be supplemented by others which require the making of things similar to, different from, or the opposite of, the model—such as building a tower of blocks, building a fence, making a mat with a designated shape, and so on. Not only making things, but "unmaking them," or tearing them apart, can be very meaningful and pedagogically useful.

In both formal teaching situations, as well as in connection with many other activities in the classroom, these types of perceptual experiences can lay the groundwork for the basic vocabulary and conceptualization of the primary qualities of quantitative concepts. Again, there are some useful references which offer suggestions for the teacher along the lines indicated.[25]

Basic concepts of space and size can be related to concepts of time and position. The child has to be taught the concrete meanings of such concepts as "now" and "later," and of "up" and "down," for example. People and objects in the room can be utilized in making simple perceptual discriminations and in forming these concepts. "John will do this *now,"* and "Mary will do this *later,* after John," or "A boy will do this

---

[24] Perry, *op. cit.*

[25] See: Brueckner, L. J., and Grossnickle, F. E., *How to Make Arithmetic Meaningful.* New York: Holt, Rinehart & Winston, Inc., 1947; Hickerson, J. A., *Guiding Children's Arithmetic Experiences: The Experience-Language Approach to Numbers.* Englewood Cliffs, N.J.: Prentice-Hall, Inc., 1952; Hauessermann, E., *Developmental Potential of Preschool Children: An Evaluation of Intellectual, Sensory, and Emotional Functioning.* London: Grune & Stratton, 1958.

now," and "A girl will do this *later,"* are rubrics for teaching this kind of time perception. Similar rubrics can be employed for teaching *position.*

The use of color dominoes and form dominoes can profitably be employed at later stages in the learning process, to reinforce as well as to enrich the learning experiences. Later still, the use of these concepts can be applied in the counting of money, keeping time with music, counting the number of children in a game, doing art work, and in various craft activities. These lead quite easily to activities and projects in which children, singly and in groups, can engage in useful, meaningful, and contextually relevant experiences.[26]

During the later stages of the primary grades, or at the beginning of the intermediate grades, the learning of quantitative concepts is followed by learning the fundamentals of arithmetic and, later still, by the learning of mathematical thinking of a simple kind. There have been a number of studies of the psychological processes involved in the four fundamental arithmetical operations.[27] Although the principles discovered in these studies are applicable to the teaching of retarded children, various adaptations in methods of teaching these skills will need to be made. Again, the principle that the learning must be immediately meaningful to the child has special relevance. Sheer drill in fundamental operations is likely to be ineffective. On the other hand, fundamental operations that are tied in with activities and projects arising out of the child's needs are likely to be reinforced much more rapidly.

It is also worth re-emphasizing the virtues of *concrete demonstrations* of the four fundamental operations with this type of child, because of his relative difficulty in generalizing and abstracting. Experiences in which he adds things, subtracts things from a group of things, multiplies things, and divides things can be utilized repeatedly until the concepts are thereby firmly entrenched. Counting blocks or marbles, dividing these up into groups, putting a number of blocks together in patterns to demonstrate multiplication, dividing a cake among a number of children, or subtracting objects from a larger number in a pile as a result of losses as in a game—these kinds of concrete demonstrations as part of on-going activities are useful.

Only after these operations are understood at the concrete level is drill in the mechanics of the fundamental operations justified. And the drills themselves need to be motivated—so that the child can actually see and understand how much he can gain from acquiring these skills.

---

[26] Stern, *op. cit.*

[27] See: National Society for the Study of Education, *The Teaching of Arithmetic,* Part II, 1951.

The teaching of arithmetic to the educable retarded at the secondary school level should be pointed toward the dual goals of assisting in the general area of social skills needed for effective and relatively independent living in the home and in the community, and assisting in and preparing for some degree of vocational competence. In a useful guide for teachers of retarded children at the secondary school level, the Kansas City, Missouri Public Schools have suggested that, "To live comfortably as an adult one should be able to use money, make change, have a concept of time, the calendar, time tables, weights and measures, etc."[28] They also suggest the training in skills which makes one a useful and contributing member of society.

The specific content which is proposed in this guide for children with M.A.'s of nine years and up—a range in mental maturity that is reasonable for most educable retarded at the secondary level—is divided into four major areas. In the first, dealing with arithmetical vocabulary, such concepts as *second, payment, annual, weekly, F.O.B.,* and *depth* are included. In the second, dealing with skills in the use of numbers, there are included such concepts as continuous adding using thought problems, the meanings of fractions like ⅔, ⅕, and even ⅞, complex multiplication skills like multiplying a three-place number with one or more zeros in it by a one-place number, and skills in division involving problems up to a three-digit quotient.

In the third area, on the use of money, the concepts of installment account, down payments, the skills in making change for $50.00 and $100.00, and ability to pay utility bills and other bills are included. And, in the fourth area, involving measurements, such items as concepts of weather (spring, summer, fall, and winter), ability to set a clock, ability to read train schedules, ability to read weather reports, ability to keep a graph of temperature, ability to measure in terms of pint, quart, and gallon, and concepts of ounce and 100 pounds are included. This sampling of content areas suggests the wide range of skills and concepts that focus on the practicable and useful, which are so important for these children.

NEEDED RESEARCH

We cannot leave this chapter without saying a word about the kind and amount of research that is urgently needed in order to make the teaching of the mentally retarded more meaningful and more effective. Although the reader will have become fully aware of the great

---

[28] "A Curriculum guide for teachers of pupils, educable but mentally retarded, Grades 7–12." Kansas City, Mo.: Public Schools, July 1959. (*Secondary Curriculum, Bulletin,* 109.)

strides that have been made since the time of Itard, and especially of the quickening pace of research in the past decade, it should be equally clear that a great deal still remains to be done.

One type of research that is still badly needed is that of basic research into the learning processes of the retarded child. In this area we have barely scratched the surface, and are still prone to accept psychology's findings about the learning processes of the normal child as applicable to that of the retarded child. As we have seen, however, even the retarded show wide variations in the processes and sequences of processes by which they learn. We can no longer assume that there is a simple, linear relationship between the level of mental development and the amount of learning that takes place. Nor can we assume, any longer, that learning proceeds by the same general principles at all mental levels and for all areas of content. The interesting relationships between sensory experience and concept formation, between type of overlearning and retention, between discriminal attention and rigidity in learning, and between amounts of anxiety and effects on learning processes need to be explored more adequately, probed more deeply, and evaluated more carefully.

Again, what constitutes effective readiness for the various content areas in the curriculum? We have some answers, but they are still only barely adequate. And such more general problems as the effect of the emotional climate upon the learning process, the nature of teacher personality and pupil personality interaction, and the effects of degree of heterogeneity in mental maturation within the class upon the learning of the class, need continuing exploration.

In the areas of teaching methods and of content materials a great deal has been "learned" by virtue of the creative, and even bold, new approaches being utilized by the modern teacher of the mentally retarded child. However, much of our knowledge is still essentially anecdotal. The relatively few rigorous research studies that have been done have been limited in scope and in generalizability. The specific factors that make one method of teaching superior to another, at one time in the life sequence of the child rather than at another, are now known only in the broadest and vaguest terms.

Research on teaching methods poses difficult methodological problems, yet the returns, as even the relatively little research that has been done demonstrates, can be extremely useful. Much of this research will need to be preceded, rather than followed, by experimental research in the laboratory, where conditions can be manipulated more precisely. In the laboratory, conditions of selection of subjects, control or measurement of motivational factors, control for difficulty level, and specific teaching procedures can be dealt with in ways to bring out the relevant and significant variables, some of which can now only be guessed at.

The whole area of problems concerned with interactions between school instruction and home and community experiences needs to be explored much more systematically than has been done heretofore. Under what conditions does subcultural deprivation affect types of learnings and learning sets most significantly? How does the level of aspiration of the parents influence the learning that is taking place in the school? How does the development of the child's identity or of his self-concept become influenced by the kinds of relationships established between school and home, and how does this affect learning in content areas? These are some of the questions which, when answered, will offer considerable improvement in our knowledge of what is going on in the learner, and of how we may be able to teach him far more effectively than at present.

ch. 13

SOCIETY'S ROLE IN

PROGRAMS FOR THE

MENTALLY RETARDED

IT SEEMS APPARENT THAT CHILDREN WHO FUNCTION AT A RE-
tarded intellectual level will be with us always. It is even probable that
the total number of such children will increase with the passing of time.
One reason for such a probable increase lies in the fact that medical science, which has made such tremendous strides during the past few years,
has lengthened the life span considerably. There have been significant advances in many medical specialties, such as surgery, internal medicine,
and the like. Advances have been made in the control of both acute
infectious and chronic types of disease. As a result, children who would
have probably succumbed to such illnesses in prior years have survived.
But many illnesses sometimes leave severe after-effects, including brain
damage, and, in turn, this may result in lowered intellectual functioning. Moreover, present-day medical treatment enables some children
with quite severe brain damage from other causes to survive. But even
though more disease processes involving injury to the brain are successfully being treated, too often their sequelae remain and result in severe
problems. As yet, little has been found to reduce the effects of many such
residuals, and until further advances in medical treatment occur we may
expect an increasing number of mentally retarded children.

Another reason for this probable increase is our rapidly expanding population. We should bear in mind that, even though the approximate ratio of such children to the general population might remain constant, the total number will increase. We can see, therefore, that the problem of retardation is likely to become an ever-increasing burden unless we understand its nature, its extent, and its implications. The problem will be alleviated only in direct proportion to the success of the research devoted to its prevention. This will be discussed later in this chapter.

In the succeeding sections of this chapter we shall discuss some general considerations of society's role in developing programs for the retarded child, and then discuss some desirable programs that it could and should provide.

SOME GENERAL CONSIDERATIONS

It is hoped that, in the preceding chapters, we have made clear to the reader the extent and complexity of the problems of mental retardation. We also hope that we have developed the point of view that there are many different "kinds" of mental retardation in children. It has been stressed repeatedly throughout the book that this condition occurs in a "whole child" whose total behavioral pattern must be understood in order that he be provided with the program that is best suited to his needs. Further, it has been emphasized that the child's behavior is the complex resultant of the interaction of a biological organism living in a particular culture and subject to individual psychological stresses and strains. We regard mental retardation, thus, not as an entity in itself, but as a condition occurring within a complex organism which has complex interactions with many external forces. The personality characteristics of the child influence his behavioral reactions, to a significant degree, and help to determine his responses to life situations.

We must also be concerned with the reactions of society itself to mental retardation. Many of the behavioral reactions of the retardate are "learned" reactions which are a function of his social environment. Further, in the last analysis, the reactions of society also determine the programs that are provided for appropriate care and management. To this extent it is a circular process. Since we regard mental retardation as the complex resultant of the interaction of a biological organism with the psychological and social forces that impinge upon it, we need to stress the fact that any approach to its solution must be a "multiple" approach including that of social and cultural forces.

The nature of society is thus, in itself, an important variable in the determination of the behavior of the child. Fromm has commented on the relation between the structure of society and the development of maladaptive behavior.[1] He feels that our society is irrationally organized in many ways, and he questions our basic overemphasis on the production of more wealth, the lack of opportunity for feelings of "belonging" and "togetherness," the lack of responsible participation in the determination of work and living conditions of the vast majority of people, and the lack of a world community and a true "brotherhood of man." Whether or not we wish to go as far as Fromm in categorizing the nature of our present-day society, we still need to recognize the far-reaching effects of societal conditions upon the mentally retarded child.

The problems of such a child have been recognized by society at many levels. Even though, in many instances, there has not been adequate *explicit* concern with his problems, they have been recognized *implicitly*. As an appreciation of the dignity of man has developed in our culture, there has been, at the same time, an increasing concern with the adequate total well-being of all children—in particular, there has been an increasing amount of attention paid to the problems of specific groups of exceptional children. At the national level there have been many important developments. President Theodore Roosevelt, who was very much interested in the problems of childhood, organized the Children's Bureau. This was originally placed in the Department of Labor, but is now a part of the Federal Security Agency. He also called the first White House Conference on Childhood. Such conferences were then planned to be convened once every ten years, and to deal with all aspects of the well-being of the child. The second White House Conference was held in 1920, during President Wilson's administration, and dealt with child labor laws and the general health problems of exceptional children. The third conference was convened by President Hoover in 1930, and had as its basic theme "Child Health and Protection." One of the more important outcomes of the 1930 conference was the development of the *Children's Charter*. This pertained to the welfare of all children and is, of course, pertinent to the problems of the mentally retarded child. Further, and of even more importance for the exceptional child, what became known as the *Bill of Rights for Children* was formulated at that time. A pertinent section of it is summarized below:

Each handicapped child is entitled to:

I. As vigorous a body as human skill can give him.

II. An education so adapted to his handicap that he can be economically independent and have the chance for the most complete life of which he is capable.

[1] Fromm, E., *The Sane Society*. New York: Holt, Rinehart & Winston, Inc., 1955.

III. Be brought up and educated by those who understand the nature of the burden he has to bear and who consider it a privilege to help him bear it.

IV. Grow up in a world which does not set him apart, which looks at him, not with scorn, or pity, or ridicule, but which welcomes him, exactly as it welcomes every child, which offers him identical privileges and identical responsibilities.

V. A life in which his handicap casts no shadow but which is full day by day with those things that make it worth while, with comradeship, love, work, play, laughter and tears, a life in which these things bring continually increasing growth, richness, release of energy, joy in achievement.

The fourth White House Conference was held in 1940, during the administration of President Roosevelt, and was concerned with "Children in Democracy." The fifth conference, held in 1950 during the administration of President Truman, was known as the "Mid-Century Conference." It summarized the progress made since the first White House Conference, and attempts were made to develop a long-range program for providing more adequate services for children for the next 50 years. The value of these conferences has been inestimable, in focusing attention on the need for promotion of the adequate development of *all* children, the normal, the mentally retarded, and those with other types of handicaps.

THE PRESIDENT'S PANEL ON MENTAL RETARDATION

On October 17, 1961, President Kennedy appointed a Panel that was instructed to explore the major aspects of mental retardation, and also prepare a comprehensive and long-range plan to deal with the central problems involved.[2] The Panel was organized into six "Task Forces," each of which assumed responsibility for the detailed study of one major area. Task Force I studied *Prevention* (Institutional and Clinical); Task Force II dealt with *Education and Habilitation;* Task Force III dealt with *Law and Public Awareness;* Task Force IV dealt with *Biological Research;* Task Force V dealt with *Behavioral and Social Research;* and Task Force VI dealt with problems of *Coordination.* The report of the Panel was published in October, 1962.

The President's Panel on mental retardation cited many statistical findings in order to underline the magnitude and severity of the problems associated with mental retardation. These are summarized briefly in the following statements:

Mental retardation affects twice as many people as blindness, polio, cerebral palsy, and heart disease *combined.*

---

[2] The President's Panel, *A Proposed Program for National Action to Combat Mental Retardation.* Washington: Sup't. of Documents, 1962.

Only four significant disabling conditions (which all come late in life) have a higher prevalence than mental retardation. These are: mental illness, cardiac disease, arthritis, and cancer.

———

400,000 of the mentally retarded require constant care and supervision. The other 5,000,000 are only mildly disabled.

———

Over 200,000 mentally retarded persons are cared for in public institutions. States and localities spend *$300,000,000.00* per year in capital and operating expenses for these institutionalized mentally retarded persons.

———

In addition, states and localities spend *$250,000,000.00* more for special education and other benefits.

———

In addition, the Federal government spends *$164,000,000.00* on the mentally retarded.

———

Fifteen to twenty million people live in a family in which there is a mentally retarded child.

———

Four per cent of all persons examined for induction into the armed forces during World War II were mentally retarded.

———

Mental retardation is a serious problem to one out of 12 people.

———

Mental retardation disables 10 times as many people as diabetes, 20 times as many as tuberculosis, 25 times as many as muscular dystrophy, and 600 times as many as infantile paralysis.

———

By 1970, there will be *1,000,000 more* retarded people than at present.

———

One out of every four beds in a mental institution is occupied by a mentally retarded person.

———

The average state hospital has 367 more patients than its rated capacity. The average number of people on the waiting list per hospital is 340.

———

Every year 126,000 babies are born who will be mentally retarded.

———

Ninety-six per cent of all mentally retarded persons live in private homes.

———

These facts, which speak for themselves, reveal the enormity and social significance of the problem.

In outlining his charge to the Panel, President Kennedy stated that one of the most important goals in coping with mental retardation was to *prevent* the occurrence of the condition, but that if this goal was not possible to attain, then every opportunity should be provided for the afflicted child *"to attain the full social development that is the birthright of every American child."* He noted that the current problems demanding consideration included those of: research, diagnosis, evaluation, care, appropriate training and education, family guidance, the need for sympathetic environment, a lack of public understanding, and a lack of sufficient private and public facilities.

The President was cognizant of the fact that very little is provided by society in terms of a positive program approach to the problems of the retarded child, and he stated: "For a long time we chose to turn away from these problems. *The standard treatment consisted of commitment to institutions, segregation from society, and silence about the affliction."* Parents of, and persons working closely with, retarded children know the truth of this only too well!

President Kennedy charged the Panel with the following tasks, which are presented here in summary form:

1. *Personnel.* It was recognized that the present-day shortage of adequately trained personnel needed to work with the retarded child is a major problem. The Panel was requested to recommend how proper personnel could be provided.

2. *Programs.* The Panel was instructed to review all possible approaches, in order to determine which programs offered the most hope for the retarded child, and then to determine how they could be implemented.
3. *Rehabilitation.* The Panel was requested to review all presently ongoing programs of treatment, education and rehabilitation.
4. *Cooperative approaches.* The need for truly collaborative and cooperative programs between federal, state and private resources in dealing with the problems of mental retardation was an important task that was assigned to the Panel for review and recommendation.

President Kennedy had a dynamic grasp of the problems associated with mental retardation, and it was quite probable that this came from personal knowledge. Some of his remarks are so pertinent and so clearly expressed that they are reproduced in the following paragraphs verbatim. If they were to be paraphrased they would lose their effectiveness.

Much of the world's population still struggles for mere survival; others for domination of the weaker. Our aim is national and individual dignity. Our fortune is scientific and technological ability. Our obligation is to search for the secrets of the human mind and to share our knowledge throughout the world.

Discoveries of the wheel, the internal combustion engine, and principles of thermodynamics have liberated mankind from much physical labor. Two hundred years ago man demonstrated, through the discoveries of Lavoisier and Harvey, that human life is governed by universal physical laws. Major progress in science and medicine can be measured from that date. Until the last two decades, however, little research was concentrated on the nature of the living cell and its reproduction. But great strides have been made in that direction through the understanding of the chemical basis of genes and chromosomes and their governing role in life itself.

The future belongs to those who can carry forward these achievements. It is now possible to attack the causes and prevention, as well as the treatment, of mental retardation. This will require new breakthroughs, but it will pay enormous dividends in knowledge about ourselves, for the functions of the brain represent an almost completely uncharted frontier. The basic research entailed in such an effort will prove the essence of human development, and its results may far exceed its objectives. Exploration and discovery in this field may uncover the secrets of life and man's capacities, and the answer to many mysteries of social behavior. Perhaps even more important, an understanding of the motivation and effect of human behavior offers the hope of fostering the rational behavior of nations.

Progress in the natural sciences during the past fifteen years have been impressive, but achievements in the prevention and therapy of mental retardation can be even more spectacular and can bring important benefits to mankind.

The mentally retarded child surely had a vigorous champion in President Kennedy!

State governments have also been active within recent years in dealing with the problems of the mentally retarded, and numerous advances have been made at this level. Residential facilities for retarded children have been improved in many states. State aid programs for public school special classes have been inaugurated and expanded, vocational rehabilitation programs integrated, medical and research programs strengthened, and, in many instances, support and impetus has been given to local programs for these children. But they all leave much to be desired.

Tremendous growth has occurred at local levels, largely motivated by the parents of retarded children. Such parents have refused to accept either the cultural stereotypes of the retarded child or the pessimistic approaches to his problems. Rather, they have, chiefly through programs of education of the community, partially succeeded in the establishment of a more positive attitude. This has resulted, in many instances, in the establishment of programs in the local public school systems. In addition, the parents themselves have provided services for those children who were so severely afflicted that they were not accepted by the public schools.

As Cianci has pointed out, established institutions (usually at the state level) can offer care to only *one out of ten* of our retarded children.[3] The community itself must provide services for the greater number of them. Unfortunately, the community has not fully accepted its responsibilities. Cianci feels that part of the reason for this lies with the prevalent philosophy of our time, which overemphasizes the producing value of the individual. At the same time it neglects the importance of the human qualities inherent in all persons.

Extensive as the developments have been, however, they still are far from adequate. We shall turn our attention next to a consideration of some of the ways in which existing programs for the mentally retarded child can be improved.

SOME NEEDED DEVELOPMENTS

Although society as a whole is becoming more aware of the problem posed by the retarded child, such an awareness is slow in developing, and needs careful nurture. Many individuals are beginning to explore the "total program" needs of the child. An example of such an approach

[3] Cianci, V., "The problem of the severely retarded child in public school," *Amer. J. ment. Defic.*, 1954, *58*, 625–632.

is that cited by Roselle, who states that the following major facilities
need to be provided:[4]

1. Adequate diagnostic and guidance facilities
2. Expanded educational facilities and programs
3. Occupational training, job finding, and supervision
4. Social service and parental training
5. Community day-care centers
6. Sheltered workshops
7. Recreational facilities
8. Personnel training facilities in universities
9. Research

With the recognition of the *presence* of the problems of mental retardation, there is also a growing desire by society to "do something
about it." Unfortunately, there is a large gap between the development
of this wish and its actual realization through some form of organized
social action. Let us look, in the following pages, at some of the elements of a program for the retardate which we feel society *should* and
could provide.

Assessment programs

There is need for the development of more adequate assessment
programs to explore the assets and liabilities of the retarded child.
Such services should be continuing in nature, extending from infancy
to adulthood, and should be repeated at frequent intervals. Adequate
assessment programs could be developed, as they have been in some
instances, within the framework of the public school systems. This
pattern of development is particularly desirable, since the problems of
the child are so closely related to the total educative process. If such a
program is to be really effective it means that, at the least, consultant
services of physicians, psychiatrists, psychologists, social workers, and
special teachers need to be made readily available to the school system.
It is usually not feasible for each school system to provide such services
individually, due to lack of trained personnel, as well as to lack of
local funds. However, they can be provided, in many instances, by cooperative arrangements on the part of a group of schools. Some states
are experimenting with a "traveling clinic"; that is, a group of experts
who visit different communities on a regularly scheduled basis in order
to consult with local public school personnel and to examine pupils.

---

[4] Roselle, E. N., "New horizons for the mentally retarded when a state looks at
the problem as a whole," *Amer. J. ment. Defic.*, 1955, *59*, 359–373.

In some instances, such assessment services are provided through the facilities of the community mental health clinic. In other cases, they are provided through out-patient departments of state institutions for the mentally retarded, and through the facilities of the training clinics of universities and colleges. However, such facilities are far too few, and are not generally available to all persons. It is only in the case of large cities and large public school systems that the appropriate professional personnel can be part of the school system itself.

Not only is there need for the development of such assessment programs for the child himself, but there is also need for the development of concurrent programs of guidance for the parents. (We have seen how important the role of the parent is in the total treatment of the retarded child.) Such programs for the parents could also be provided through the same agencies available for the children. A good example of such services is furnished by the Morris J. Solomon Clinic for mentally retarded children, located in the Jewish Hospital in Brooklyn, New York, where continuing guidance and consultation services are provided for the parents.[5]

Education of the community

The community requires continuing education with respect to the needs of mentally retarded children. Not only should the needs of these children be made quite explicit to the community, but there should also be explicit education concerning proposed programs for them and methods of *implementing* these programs. Too often such educational programs "bog down" because of inadequate information about workable programs and methods of achieving them. The community should be made aware not only of its social responsibilities toward the retarded child, but also of how they can be achieved.

The President's Panel was fully aware of the need to educate the entire community to the needs of the mentally retarded child. To do so, it was proposed that all communication media be utilized. For instance, it was suggested that illustrated, printed material (brochures) be prepared and distributed, and that films and film strips dealing with general information about the retarded child, special educational methods and principles, vocational training methods, and the need for research be disseminated to all interested groups.

[5] Wortis, J., "Toward the establishment of special clinics for retarded children: experiences and suggestions," *Amer. J. ment. Defic.*, 1954, *58*, 472–478.

Guidance and treatment of the parent

We have discussed at length the needs of the parents for guidance and treatment (see Chapter Ten). Without the understanding and full cooperation of the parents, the school cannot offer the maximum benefits of its program to the retardate. Too often this point of view has been overlooked and, as a result, the special class teacher struggles to achieve progress with the child, only to meet continued frustration due to the reactions and attitudes of the parent. It is our conviction that the parent must be drawn into the total guidance and treatment process before the child can receive the full benefits of any program. Facilities for such programs need to be provided within the community. Certainly within the school system itself there *could* be developed provisions for at least part of such activities. For example, groups of parents could be formed to meet regularly with a special class teacher, provided one were suitably trained to offer such services, or with a consultant in the event the teacher lacked such training. If it were evident that a parent had severe emotional problems, he could then be referred to a source where more appropriate help would be available for him (such as the community mental health clinic, the school clinic, or a psychotherapist in private practice).

Even though, in most instances today, the public schools do not usually offer effective guidance and educative programs to parents, with a little planning most could do so at relatively little increase in cost. It should be realized that the community would ultimately benefit from such programs, because the child would be better prepared to function as a contributing member of society. He would, therefore, need less continuing care, and would be less of a burden to society.

Re-evaluation of residential facilities

We have previously discussed (in Chapter One) the extent of the residential facilities available for retarded children. It is certainly evident, from the data we cited, that available facilities for such children are far too few, and are not adequate to meet their needs. Following a study of the residential facilities available for such children, Dunn pointed out that less than seven per cent of the estimated total number of persons of all ages in the United States classified as mentally deficient were reported in residential schools, as of 1954.[6] The situation is even

---

[6] Dunn, L., "Services for exceptional children," in *Services for Exceptional Children*. Langborne, Pa.: The Woods Schools for Exceptional Children, 1956, pp. 17–29.

more critical when it is realized, as Dunn points out, that such services are often concentrated in a specific geographical area, whereas other areas of the country have few such facilities. He cites the state of Tennessee as an example of such a situation. It probably contains 20,000 mentally retarded persons. Of these, 3,300 are in need of institutional care, but the state has residential facilities to take care of only 1,200 of them. This lack of residential facilities, however, is not unique to the state of Tennessee; it is characteristic, to some degree, of all our states. An increase in residential facilities is badly needed, and to obtain it society must be made aware of the need.

The lack of residential facilities sometimes produces tragic results. Too often we have seen children who are severely retarded, who need the benefits of residential care, and who have finally been recommended for such placement, but have no facilities available for them. It is fruitless, and even dangerous, to work with parents, and to work through their problems and feelings in regard to placement of the child, when actual placement cannot be accomplished because there is no place for the child to be institutionalized. Parents who apply for admission of their child are often told: "We have a waiting period of several years. We will put your name on the list and notify you when we will be able to take your child." In the meantime, with the passing of time, the problems of the child and his parents usually increase in severity. Further, the possibilities of promoting the emotional development of the child decrease as his problems continue to mount.

The problems posed by the inadequate extent of residential facilities are not as great for those parents who have sufficient funds to provide private residential school care for their severely retarded children. The costs of such private care are very high, however, and are beyond the means of most parents. The majority are forced to rely upon the facilities provided by society.

The President's Panel stated that residential facilities for the *present* number of mentally retarded children are woefully inadequate. As of today, facilities for an additional 50,000 retardates are needed, and this need will increase with the increase in population.

It is gratifying to note that the Panel took cognizance of the fact that, in too many instances, existing institutions are too large, and, by their very size, probably work against providing the best possible programs for the retarded child. The Panel has recommended that existing institutions gradually reduce their bed capacity, until a maximum of 1,000 beds per institution is achieved. But since it is recognized that even this is not the best possible situation, it has been recommended that new institutions limit their bed capacities to 500 beds per institution (or even less), so that the best possible degree of care be provided for their patients. In addition, the Panel has recommended that institutions for mentally retarded persons take on an active role in the community; that they become a center of training and research, as well as treatment. Such programs require not only funds, but personnel, and it is the abject shortage of adequately trained personnel that is one of the most demanding needs in our present institutions.

We have been discussing, up to this point, the need for *increased* residential facilities for the severely retarded child. In addition to the need for a *quantitative* increase in such facilities, there is also a need for *qualitative* improvement in the facilities that are provided. In too many instances, our residential schools are pitifully understaffed— there is a lack of doctors, psychiatrists, psychologists, social workers, teachers, and specialists of all kinds. It is recognized that the retarded child requires and can profit from more than custodial care. He needs positive, dynamically oriented education, training and guidance on an intensive, individual basis. Adequate programs cannot be developed without the necessary trained personnel. These are more important to the development and well-being of the child than are buildings. Of course, we do not mean to give the impression that adequate physical facilities are not important. But of what use are excellent, modern buildings, when the same outmoded custodial program is continued in them? More adequate staffing patterns for the residential schools are also of prime importance.

Increasing the facilities of day-school special classes

The number of day-school special classes has shown a remarkable growth within the last 50-year period. Such classes have been organized, both within and outside the public school systems, by the parents themselves.

Dunn has prepared an analysis of the number of children in special school classes of various types. His data are reproduced in Table 10.

Inspection of Table 10 indicates that the increase in provisions for mentally retarded children in day-school special classes has been tremendous—from a total of no children in 1895 to 114,000 in 1953. In addition to such classes, as Dunn points out, there were (in 1953) 125,000 individuals of all ages in residential schools, and, of these, 25,000 were of school age. Thus, there were a total of 139,000 children enrolled in day and residential schools for retarded children. However, the services

TABLE 10. Historical Summary of Statistics Reported to the United States Office of Education on Special Day-Schools and Classes for Mentally Retarded Children*

Year	Number of pupils (Recorded to the nearest thousand)
1895	Nil
1922	23,000
1927	52,000
1932	75,000
1936	99,000
1940	98,000
1948	87,000
1953	114,000

* Reproduced from Dunn, *op. cit.*

provided are inadequate. Dunn's statements in this regard are so important that they are quoted verbatim:

(1) Less than 20 per cent of the estimated total number of school-aged children in the United States classified as "trainable" mentally retarded were reported in special day-schools in 1952; and (2) less than 8 per cent of the estimated total number of school-aged children in the United States classified as "trainable" were reported in special day-schools and classes in the public schools, as of 1952.

These findings serve to emphasize further the need for increased and improved facilities for mildly and moderately retarded children.

We would like to point out that the data cited above refer essentially to children of *school age*. We must not forget that retarded children of *preschool* age also present serious problems, and are also in need of specialized treatment. It is true, of course, that the major responsibility for the child at such an age lies with the parents in the home, but such parents need appropriate guidance, and the child himself needs specialized experiences outside the home. The facilities for providing such care are almost totally lacking. There is a great need to extend our day-school program downward to reach the preschool age group, and also to "tie" the parent very closely into such a program. We have discussed at length the emotional development of the child, and have stressed the importance of early emotional trauma upon his total personality development. By extending the day-school special class programs downward, even for only one year, valuable experiences could be provided for both the child and his parents at the time when they are urgently needed and would be highly effective.

At the same time, the day-school special classes also need to be extended *upward* beyond the age of adolescence. We know that, in most cases, the mildly and moderately retarded child is capable of responding to vocational training. However, as we have pointed out, he matures slowly, and does not reach full maturation until beyond the normal adolescent age. It is during this latter period that vocational training programs should be stressed. The retarded child often needs continued vocational training for many years in later adolescence. Further, during his initial job placement and often for a considerable length of time afterward, the child needs guidance by skilled personnel, so provision should be made for "follow-up" services. Some communities have provided *sheltered workshops* for the retarded individual, in which additional training, placement services, and follow-up supervision are provided.

As we have stressed, one of the major goals of the day-school special class is to equip the child, insofar as possible, to be a self-sustaining and contributing member of society. An implication of this point of view is that, to be most effective, the usual program offered should be extended both upward and downward to cover a larger extent of the child's life, and thus increase the possibility of attaining this objective.

The information furnished by the President's Panel in regard to the extent of the programs of special education needed by the retarded child leads us to be somewhat pessimistic as to what will be accomplished in the immediate future. It was stated by the Panel that, between 1948 and 1958, the number of day and institutional schools offering special education facilities for retardates increased in number from 868 to 3,202. This is an increase of approximately 270%. But the present-day demand is many times this, and the gap between the need and what actually exists is very great.

Much of the difficulty in providing facilities stems from the lack of adequately trained special class teachers. In 1962, some 500 new teachers, trained to teach retarded children, were graduated from our training institutions. The Panel noted that this number hardly served to replace those who left the profession for various reasons! It is estimated that, in order to meet the educational needs of the children presently known to be retarded, 75,000 teachers would be required. It was stated that it would be necessary *to add 6,000 new teachers per year* to our existing pool of trained teachers in order to meet the existing needs. This goal can not be attained in the near future, unless drastic steps are taken.

In addition to the *quantity* of the available day-school facilities, we should be concerned with the *quality* of such programs. They will only be as good as the staffs available for their implementation. Specially trained teachers in sufficient numbers are a necessity for such services. Specialists from many areas should be available to the special class teacher, who carries the major responsibility for the continuing program, for additional specialized help and guidance.

Vocational programs

The community should become aware of the fact that the mentally retarded individual is capable of contributing a great deal to industry, and that there are many tasks that he can perform quite adequately if given the opportunity. It should become common knowledge that he can "hold down a job" adequately in his own right, and does not need to be given a job "out of pity." In other words, in many situations such an individual can "pull his own weight." There is a very interesting and pertinent study by Downing which supports this point of view.[7]

Downing studied 3,787 retarded individuals in Onondaga County in New York. One major concern of his study was to determine the *prevalence* of mental retardation in the county. He noted that the number of children suspected of being so afflicted increased up to age 14, but that, beyond that age, suspected cases tended to decline. One suggested explanation is that, during the school years, the criterion of academic success is a primary factor in the assessment of the child as mentally retarded. At a later age, school work is less important, and criteria of social competence are applied. As a consequence, some individuals formerly perceived as mentally retarded are now judged *not* to be. Probably, it is not the individual who has changed, but, rather, *society's perception of the individual* that is different. Many other studies have shown that the child diagnosed as being mentally retarded in early life often makes very good adjustments during later life, and functions well in the community. It has been suggested by some persons that there has been a "spontaneous cure." We question this conclusion, and believe, instead, that the criteria being applied in judging retardation are different. Moreover, retarded children can, and often do, function well in the nonacademic areas.

The apparent decline in the number of individuals perceived as being mentally retarded in later life is based on the fact that such individuals are capable of achieving vocational success, and of becoming relatively self-supporting members of the community. Although such persons do so without significant outside help, many more could ac-

---

[7] Downing, J. J., "The community recognition of mental retardation," in *Services for Exceptional Children*. Langhorne, Pa.: The Woods Schools for Exceptional Children, 1956, pp. 98–111.

complish this goal if provided with specially designed programs of vocational training, guidance, and placement.

Industry should be acquainted with the potentialities of the retardate, and should be helped to see that he can be an economic asset. The achievement of this kind of objective has been partially accomplished in the cases of other special groups, such as the crippled and "mentally ill." There is no reason why it could not be similarly accomplished in the case of the mentally retarded.

Prevention

In the foregoing pages we have discussed various programs for dealing with the existing problems of the retarded child. But it is of primary importance that efforts also be devoted to attempts to reduce the number of children who are afflicted with this condition, so that problems associated with mental deficiency may be alleviated at the source, that is, prior to birth. For this purpose, efforts need to be exerted in two primary directions simultaneously: first, we must continue and expand research programs in order to deal more effectively with the problems of children who already are retarded, and who may be helped; and second, we must continue and expand research in an attempt to prevent the occurence of retardation. In the latter approach, we are concerned essentially with the welfare of as yet unborn future generations.

An analogy here is the reduction in poliomyelitis which occurred dramatically following the successful production of the polio vaccines. However, as we have seen in Chapter Four, the etiology of mental retardation is quite complex. It has been stressed that this condition does not stem from any one basic defect or cause, but that, rather, it is a condition which has multiple causation. We may consider mental retardation as a symptom, and only a few of its specific etiological causes have been pinpointed with a high degree of accuracy. Too many of the factors contributing to retardation are still obscure or unknown.

Some of the factors contributing to its occurrence have been reduced significantly by certain medical advances not developed to combat mental retardation as such. For instance, one cause relatively common a few generations ago was congenital syphilis. When blood tests are routinely applied to pregnant women and a syphilitic infection is discovered, medical treatment procedures are instituted which, in many instances, prevent infection of the child and the subsequent brain damage.

Also, research into blood incompatibilities, such as Rh factors (see Chapter Four), the development of improved obstetrical practices, and discovery of phenylketonuria (PKU) are examples of how medical advances have served to reduce the possible occurrence of retardation in many instances. We have also seen, however, that some advances in medical practice may have served to increase its incidence.

President Kennedy's Panel was deeply concerned with problems relating to the prevention of mental retardation. The factors mentioned in the preceding material were noted by the Panel, and, in addition, other significant areas were discussed where preventative methods may be applied. For instance, the increased understanding of enzymatic diseases which precede faulty metabolism, knowledge of the relationships between maternal infections during pregnancy to retardation (such as in the case of Rubella, or German Measles), knowledge of the effects of toxiplasmosis and cytomegalic inclusion body disease, and increased awareness of the effects of ionization radiation, as well as awareness of the relationship of other bodily diseases of the mother (such as thyroid problems, urinary tract infections and diabetes), have all served to lead to the initiation of preventative measures which reduce the probability of mental retardation in the child.

We have seen that premature birth *may* be associated with mental retardation. (See Chapter Four.) Studies made at Johns Hopkins University, School of Hygiene, in regard to prematurity and cited by the President's Panel, are of such importance that they are summarized in the following statements:

(1) As the birth weight of the infant decreases, the more probable is the increase in disability.

(2) 26.3% of children with birth weights below 1500 grams (3.3 lbs.) have serious neurological disabilities. 22.8% have cerebral damage which leads to significant learning and behavioral difficulties.

(3) Prematurity has a general deleterious effect, and 50% of premature infants have handicaps ranging from minimum neurological damage to severe mental deficiencies.

If the incidence of prematurity is reduced, or if ameliorative treatment can be offered, then it is to be expected that the probability of mental defect in the child will also be reduced. Studies indicate that proper prenatal care of the expectant mother does reduce the incidence of prematurity. For example, the President's Panel noted that the prematurity rate among women in the District of Columbia with no prenatal care is 22.7%, while the rate among those receiving prenatal care is only 10.4%. This is a highly significant reduction in the incidence of premature births, and so the Panel recommended the establishment of medical clinics for all expectant mothers, which would be supported in part by federal funds, so that all women, regardless of socioeconomic status, could obtain proper prenatal care. Also, increased knowledge in regard to genetics and chromosome aberrations led the Panel to recommend the establishment of genetic counseling services to assist persons prior to marriage.

It appears, therefore, that a promising way to attack the problem of the prevention of mental retardation is to work intensively with the expectant mother. More and more, it is becoming apparent that many of the etiological factors related to some forms of retardation are related to what happens to the infant in utero, and, of course, as the preceding material indicates, the well-being of the mother is of paramount importance here. The establishment of such programs as these demands the expenditure of a considerable amount of money. Whether or not such funds are made available depends upon the degree of responsibility which society wishes to assume for the welfare of retardates. It concerns not merely one segment of society, but is of vital concern to society at large.

Continuing services

The responsibilities of society to the mentally retarded individual do not end when such a person has passed beyond the usual school age. He needs continuing guidance, and sometimes needs the support of some individual during periods of acute stress. In many instances, the availability of such a person is a deciding factor in determining whether that individual becomes capable of achieving a self-supporting role, or whether he will need continued total care by society. For its own best interests, as well as for the interests of such an individual, society must assume the responsibility for providing the support and guidance needed.

This necessitates the establishment of facilities designed to implement the proposals outlined in the preceding pages. The total program of continuing care for the mentally retarded has been excellently summarized by President Kennedy's Panel. It is reproduced in Table 11.

A FINAL COMMENT

As in our first edition of this text, we have discussed at length the development, guidance and education of the mentally retarded child, but have done so in the light of newer developments. Also, detailed attention has been paid to the problems of the parents, and the responsibilities of society have been delineated. We have stressed repeatedly the fact that the retarded child follows the same psychological principles

TABLE 11. AREAS OF DIRECT SERVICES FOR THE RETARDED[1], [2]

Life stage	Physical & mental health	Shelter nurture protection	Intellectual development	Social development	Recreation	Work	Economic security
Infant	Specialized medical follow-up; Special diets, drugs or surgery; Home nursing	Residential nursery	Sensory stimulation; Home training; Environmental enrichment	Child welfare services			
Toddler	Correction of physical defects; Physical therapy	Foster care	Nursery school; Trained baby sitter		Playground programs		
Child	Psychiatric therapy; Dental care; Day care	Homemaker service	Classes for slow learners; Special classes—educable; Special classes—trainable; Religious education		Scouting; Swimming		
Youth	Short-stay home; Psychotherapy	Boarding school	Work-school programs; Speech training; Occupational training	Social clubs	Day camps; Residential camps; Youth groups		
Young adult	Half-way house; Facilities for retarded in conflict	Guardianship of person	Vocational counseling—Personal adjustment training; Marriage counseling			Sheltered workshops; Selective job placement; Sheltered employment	"Disabled child's" benefits; Health insurance; Total disability assistance
Adult		Long-term residential care; Group homes	Evening school	Social supervision	Bowling; Evening recreation		Guardianship of property; Life annuity or trust
Older adult	Medical attention to chronic conditions	Boarding homes					Old age assistance; OASI benefits

[1] Not included are diagnostic and evaluation services, or services to the family; the array is set forth in an irregular pattern in order to represent the overlapping of areas of need and the interdigitation of services. Duration of services along the life span has not been indicated here.

[2] Reproduced from: The President's Panel. *A Proposed Program for National Action to Combat Mental Retardation.* Washington: Sup't. of Documents, 1962, p. **76**.

of development as do *all* children, and we have tried to elaborate the more important of these, so that our insight into and grasp of the problems of retardation be clearer and more extensive. We have also stressed the fact that this condition is a very complex phenomenon that embraces *all* aspects of the child's life.

Since mental retardation is a multi-determined condition, it requires the integrated efforts of specialists in all fields to deal with the existing problems and to mount the best possible attack upon its etiology. But it is obvious that such efforts cannot be either initiated or maintained without wholehearted support from society at large. However, this support depends, to a significant extent, upon an informed and interested society. Since the problem affects *all of us*, whether we realize it or not, it is incumbent upon all of us to assume some degree of responsibility for the initiation, development and maintenance of appropriate programs for the mentally retarded at all levels.

There is no doubt that significant progress has been made in the way in which mental retardation is regarded, and the clouds of shame, denial and neglect that surround the problems of the afflicted child are, to some extent, dissipating. Some remnants still linger, though, and probably will continue to do so for a few more generations.

In this edition we have been very much heartened by being able to report upon the many advances that have been made into the etiology of mental retardation and upon the significant advances that have been made in treatment and prevention programs. But it would be very easy to become disheartened by the advances that have *not* been made. So we must once again bring the text to a close with the same type of observation that was made in the previous edition.

Despite what has been accomplished, we are still in a state of relative ignorance as to the nature of mental retardation, and still are confronted with a multitude of the most formidable problems. The significant research breakthrough is yet to come. Perhaps we may be able to report upon it in the next revision. We hope that this volume will be of some help in advancing the cause of the mentally retarded child, and in effecting a little movement along the long and arduous road that still lies ahead of us.

SELECTED READINGS

Abraham, W., *Barbara: A Prologue*. New York: Holt, Rinehart & Winston, Inc., 1958.

Abt, L. E. and Bellak, L., *Projective Psychology*. New York: Alfred A. Knopf, Inc., 1950.

Allport, G. W., *Pattern and Growth in Personality*. New York: Holt, Rinehart & Winston, Inc., 1961.

American Association on Mental Deficiency—Woods Schools Conference, "Symposium on research design and methodology in mental retardation." *Amer. J. ment. Defic.*, 1959, *62:2*, 227–430.

Anderson, H. H. and Anderson, G. L., *An Introduction to Projective Techniques*. Englewood Cliffs, N. J.: Prentice-Hall, Inc., 1951.

Angus, L. R., "Psychiatry in the field of mental deficiency," *Amer. J. ment. Defic.*, 1949, *54*, 313–327.

Baumgartner, B. B., *Helping the Trainable Mentally Retarded Child*. New York: Bureau of Publications, Teachers College, Columbia University, 1960.

Bayley, N. and Schaefer, E. S., "Maternal Behavior and Personality Development from the Berkeley Study," presented at Regional Res. Council, Child Develpm. and Child Psychiat., Iowa City, Iowa, April, 1960.

Beck, S. J., *Rorschach's Test*. New York: Grune & Stratton, Inc., 1944 (3 vols.).

Benda, C. E., *The Child with Mongolism*. New York: Grune & Stratton, Inc., 1960.

Bender, L., *Psychopathology of Children with Organic Brain Disorders*. Springfield, Ill.: Charles C. Thomas, Publisher, 1956.

417

Benedek, T., "Adaptation to reality in early infancy," *Psychoanal. Quart.*, 1938, *7*, 200 *ff.*

Blodgett, H. E. and Warfield, G. J., *Understanding Mentally Retarded Children*. New York: Appleton-Century-Crofts, Inc., 1959.

Bridge, E. M., *Epilepsy and Convulsive Disorders in Children*. New York: McGraw-Hill, Inc., 1949.

Brody, S., *Patterns of Mothering*. New York: International Universities Press, Inc., 1956.

Brownell, W. A., "Arithmetic readiness as a practical classroom concept," *Elem. Sch. J.*, 1951, *51*, 15–22.

Brueckner, L. J. and Grossnickle, F. E., *How to Make Arithmetic Meaningful*. New York: Holt, Rinehart & Winston, Inc., 1947.

Buros, O. (ed.), *Tests in Print: A Comprehensive Bibliography of Tests for Use in Education, Psychology and Industry*. Highland Park, N. J.: Gryphon Press, 1961.

Burt, C., *The Backward Child*. London: University of London Press, 1958, 4th Ed.

———, *The Causes and Treatment of Backwardness*. New York: Philosophical Library, Inc., 1953.

Caplan, G. (ed.), *Prevention of Mental Disorders in Children*. New York: Basic Books, Inc., 1961.

Cardwell, V. E., *Cerebral Palsy: Advances in Understanding and Care*. New York: Association for the Aid of Crippled Children, 1956.

Carlson, B. and Gingland, D., *Play Activities for the Retarded Child*. Nashville: Abingdon Press, 1961.

Casler, L., "Maternal deprivation: a critical review of the literature," *Monogr. soc. Res. Child Develpm.*, 1961, *26*, 1–64.

Clarke, A. M. and Clarke, A. D. E. (eds.), *Mental Deficiency: The Changing Outlook*. London: Methuen & Co., Ltd., 1958.

Colby, K. M., *A Primer for Psychotherapists*. New York: The Ronald Press Company, 1951.

Cromwell, R. L., "Selected aspects of personality development in mentally retarded children," *Except. Child.*, 1961, *28*, 44–51.

Cronbach, L. J., *Essentials of Psychological Testing*. New York: Harper & Row, Publishers, 1960.

Crothers, B. and Paine, R. S., *The Natural History of Cerebral Palsy.* Cambridge, Mass.: Harvard University Press, 1959.

DeProspo, C. J. and Hungerford, R. H., "Services of the specialist in guidance and placement of the mentally retarded," *Amer. J. ment. Defic.*, 1944, *48*, 299–301.

Doll, E. A., "Definition of mental deficiency," *Train. Sch. Bull.*, 1941, *37*, 163–164.

———, "Etiology of mental deficiency," *Train. Sch. Bull.*, 1944, *41*, 129–137.

———, "The feebleminded child," in *Manual of Child Psychology* (L. Carmichael, ed.). New York: John Wiley & Sons, Inc., 1946.

———, *The Measurement of Social Competence.* Minneapolis: Educational Test Bureau, Educational Publishers, 1953.

Dunn, L. M. (ed.), *Exceptional Children in the Schools.* New York: Holt, Rinehart & Winston, Inc., 1963.

Dunn, L. M. and Capobianco, R. J., "Studies of reading and arithmetic in mentally retarded boys," *Monogr. Soc. for Res. in Child Develpm.*, 1954, *19*, No. 1.

Eisenberg, L., "Emotional determinants of mental deficiency," *A.M.A. Arch. Neurol. Psychiat.*, 1958, *80*, 119–121.

Farber, B., *Effects of a Severely Mentally Retarded Child on Family Integration*, Monogrs. of Soc. for Res. in Child Develpm., 1959, *71*.

———, *Family Organization and Crisis: Maintenance of Integration in Families with a Severely Mentally Retarded Child.* Lafayette, Ind.: Child Development Publications, 1960.

Farber, B., Jenne, W. and Toigo, R., *Family Crisis and the Retarded Child.* Washington: Nat. Educ. Ass., 1960.

Finch, S., *Fundamentals of Child Psychiatry.* New York: Grune & Stratton, Inc., 1960.

Flavell, J., *The Developmental Psychology of Jean Piaget.* Princeton, N. J.: D. Van Nostrand Co., Inc., 1963.

Fraenkel, W. A., *The Mentally Retarded and Their Vocational Rehabilitation: A Resource Handbook.* New York: Nat. Ass. for Retarded Child., Inc., 1961.

Frampton, M. E. and Gall, E. D., *Special Education for the Exceptional.* Boston: Porter Sargent, Publisher, 1955 (3 vols.).

Francis, R. J. and Rasick, G. L., *Motor Characteristics of the Mentally Retarded.* Washington: U.S. Dep. of Hlth., Educ. and Welf., 1960.

French, E. and Scott, J. D., *Child in the Shadows.* Philadelphia: J. B. Lippincott Co., 1960.

Gallagher, James J., *A Comparison of Brain-Injured and Non-Brain-Injured Mentally Retarded Children on Several Psychological Variables*, Monogrs. of Soc. for Res. in Child Develpm.

Gardner, W., "Personality concomitants of mental retardation," in Wilcox, R. K. (ed.), *Strategies for Behavioral Research in Mental Retardation.* Madison: University of Wisconsin Press, 1961.

Garrison, K. C. and Force, D. G., *The Psychology of Exceptional Children.* New York: The Ronald Press Company, 1959, 3rd Ed.

Garton, M. D., *Teaching the Educable Mentally Retarded.* Springfield, Ill.: Charles C. Thomas, Publisher, 1961.

Gates, R. R., *Human Genetics.* New York: The Macmillan Co., 1946 (2 vols.).

Gellner, L., *A Neurological Concept of Mental Retardation and Its Educational Implications.* Chicago: The Dr. Julian D. Levinson Research Foundation for Mentally Retarded Children, 1959.

Glidewell, J. (ed.), *Parental Attitude and Child Behavior.* Springfield, Ill.: Charles C. Thomas, Publisher, 1962.

Glover, E., "The unconscious function of education," *Int. J. Psychoanal.*, 1937, *18*, 180 *ff.*

Goldfarb, W., *Childhood Schizophrenia.* Cambridge, Mass.: Harvard University Press, 1961.

Goldstein, J. and Palmer, J., *The Experience of Anxiety: A Casebook.* New York: Oxford University Press, Inc., 1963.

Goodenough, F. L., *Mental Testing.* New York: Holt, Rinehart & Winston, Inc., 1949.

Gunzburg, H., *Social Rehabilitation of the Subnormal.* Baltimore: The Williams & Wilkins Co., 1960.

———, *Subnormal Personalities—Their Clinical Investigation and Assessment.* Baltimore: The Williams & Wilkins Co., 1961.

Hall, C. S., *A Primer of Freudian Psychology.* Cleveland: The World Publishing Company, 1954.

Haring, N. G., *et al., Attitudes of Educators toward Exceptional Children.* Syracuse, N.Y.: Syracuse University Press, 1958.

Hartman, H., *Ego Psychology and the Problem of Adaptation.* New York: International Universities Press, Inc., 1959.

Hauessermann, E., *Developmental Potential of Preschool Children: An Evaluation of Intellectual, Sensory, and Emotional Functioning.* London: Grune & Stratton, 1958.

Heck, A., *The Education of Exceptional Children.* New York: McGraw-Hill, Inc., 1953.

Heiser, K. F., *Our Backward Children.* New York: W. W. Norton & Company, Inc., 1955.

Hill, Arthur S., *The Forward Look: The Severely Retarded Child Goes to School.* Washington: Federal Security Agency, U.S. Office of Education, Bulletin 11, 1952.

Honigmann, J. J., *Culture and Personality.* New York: Harper & Row, Publishers, 1954.

Hopkins, T. W., Bice, H. V. and Colton, K. C., *Evaluation and Education of the Cerebral Palsied Child.* Washington: Int. Council for Except. Child., 1954.

Hudson, Margaret, *Procedures for Teaching Trainable Children.* Washington: Council for Except. Child., NEA Res. Monogr., Ser. A, No. 2, 1960.

Hunt, J. McV., *Intelligence and Experience.* New York: The Ronald Press Company, 1961.

Hutt, M. L. and Feuerfile, D., "The clinical meanings and predictions of a measure of perceptual adience-abience for a deaf-retarded group," Paper presented at Amer. Psychol. Ass. Convention, Philadelphia, Sept., 1963.

Hutt, M. L. and Gibby, R. G., *The Child: Development and Adjustment.* Boston: Allyn and Bacon, Inc., 1959.

———, *Patterns of Abnormal Behavior.* Boston: Allyn and Bacon, Inc., 1957.

Illingworth, R., *An Introduction to Developmental Assessment in the First Year.* London: National Spastics Society, 1962.

Ingham, H. V. and Love, L. R., *The Process of Psychotherapy*. New York: McGraw-Hill, Inc., 1954.

Jordan, T. E., *The Mentally Retarded*. Columbus, Ohio: Charles E. Merrill Books, Inc., 1961.

Kanner, L., "Conception of wholes and parts in early infantile autism," *Amer. J. Psychiat.*, 1951, *108*, 23–26.

Kansas City Public Schools, *A Curriculum Guide for Teachers of Pupils, Educable but Mentally Retarded: Grades 7–12*. Kansas City, Mo.: Bull. No. 109, 1959.

Kennedy, Ruby Jo., *The Social Adjustment of Morons in a Connecticut City*. Hartford, Conn.: Social Service Department, 1948.

Kent, G. H., "Use and abuse of mental tests in clinical diagnosis," *Psychol. Rev.*, 1938, *2*, 391–400.

Kirk, S. A., *Educating Exceptional Children*. Boston: Houghton Mifflin Company, 1962.

Kirk, S. A. and Johnson, G. O., *Educating the Retarded Child*. Boston: Houghton Mifflin Company, 1951.

Kirk, S. A., et al., *You and Your Retarded Child: A Manual for Parents of Retarded Children*. New York: The Macmillan Co., 1955.

Kittman, Laura L., *The Mentally Retarded Child at Home: A Manual for Parents*. Washington: U. S. Government Printing Office, 1959.

Klopfer, W., *The Psychological Report*. New York: Grune & Stratton, Inc., 1960.

Kugelmass, I. N., *The Management of Mental Deficiency*. New York: Grune & Stratton, Inc., 1954.

Lagache, D., *Psychoanalysis*. New York: Walker & Company, 1963.

Lanzkron, J., "The concept of pfropfschizophrenia and its prognosis," *Amer. J. ment. Defic.*, 1957, *61*, 544–547.

Lehner, G. F. J. and Kube, E. A., *The Dynamics of Personal Adjustment*. Englewood Cliffs, N. J.: Prentice-Hall, Inc., 1955.

Leibowitz, H., Waskow, I., Loeffler, N. and Glaser, F., "Intelligence level as a variable in the perception of shape," *Quart. J. Exp. Psychol.*, 1959, *11*, 108–112.

Levinson, A., *The Mentally Retarded Child: A Guide for Parents*. New York: The John Day Company, Inc., 1952.

Levinson, A. and Bigler, J. A., *Mental Retardation in Infants and Children*. Chicago: Year Book Medical Publishers, Inc., 1960.

Lewis, H. (ed.), *Deprived Children: A Social and Clinical Study*. New York: Oxford University Press, Inc., 1954.

Lippman, H., *Treatment of the Child in Emotional Conflict*. New York: McGraw-Hill, Inc., 1962.

Lowenfield, V., *Creative and Mental Growth*. New York: The Macmillan Co., 1952.

Magary, J. F. and Eichorn, J. R., *The Exceptional Child: A Book of Readings*. New York: Holt, Rinehart & Winston, Inc., 1960.

Maseland, R. L., Sarason, S. B. and Gladwin, T., *Mental Subnormality: Biological, Psychological and Cultural Factors*. New York: Basic Books, Inc., 1958.

Maslow, A. H., *Motivation and Personality*. New York: Harper & Row, Publishers, 1954.

May, R., *The Meaning of Anxiety*. New York: The Ronald Press Company, 1950.

Maynard, B., *The Nature of Ego*. New York: Philosophical Library, Inc., 1962.

Mednick, M. and Mednick, S., *Research in Personality*. New York: Holt, Rinehart & Winston, Inc., 1963.

Metropolitan School Study Council, *The Slow Learner in the Average Classroom*. New York: The Council, 1954.

Michal-Smith, H., *Management of the Handicapped Child*. New York: Grune & Stratton, Inc., 1957.

Michal-Smith, H. (ed.), *Pediatric Problems in Clinical Practice*. New York: Grune & Stratton, Inc., 1954.

Michal-Smith, H. and Kastein, S., *The Special Child: Diagnosis, Treatment, Habilitation*. Seattle: New School for the Special Child, 1962.

Miller, D. R. and Swanson, G. E., *Inner Conflict and Defense*. New York: Holt, Rinehart & Winston, Inc., 1960.

Murphy, L., *Personality in Young Children*, Vol. 1. New York: Basic Books, Inc., 1956.

Murray, H. A., "Thematic apperception test," in *Contributions toward Medical Psychology* (A. Weider, ed.). New York: The Ronald Press Company, 1953, Vol. II, pp. 636–649.

National Society for the Study of Education, *The Teaching of Arithmetic*, Pt. II, 1951.

O'Connor, N. and Tizard, J., *The Social Problem of Mental Deficiency.* New York: Pergamon Press, Inc., 1956.

Penrose, L. S., *The Biology of Mental Defect.* New York: Grune & Stratton, Inc., 1949.

Perry, N., *Teaching the Mentally Retarded Child.* New York: Columbia University Press, 1960.

Piaget, J., *The Construction of Reality in the Child.* New York: Basic Books, Inc., 1954.

Pinneau, S., *Changes in Intelligence Quotient: Infancy to Maturity.* Boston: Houghton Mifflin Company, 1961.

Pollock, M. P. and Pollock, M., *New Hope for the Retarded: Enriching the Hopes of Exceptional Children.* Boston: Porter Sargent, Publisher, 1953.

Riessman, F., *The Culturally Deprived Child.* New York: Harper & Row, Publishers, 1962.

Rothstein, J. H., *Mental Retardation: Readings and Resources.* New York: Holt, Rinehart & Winston, Inc., 1961.

Roucek, J. (ed.), *The Unusual Child.* New York: Philosophical Library, Inc., 1962.

Schlotter, B. and Svendsen, M., *An Experiment in Recreation with the Mentally Retarded.* Chicago: Behav. Res. Fund, Ill. Dep. of Publ. Welf., 1951, Rev. Ed.

Schonell, F., Richardson, J. and McConnel, T., *The Subnormal Child at Home.* London: Macmillan and Co., 1958.

Schwartz, P., *Birth Injuries of the New Born.* New York: Hafner Publishing Co., 1961.

Sherman, M. (ed.), *A Rorschach Reader*. New York: International Universities Press, Inc., 1961.

Siegel, E., *Helping the Brain Injured Child*. New York: Association for Brain Injured Children, 1961.

Slaughter, S. S., *The Mentally Retarded Child and His Parent*. New York: Harper & Row, Publishers, 1960.

Slavson, S. R., *The Practice of Group Therapy*. New York: International Universities Press, Inc., 1947.

Smith, J. O., "Group language development for educable mental retardates," *Except. Child.*, 1962, *58*, 111–123.

Smith, N. B., "Helpful books to use with retarded readers," *Elem. Sch. J.*, 1952, *52*, 390–397.

Stacey, C., et al., *Counseling and Psychotherapy and the Mentally Retarded: A Book of Readings*. New York: Free Press of Glencoe, Inc., 1957.

Stern, C., *Children Discover Arithmetic: An Introduction to Structural Arithmetic*. New York: Harper & Row, Publishers, 1949.

Storr, A., *The Integrity of the Personality*. Baltimore: Penguin Books, Inc., 1963.

Strauss, A. A. and Lehtinen, L. E., *Psychopathology and Education of the Brain-Injured Child*. New York: Grune & Stratton, Inc., 1947.

Symonds, P. M., *The Dynamics of Parent-Child Relationships*. New York: Columbia University Press, 1949.

Theodore, Sister Mary, *The Challenge of the Retarded Child*. Milwaukee: The Bruce Publishing Co., 1959.

Tizard, J. and Grad, J., *The Mentally Handicapped and Their Families*. New York: Oxford University Press, Inc., 1961.

Training School at Vineland, N.J., *Conference on Practical Problems of Coordinating all Services Related to the Treatment—Training—and Management of the Mentally Retarded*. Vineland, N. J.: Vineland Training School, May 11–12, 1959.

Traxler, A. E., et al., *Introduction to Testing and the Use of Test Results in Public Schools*. New York: Harper & Row, Publishers, 1953.

Tredgold, R. F. and Soddy, K., *Mental Deficiency*. Baltimore: The Williams & Wilkins Co., 1957, 9th Ed.

Waelder, R., *Basic Theory of Psychoanalysis.* New York: International Universities Press, Inc., 1960.

Wallin, J. E. W., *Mental Deficiency in Relation to Problems of Genesis, Social and Occupational Consequences, Utilization, Control, and Prevention.* Brandon, Vt.: J. clin. Psychol., 1956.

Warren, D. M., "Reading needs of the mentally retarded," *Educ.,* 1951, *71,* 548–551.

Whyte, L., *The Unconscious before Freud.* London: Tavistock Publications, 1962.

Williams, J. R. and Belinson, L., "Neurosis in a mental defective," *Amer. J. ment. Defic.,* 1953, *57,* 601–612.

Windle, C., "Prognosis of mental subnormals," *Amer. J. ment. Defic. Monogr. Suppl.,* 1962, *66,* 1–180.

Wolberg, L. R., *The Technique of Psychotherapy.* New York: Grune & Stratton, Inc., 1954.

Woods Schools, *Counseling Parents of Children with Mental Handicaps,* Proceedings of the Thirty-third Spring Conference of the Woods Schools, Langhorne, Pa., 1958.

Woodworth, R. S., *Dynamics of Human Behavior.* New York: Holt, Rinehart & Winston, Inc., 1958.

INDEX OF NAMES

INDEX OF SUBJECTS